WESTERN GEOPHYSICAL

VERTICAL SEISMIC PROFILING

By E. I. Gal'perin

Translated by Alfred J. Hermont
Edited by J. E. White

SOCIETY OF EXPLORATION GEOPHYSICISTS

Special Publication No. 12

Originally Published in Russia by Nedra
Moscow, 1971

Library of Congress Catalog Card Number: 74-83416

Society of Exploration Geophysicists
P. O. Box 3098
Tulsa, Oklahoma 74101

Published 1974.

Printed in the United States of America.

CONTENTS

DESIGNATIONS USED IN THE MONOGRAPH

H depth of observation point

h depth of charge

H_r maximal depth of raypath penetration

H_v depth of boundary of section in borehole (along the vertical)

H_N distance to boundary of section below the shotpoint (along the normal to the boundary $H_N = l \sin \phi + H_v \cos \phi$)

Q weight of charge

l distance from shotpoint to vertical profile (i.e. the top of the borehole); the $(+)$ sign is assumed when the shotpoint is located in the direction of the horizon dip (with respect to the top of the hole)

L distance along boundary from borehole to projection of shotpoint on boundary ($L = l \cos \phi - H_v \sin \phi$)

v_P propagation velocity of longitudinal waves

v_s propagation velocity of transverse waves

v_0 initial velocity

v_{av} average velocity

v_{avN} average velocity in bed located between H_v and point of observation H

v_a apparent velocity

v_b boundary velocity

v_{LR} velocity in the layer

β coefficient of velocity increase

p parameter determined by Snell's law:
for $\phi = 0$ $p = \sin i_0 / v_0 = \sin i_1 / v_1 = \sin i_n / v_n$;
for $\phi \neq 0$ $p = \sin i_1 / v_1 = \sin i_2 / v_2$

ϕ angle of dip of horizon. Positive values are those above the horizontal with reference to which the angle is defined ($0 \leq \phi \leq \pm 90°$)

i angle of incidence of refracted wave upon the boundary (reckoned from the normal to the latter; from 0 to $\pi/2$)

i_0 angle of ray as it emerges from the source

i_H angle of raypath as it exists at point H of profile

i_{cr} critical angle ($i_{cr} = \arcsin v_n / v_{n+1}$, where v_n = velocity in nth layer of the cross-section, $v_n < v_{n+1}$)

ψ angle of inclination of seismometers with reference to the horizontal

d_n thickness of the nth layer

m order of multiples as determined by the number of reflections from the lowest horizon

λ wavelength

f frequency of oscillation

In describing the wave fields, the following designations are introduced:

t_P, t_S direct longitudinal and transverse waves (i.e., times of arrival)

t_P^1, t_S^1 longitudinal and transverse waves reflected from boundary 1

t_P^{101}, t_S^{101} multiply reflected waves, reflected sequentially from boundaries 1, 0, 1

t_{cv}^1, t_{cv1} converted reflected and converted transmitted waves formed at interface 1

t_{HD1} head wave associated with interface 1

t_{RR} refracted wave

FURTHER DESIGNATIONS AND ABBREVIATIONS USED IN TRANSLATION

ACA	automatic control of amplification
CDR	Controllable directional reception
CMRRW	correlational method of refracted waves
DSS	deep seismic sounding
ECA	exponential control of amplification
MCTTC	method of converted traveltime curve
MRLW	method of reflected waves
PSA	polarized seismic analyzer
SP	shotpoint
SWL	ultrasonic and sonic (acoustic) well logging
t_{BT}	arrival time from crystalline basement
t_{FL}	wave propagating along fluid column
t_T	pipe (tube) wave
VSP	vertical seismic profiling
ZLV	zone of low velocity

Note: On the figures, cek = sec or second.

FOREWORD

Among the tools for disclosing subsurface lithologic information, there is no competitor for the drill. Once a hole has been drilled through a geologic section of interest, the opportunity exists at last to check projections of surface measurements against "ground truth" and to achieve a precision not obtainable from surface measurements alone. This opportunity is exploited in some fashion by all prudent oil producers. However, powerful economic and psychological factors stand in the way of full use of this opportunity. If a well is a producer, every day of down-hole measurements represents a delay of income and, more importantly perhaps, every down-hole operation poses some threat of damage to the well. If the well is dry, the owner may not be interested in spending additional money on an already costly failure, particularly if his limited land holdings were condemned by the dry hole and the subsurface information gained would primarily be of interest to competitors holding adjacent leases. For whatever reasons, general practice in the United States does not make full exploration use of the holes drilled. To be sure, the suite of logging tools is comprehensive and log interpretation is sophisticated. Furthermore, surface seismic sources and down-hole geophones have been used to delineate boundaries of salt domes, as well as to indicate average vertical velocity to selected depths. The fact is, however, that no method has been put into general use which combines surface and down-hole measurements in a complementary fashion and extends surface geophysical methods into the third dimension.

Within the Soviet Union, a method has been developed and put into general use which intimately combines the full seismograms from a vertical spread of borehole geophones with normal reflection records from a surface spread. This combination of special equipment, standardized field procedures, and theoretical foundation for interpretation is known as Vertical Seismic Profiling. Spurred by the same need for better subsurface delineation, the oil industry of the USSR has sponsored the development of VSP and welcomed the opportunity to try out the new method in a wide variety of geologic provinces.

From basic principles and from initial field experience reported in this book, Vertical Seismic Profiling offers many unique advantages. Seismic noise levels are lower at interior points of the medium, and there three-component motion is more simply related to individual shear or compressional waves. VSP records provide a reliable correlation between reflections observed on surface profiles and the interfaces or thin-layered sequences which give rise to each reflection. Multiple reflections are identified. Average velocities are obtained by direct observation over paths required for CDP stacking. A major benefit from VSP is the improved interpretation of records obtained along surface profiles in the area.

Foreword

In the book, "Vertical Seismic Profiling", Dr. E. I. Gal'perin gives us a close look at a new exploration tool. It is hoped that this translation into English will speed the application of this tool to the search for oil in additional areas of the world.

Translation of this book by Dr. A. J. Hermont was implemented by the SEG Translations Committee and the SEG Executive Committee. Special thanks go to Mr. Jerry W. Henry, who contributed to the editorial process far beyond his normal role as Publication Manager of SEG, and to Dr. Ronald W. Ward, who assisted in final manuscript preparation. The cooperation of Mezhdunaroknaja Kniga is gratefully acknowledged, particularly for making available the originals of the figures.

J. E. WHITE, *Editor*
Moscow, December 1973

INTRODUCTION

Seismic investigations are essential in the catalog of geophysical methods of exploration for petroleum and gas. An overwhelming number of oil and gas fields has been discovered on structures which have been selected for drilling by means of seismic methods of exploration. In mining geology, seismic investigations permitted the transition from geologic mapping to the study of formations containing ore bodies and the structures which control those bodies. The number of seismic exploration parties increases each year.

During the last 10-15 years, substantial progress has been made in the development of instrumentation, methods of observation, and means of processing data acquired in seismic exploration. This may be explained, to a notable degree, by the development of the dynamic theory of wave propagation and the experimental study of seismic waves for a wide range of frequencies under field conditions and on models. Each year, seismic investigations are concerned with even more complicated problems associated with the necessity to increase the depth of penetration and at the same time to improve the detail and accuracy of investigations. The exploratory capabilities of seismic methods, however, increase at a slower rate than do the difficulties of related problems. This situation stems from the fact that, lately, the geologic effectiveness of seismic investigations does not advance with sufficient rapidity.

The basic difficulties associated with seismic investigations and with the interpretation of data are related to the complexity of actual media in which the seismic waves propagate. The results obtained during the last few years indicate that, as the detailed study of the media progresses, it appears to be more and more complex, heterogeneous, and thin-layered. The wave pattern observed on seismograms is characterized by a large number of various wave types and by extensive zones of their interference.

As penetration increases, the intensity of useful waves sharply decreases. The lack of objective means for identifying useful waves against a background of intensive regular and irregular noise reduces the reliability of the results.

The future refinement of seismic methods is unthinkable without a detailed experimental study of seismic waves in actual media. Although in the domain of seismic wave theory (and in that of the implementation of various computational schemes) advances in principle have been achieved, the physics of the process of generation and propagation of seismic waves in actual media has not been pursued with sufficient vigor. The rigorous principles of characteristics associated with realistic models have not as yet been worked out.

Until recent times, the experimental study of seismic waves was based on the increasingly detailed analysis of wave fields observed, usually on the surface. Such a method was sufficiently effective under conditions of simple media. For more complicated seismogeologic conditions, data associated with the kinematic and dynamic aspects of waves, as they are obtained in surface observations, are insufficient for the understanding of the physics of their generation and propagation. As a result, reliable criteria for the unique determination of the nature of waves recorded on a seismogram are not always available. Also, a gap frequently exists in the physically substantiated methods of interpretation of observed data. In this context, there does not at present exist a clear comprehension of the influence of various types of inhomogeneities of the cross-section on the wave field. In spite of the complexity of observational systems (which leads to increased costs of seismic investigations), the authenticity of geologic interpretation is often doubtful.

In the search for ways to overcome these difficulties, it seemed expeditious to alter in principle the approach to the experimental study of various wave types in the propagating wave field, and to go on to the investigation of the very formation process of particular waves; i.e., to the wave field formation as a whole. Procedurally, this leads to a shift from mostly surface observations to observations in the interior of the medium — in boreholes. For a long time, seismic observations in boreholes have been applied to the practice of seismic exploration. Most of these are only for the study of first arrival times of waves, from shots near the top of the well in question. The scope of such investigations is basically restricted to the study of average wave velocities. To begin with, it was necessary to refine substantially the techniques for the study of seismic waves by means of observations at points in the interior of the medium. It appeared most promising to utilize not only the first arrivals but also the subsequent events of the record. The effectiveness and the yield of this approach may be compared to the effectiveness of an analogous transition for surface observations taking place in the 1930s.

Field work in this direction, instigated by the Institute of Physics of the Earth of the Academy of Sciences of the USSR in 1959, led to the development of the method of vertical seismic profiling (VSP). As for its physical approach and its orientation, the VSP method appears to constitute a further development of the principles of experimental studies of seismic waves in actual media as they were conceived over a period of many years by

G. A. Gamburtsev. In the process of the method's development, the first instrument systems were created, the procedures and the survey techniques were developed, and the mode of data interpretation was conceived. Experimental investigations were carried out covering regions of different geologic structures. Observations were made on platforms, the sedimentary section of which consisted of thin layers with increased propagation velocity and with weak velocity differentiation (Kuibyshev district). Work was also done in an area having a thick, high-velocity carbonate bed overlying a basement of highly variable depth (Volgograd district). Further investigations included regions of terrigenous deposits associated with a shallow basement (Krasnodar district). Also, observations involved inflected thick beds of coarsely fragmented terrigenous deposits (Northern Tyan-Shan) as well as beds composed of thin-layered sandy clays (Krasnodar).

These investigations showed that the wave fields observed on seismograms obtained on the surface are considerably more complicated than one could have assumed and that it is the upper portion of the cross-section that is highly, and in many cases decisively, responsible for their formation. The investigations not only permitted the study of particular features of seismic wave propagation in various structurally different media, but also clarification and appraisal of basic capabilities of the method. It was also determined that VSP enables the identification of the nature of waves in a more reliable and unique manner than is possible for surface observations. Also the method lends itself to the stratigraphic correlation of waves and permits the evaluation of exploratory possibilities of seismic surveys, so that in each particular geologic situation, one may select the optimal mode of observation. All these questions, in essence, determine the effectiveness of seismic investigations and play a dominant role in the practice of seismic exploration. The combination of surface observations with VSP seems to be most promising.

The results at hand indicate the necessity of a critical review of some basically and practically important propositions concerning the meaning of various wave types involved in the formation of the overall wave field, as well as of the exploratory capabilities of seismic investigations. The essential bulk of observations was carried out within the seismic frequency band. However, much of the material can also be helpful in understanding the particulars of wave fields observed in deep seismic sounding and in earthquake seismology.

This work is devoted to a description of VSP, the capabilities of which are illustrated through the study of basic types of seismic waves in actual media. In the first (methodological) part the fundamental essentials of VSP are discussed: questions of instrumentation, methods of observation, the kinematics and the correlation of waves. Special attention is given to the study of the directions of particle motion in the medium. The latter, for VSP, in contrast to surface observations, may be utilized for subsequent qualitative processing of data.

In the second part of the work, certain particulars of generation and propagation of longitudinal reflected-refracted waves are studied in detail. These waves form the essential basis for methods of seismic investigation. But transverse and converted waves (both reflected and refracted) are also considered in detail. Attention is focused on the examination of wave fields associated with the upper portion of the cross-section. This is reasonable in view of the very strong influence that the upper portion of the cross-section exerts on the wave field at interior points of the medium as well as

at the surface for source-detector distances commonly used in the method of reflected waves (MRLW),[1] correlational method of refracted waves (CMRRW), and deep seismic sounding (DSS) methods. This influence in many cases restricts the exploration capabilities of the investigations and is frequently underrated.

In this book, which is the first monograph on VSP, the author's goal is not a rigorous examination of all aspects of the method. In fact, this could hardly be achieved in the initial phase of its development. It seemed more significant to point out new possibilities of the study of the process of seismic wave propagation in actual media that is substantiated by physics. Therefore, in describing wave fields, study material is cited having to do, preeminently, with basic laws governing wave fields. In many cases we thought it possible to restrict ourselves to qualitative results which, all the same, sufficiently illustrate the VSP method and permit the evaluation of the exploratory capabilities of seismic investigations. The book includes material documented in scattered papers of the author and of other investigators.

The considerable possibilities of the method attracted to it a wide circle of specialists and, during the last two or three years, a large volume of VSP work was accomplished. Regretfully, not all results of the latest investigations could be assimilated during the preparation of the book.

The work is compiled from observational material executed by the Institute of Physics of the Earth, Academy of Sciences, USSR (IPE AS USSR) in cooperation with the production geophysical Trusts of the Ukraine, the Uzbek, and the Kazakh SSR as well as those of Kuibyshev, Krasnodar, and Volgograd. The

[1]See "Further Designations and Abbreviations used in Translation," p. vi.

field work and the data processing involved many contributors. Special recognition is given to A. V. Frolov, R. M. Gal'perina, and I. M. Muzyka who made substantial contributions during the development of the method.

I am taking this opportunity to express my gratitude to G. I. Petrashen, I. L. Nersesov, A. I. Bogdanov, B. Ya. Gelchinskiy, as well as to D. K. Ozerov who reviewed the manuscript and was responsible for many valuable comments.

PART ONE
VERTICAL SEISMIC PROFILING

Chapter 1
FUNDAMENTALS OF THE VSP METHOD

The principal difficulties of seismic interpretation are associated with the complexity of the wave fields, the lack of reliable criteria for their analysis, and the identification of the nature of the recorded waves. Under such conditions, a mere broadening of utilized wave categories will not solve the overall problem; since, for each particular method, specific difficulties arise which reduce their effectiveness. Of course, in some situations it is possible to utilize the full measure of particular exploration capabilities.

In the reflection method, as penetration increases, it becomes imperative to separate weak signals from a background of various types of regular and irregular unwanted waves. Among the regular wave types, multiples are of particular significance; these waves, in spite of considerable efforts, do not lend themselves to being suppressed and are not even recognizable on seismograms in certain cases. Multiple reflections thus are the basic reason for the limited effectiveness and penetration of the reflection method in most areas. In many areas, regular waves are altogether nonexistent on seismograms because of the intensity of seismic noise associated with the upper portion of the cross-section, the nature of which is not always clear.[1] The application of complicated directional systems of observation leads, as a rule, to a loss of detail and to a loss of the resolving power of the method, which complicates the study of dipping structures representing the major objectives for large-scale platform regions.

In the correlation method of refracted waves (CMRRW) there is no consensus on the nature of the recorded waves. Available material indicates that here the fundamental role is played not by the headwaves but by the curved-path refractions and reflected waves, the latter for large angles of incidence (see Averbukh et al, 1963; Alekseyev, 1960). The situation is complicated by insufficient data on laws governing the variation of velocity in the horizontal direction. These laws play a dominant role in the treatment of data involving curved-path refractions.

Because of the difficulties associated with the application of longitudinal waves, active development of methods involving transverse and converted waves has been going on; in principle these methods possess known advantages. However, it is not always possible to realize these advantages in a given geologic situation. It is likely that this is the reason why methods involving transverse and converted waves thus far have not found widespread application and that some of their modifications still remain in the experimental stage.

Up to now, the fundamental difficulties of the transverse-wave method are associated with the manner of their excitation. The lack of velocity data on longitudinal and transverse waves on the one hand, and the wide range of possible ratios of these waves on the other, complicate the interpretation of data obtained by the methods of transverse and converted waves.

The fundamental difficulties of the converted-transmitted waves method relate to a lack of criteria (based on the physics of the problem) which would permit the identification of longitudinal and transverse waves associated with the same horizon of a multilayered medium.

For all methods, the complexity of interpretation is, to a considerable degree,

---

[1] In this monograph, the upper portion of the cross-section is understood to be the bed (deposits) extending from the surface to the first seismic reference horizon.

determined by the strong influence of the upper portion of the cross-section on the wave field. These difficulties of interpretation are equally characteristic for seismic exploration and for methods of deep seismic sounding (DSS), including earthquake seismology; for DSS they are further aggravated by less complete systems of observation.

To overcome the enumerated problems it was necessary to develop methods which would permit the analysis of the wave pattern of seismograms with more confidence. As a first step, one has to learn to study the process of generation and propagation of different waves and the manner in which the wave field is formed. This brings us to the necessity of transition from predominantly surface observations to observations at interior points of the medium, i.e., in boreholes.

SEISMIC OBSERVATIONS IN BOREHOLES

Seismic observations in wells have been going on for about 35 years and are considered mandatory for overall seismic surveys. They may be classified under two principal categories: as an aid to the solution of problems and as a means to study the frequency range of utilized waves. Up to now, seismic observations in boreholes were basically conducted for the purpose of measuring the propagation velocities of waves and with the solution of certain structural problems in mind. Simultaneously, two different modifications were being developed: seismic well shooting and borehole seismometer exploration.

Velocity measurements in wells are carried out by using waves of different origin and emerging in different frequency ranges. Two modes of seismic well logging have evolved based on frequency, which determines the detailing capabilities and the accuracy of the measurements; i.e., work in the seismic and in the sonic frequency ranges.

Seismic well shooting

Seismic well shooting may record either direct (longitudinal and transverse) or refracted waves.

Logging of direct longitudinal waves is the most widely used form of seismic observations in boreholes. Velocity measurement of longitudinal waves by means of well observations is the topic of many publications examining questions of the method (Voyutskiy, 1937; Gamburtsev, 1937, 1938; Puzyrev, 1957) as well as the mechanics and the accuracy of interpretation (Bogdanov, 1960; Puzyrev, 1957; Dix, 1945). Interpretation of seismic well shot data is based on the assumption of a horizontally layered model of the medium. Seismic well shooting at present is considered to be one of the most reliable sources of information on average seismic wave velocities, which are so indispensable in the interpretation of seismic data, particularly when they relate to the method of reflected waves (MRLW). In the last few years the trend has been away from recording with a single seismometer to the use of multipoint systems which serve to improve not only the accuracy of determination of velocity characteristics of the medium, by measurement of interval and mean layer velocities, but also the resolving power of the method.

Well shooting based on refracted waves is less prevalent. In specific cases it increases the accuracy of velocity measurements (Ivanov, 1957; Raikher, 1958). Shots are fired at large distances from the well. At these distances the first arrival (vertical profile) is the wave refracted at a boundary located below the depth of the well.

The principle of well shooting based on direct transverse waves was introduced during the last few years, when the need arose for a detailed differentiation of the cross-section according to wave velocities

(Berdennikova et al, 1959; Zhadin, 1960). In contrast to longitudinal wave logging, three-component observations are commonly used for the registration of transverse waves. Direct transverse waves of the SH-type are studied; these are generated by a directional source (as a rule, by a horizontal impact) using special pile drivers as well as mobile arrangements mounted on cranes (Brodov, 1967; Anonymous, 1962). In the last few years directional shots have been utilized for the generation of S-waves (Puzyrev et al, 1967): this substantially increases the penetration of the investigations. Transverse wave recording permits the study of the laws of velocity variations of S-waves in media of different constitution, which significantly improves the reliability and accuracy of interpretation of data based on transverse and converted waves.

Occasionally, one applies the so-called "inverted seismic well shooting method" (frequently called "torpedoing") to seismic observations in boreholes; in this case, observations are made on the surface, whereas the explosions take place at different depths along the bore of the well. Such observations usually are conducive to the study of the upper portion of the cross-section only. In the overall range of observations they are not of essential value.

The opportunities for the study of velocity cross-sections in boreholes and the construction of velocity models in actual media are severely restricted in the seismic frequency range. It is known that, even though it is possible to obtain the average velocities from the longitudinal vertical traveltime curve, the determination of layer velocities is very difficult, especially for media with weak velocity differentiation. The same applies to the identification of thin high-velocity layers. The clarification of the nature of seismic boundaries and the study of transitional layers by methods of ordinary seismic

well shooting is practically impossible. Aiming for results that would increase accuracy and detail, attempts were made to employ high frequencies for observations along small spreads. In this direction, original work was done by Voyutskyi (1937) and by Ostrovskyi (1944). The latter placed a source of elastic waves (detonator) into a well within the immediate neighborhood of a probe consisting of two seismometers. Subsequently, various investigators utilized electric discharges (Sergeyev et al, 1963) and piezoelectric (Riznichenko, 1956) and electromagnetic transducers as sources of energy. Regrettably, however, many of these efforts did not go beyond the experimental stage, although the soundness of this approach is unquestionable.

Borehole seismometer exploration

In contrast to seismic well shooting, borehole seismometer exploration is used for the solution of independent geologic problems, in particular for the determination of stratigraphic details of steeply inclined horizons in sectors contiguous to the well and, most frequently, in the study of lateral flanks of salt domes (Bogdanov, 1960; Bondarev and Sivkov, 1963; Gardner, 1953; Ivanov, 1953, 1957; Konovalov, 1961; Riznichenko, 1946; Tumilovich, 1962; Beranek and Zounkova, 1965; Holste, 1959.) In all these endeavors, as a rule, only the first arrivals of longitudinal waves are being used. The method of fields or that of gradients allows graphical construction of the refracting boundary. Application of computers substantially extends the capabilities of fully interpreting the data.

Sonic logging

The ultrasonic method was at first introduced for the laboratory study of physical properties of rocks. This method allowed the study of physical parameters of different rocks according to their lithological composition, pressure, and temperature. It was demonstrated that one can differentiate between rocks by their physical properties. The results obtained were interesting not only as applied to engineering geology but also as they related to the interpretation of field data and, especially, the interpretation of seismic data with greater accuracy. The study of physical properties of rocks under natural conditions has substantial advantages when compared to laboratory and parametric measurements on models: the former became the basic premise for the development of ultrasonic (acoustic) well logging (SWL) (Karus and Saks, 1961; Riznichenko, 1956).

High-frequency observations are based on the study of laws governing the propagation of sonic impulses (50-5000 hz) and ultrasonic impulses (20-50 khz) in rock formations; the recording is done over small spreads which permits the differentiation of the cross-section and identification of thin layers of the order of a fraction of a meter. At present, SWL is widely utilized: (a) in production geophysics for the lithologic differentiation of the cross-section, the study of porosity, presence of caverns, and fracturing and the determination of gas-oil and water-oil contacts, as well as monitoring the quality of cementing the borehole; (b) in engineering geology for the study of mechanical and supporting properties of soils; and, (c) in seismic exploration in which SWL is the source of the most detailed information on propagation velocities in actual media.

Sonic investigations in boreholes have indeed found wide application. In this connection one should note that velocities based on SWL-data may differ from those derived within the seismic frequency band. Fundamental reasons for such differences may be the heterogeneities of the media and the frequency dispersion as well as modification of properties of the media in the neighborhood of the borehole casing as a result of fluid invasion, saturation of dry terrigenous rocks, etc.

The possibility of using SWL for the study of wave fields by the method of synthetic seismograms seems especially intriguing.

Study of waves in subsequent portions of the record

In spite of some progress in the development of borehole investigations, they still lag behind surface observations, for which the capability of correlation of useful waves has sharply increased (through frequency selectivity and various interferential systems of directional reception). For that reason, even the large volume of seismic well logging carried out everywhere could not exert much influence on the effectiveness of seismic investigations. This is so because the basic difficulties, in most cases, are associated not with insufficient data on average velocities, but with inability to analyze and correlate complicated wave fields. At the same time, even from a most general point of view, it is clear that observations at the interior points of the medium could reveal new information on the origin of recorded waves, if the treatment would involve not only the first arrival, but also waves within the subsequent portion of the record. This idea was most clearly stated by Puzyrev (1957) who wrote: "At present one is acutely aware of the lag of borehole results behind the overall level of seismic exploration. . . . Further development of the method and the technique must be along the path that guarantees correlational tracking of waves along the bore of the well."

The advantages and feasibilities of a study of waves in the subsequent portion of the record was pointed out even earlier by many authors. Sollogub and Raikher (1955) proposed recording of reflected waves in wells in order to locate the reflecting horizon more correctly. Yakobson (1956) has recorded subsequent arrivals in seismic well logging. Among many unwanted waves he was able to isolate reflected waves. Petkevich (1957,

1958) pointed out the feasibility of defining the cross-section more accurately by means of simultaneous treatment of vertical traveltime curves for first arrivals and those for reflected waves. He also described the traveltime characteristics for reflected waves. In the contributions of Levin and Lynn (1958) and Jolly (1953), reflected and multiple waves were tracked practically to the weathered layer and were correlated with waves recorded in surface observations; also, the reflection coefficients were determined. Berdennikova et al (1959), while pointing out the expediency of using subsequent arrivals, focused their attention on the practical difficulties of acquiring undistorted recordings; these distortions make it difficult to correlate waves at points in the interior of the medium as well as at the surface. These authors showed the necessity for firm contact between the probe and the casing of the well (Berdennikova et al 1959; Khalyevich, 1955; Jolly, 1953; Levin and Lynn, 1958).

The development of well logging based on transverse waves facilitated acquiring undistorted registrations at interior points of the medium. Data from wells could then be used to study the dynamics of direct longitudinal and transverse waves, the purpose being the determination of absorption properties (attenuation and dispersion) in actual media. These efforts, aside from their purely practical value, were of considerable scientific interest, since they provided initial information on the study of the mechanics of absorption. A large amount of research in this direction is credited to Zhadin (1960), Berdennikova (1959), Berdennikova et al (1959); Berdennikova and Limbakh (1966); and abroad, to McDonal et al (1958), Levin and Lynn (1958) and Jolly (1953, 1956). The contributions of Hagedoorn (1962) and Clifford (1958) are concerned with the study of particular features of wave propagation by observations

at interior points of the medium. The most complete and purposeful work in correlational tracking of subsequent arrival-time waves observed in wells was that carried out by LGU and Vniigeofizika in development of the method of transverse waves in seismic exploration (Puzyrev and Khudobina, 1962). The results of these efforts became the basis of investigations initiated by the IPE AS USSR in 1959 and culminated in development of the VSP method (Galperin, 1957, 1962, 1963a, b, 1964a, b, c, 1965a, b, 1966a, b, c, 1967a, b, 1969; Gal'perin and Kosminskaya, 1958; Gal'perin and Frolova, 1960, 1961, 1963, 1966; Gal'perin et al, 1969; Demidenko, 1964, 1966, 1967; Rudnitskiy, 1968).

FUNDAMENTAL FEATURES
OF VSP

Let us examine the fundamental features of VSP as compared to surface observations.

1) In contrast to surface observations, for which the ultimate form of the wave pattern is studied, VSP permits observation and study of the very process of generation and propagation of seismic waves in the actual medium as well as the mechanics of formation of the wave field. Sequentially observing the development of the wave process in VSP, one splits, as it were, the total wave field, and one is permitted to shed some light on the following questions: how is such a complicated wave field, as that recorded at the surface, generated from a relatively simple and short-duration impulse at the source? Where and how does this process occur and what is the role that the various heterogeneities of the medium play in the overall process? For propagation of the impulse in a homogeneous absorbing medium only its form is altered. In inhomogeneous (layered) media, secondary waves arise at the boundaries of heterogeneities and a redistribution of energy between the waves takes place. VSP per-

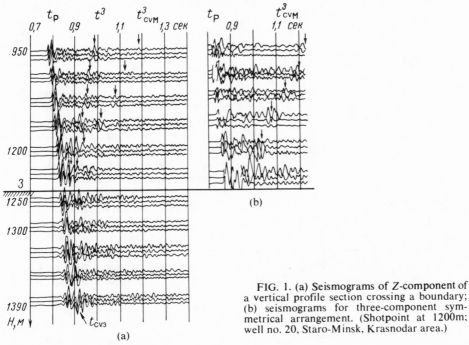

(a)

(b)

FIG. 1. (a) Seismograms of Z-component of a vertical profile section crossing a boundary; (b) seismograms for three-component symmetrical arrangement. (Shotpoint at 1200m; well no. 20, Staro-Minsk, Krasnodar area.)

mits the study of the processes of reflection and refraction and the formation of the totality of secondary waves. On seismograms of the Z-component (Figure 1a) and on those of the symmetrical three-component arrangement (Figure 1b), the direct incident wave and the secondary waves are indicated as they are formed on a boundary: two reflected and two refracted waves (longitudinal and transverse).[2] The energy distribution between secondary waves for normal and oblique incidence (the angle is larger than the critical one) is schematically indicated by the dynamic vertical traveltime characteristics of Figure 2; these are based on experimental data. For oblique incidence, in addition to the longitudinal reflected and refracted wave, reflected and refracted

converted waves are also formed. Observations from interior points of the medium permit the tracking of each secondary wave which, in turn, may become the source of new waves. Reaching the zone of low velocities, or the surface, the waves are reflected and returned into the depth of the medium (Figure 3). An avalanche of waves is the result. VSP permits the study of the wave fields corresponding to various cross-sections, and evaluation of

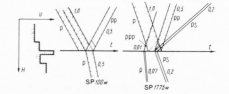

FIG. 2. Schematic graphs showing the distribution of energy for secondary waves for normal incidence (SP 100 m) and oblique incidence (SP 1775 m). This example involves a thin layer (well no. 42, Staro-Minsk). The numbers refer to the portion of the energy associated with each wave. (From Zapol'skyi, 1955.)

[2] For the sake of simplicity of discussion, the titles under the figures shall refer only to the registration of three-component and horizontal seismometers. The vertical Z-components shall not be specifically referred to.

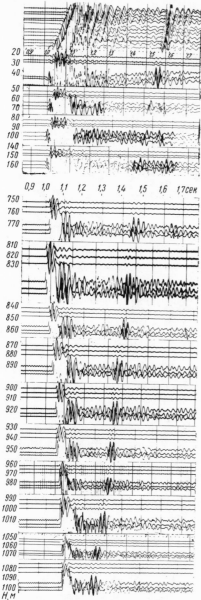

0,9 1,0 1,1 1,2 1,3 1,4 1,5 1,6 1,7сек

FIG. 3. Tracking of the longitudinal re-flected wave along vertical and horizontal profiles (well no. 2, Staro-Minsk.)

the roles that various wave types play in the process.

2) In most cases the profile in surface observations is practically parallel to the boundaries of the section; thus the loca-tion of the seismometers, in relation to the heterogeneities of the medium, remains invariant. For observations at interior points of the medium, the profile may cross the heterogeneities with which the waves are associated. Here, the differing kinematic and dynamic characteristics of various waves are sharply distinct; also distinct are the regions of their existence. For this reason, in many VSP situations the kinematic features of the waves pro-vide reliable criteria for the identification of wave types even without preliminary velocity determinations.

3) In surface observations, all horizons of the section are located below the seis-mometers, so the only direction of im-pinging waves is from below. For VSP, the horizons of the section are located below and above the seismometers so that the vertical profile comprises the registration not only of waves which impinge on the seismometer from below, but also various longitudinal and converted waves that have been subjected to reflection and con-version at the surface or at boundaries in the upper portion of the cross-section and which propagate downward. Experience with VSP indicates that the latter waves, as a rule, are distinguished by high inten-sity and may be reliably tracked at large distances from the surface. For all prac-tically accessible depths (of the order of 4000 m), the surface and the upper portion of the cross-section strongly influence the wave field. Thus a much larger number of waves is recorded at interior points of the medium than on the surface, and it is for this reason that the wave pattern of the former is characterized by its increased complexity. The study of the totality of waves permits the acquisition of most complete data on their origin and on the nature of the medium in which they propa-gate.

4) Pronounced heterogeneity and large velocity gradients in the upper portion of the cross-section cause a considerable

portion of the energy from a near-surface explosion, in the form of low-velocity waves to be propagated along the surface, so that penetration in depth is relatively small. Many of these waves interfere with each other and produce a continuous background of irregular waves, which degrades or entirely distorts surface seismograms near the shotpoint (for the MRLW) (Gal'perin, 1964b; Karayev and Lukashin, 1964; Rudakov, 1962.)

Generally, as the distance from the surface increases, the low-velocity background noise, as a rule, rapidly diminishes. Also, the filtering influence of the upper portion of the cross-section decreases. VSP is of special significance not only because of the "withdrawal" from the surface, but also because waves near the boundaries of the section may be studied. This is considered to be the paramount advantage of VSP over surface observations.

5) For observations at interior points of the medium, the direction of particle motion for simple body waves corresponds to the direction from which the waves approach the receiver, especially in the initial part of a signal. This is in contrast to surface observations, where the direction of particle motion is highly distorted by the upper portion of the cross-section. This fact can be used for a quantitative treatment of the trajectories of propagation in interpreting VSP material. Of special interest is the spatial polarization of seismic waves, a particularly sensitive parameter of the latter. Its study permits the acquisition of additional data concerning the structure of actual media and the particular features of the physics of propagation of seismic waves in these media.

6) The directions of approach of all waves observed at the surface are close to each other and vary only slightly along the profile. In VSP the direction of approach of various waves are sharply differentiated and vary markedly not only as

the source becomes more remote but also as the point of observation along the vertical profile changes. For different wave types the laws governing these variations may vary as well.

7) For observations at interior points of the medium the shape and intensity of the waves may vary in a discontinuous manner when the vertical profile crosses layers with sharply different elastic parameters.

8) The useful sensitivity of instrumentation on the surface is limited by the seismic noise background. At interior points of the medium, seismic noise decreases with depth, so that the useful instrument sensitivity may be considerably higher than for surface observations. VSP, therefore, permits the study of waves with substantially wider dynamic range; e.g., waves of very low intensities (such as head waves associated with thin layers).

The enumerated properties of wave fields at interior points of the medium and those of the VSP method determine the effectiveness and the exploratory capabilities of the latter.

VSP constitutes a further development and a generalization of all borehole investigations in the seismic frequency band, and, in particular, that of seismic well shooting and borehole seismic exploration. There is no doubt that, in the very near future, seismic well shooting will be completely replaced by VSP, since VSP provides information on the velocity cross-section and on details of horizons from both arrivals and waves registered in the subsequent portions of the record.

Combination of VSP with surface observations

The combination of horizontal and vertical profiling acquires a special meaning for the study of the origin of waves recorded on the surface. The waves observed on the surface may be tracked on the vertical profile down to the boundaries with which they are associated. For combined observations, one succeeds in utilizing the variation of wave parameters as a result of changes in the receiver-source distance, characteristic to surface observations, and of changes in the receiver-horizon distance, which is inherent in observations at interior points of the medium.

Combining VSP and SWL

The combination of VSP and SWL is of considerable interest, since synthetic seismograms computed from data of detailed characteristics of true velocities, obtained from SWL, permit the splitting of the complicated wave field and the study of the manner in which various heterogeneities of the cross-section influence that field (Gogonenkov, 1967; Karus, 1958). The application of computers provides the means of calculating wave fields involving a large number of layers and of accounting for refraction at intermediate horizons and wave absorption. The shape of the initial impulse, required for computation, may be obtained from VSP. Comparison of the computed wave pattern with data from VSP permits deciphering of the mechanism of wave formation and the realization of rigorous stratigraphic correlation of waves, and also evaluation of the influence of various elements of the cross-section on the wave field. This is particularly important in connection with the thin-layer cross-section which characterizes the actual medium. The presently available (relatively scant) experience with VSP and SWL combinations (Gamburtsev and Koptev, 1967; Gogonenkov, 1967) confirm the promising aspect of the latter. As more experience is accumulated, the possibilities of such combinations will substantially increase. In this connection it seems more expedient to change from ultrasonic observations to lower frequency sonic ones, which may be used in cased wells. With sufficient detailing, this approach should increase the possibilities of combining VSP with high-frequency observations.

The specific feature associated with observations in boreholes is the existence of a large amount of various types of unwanted waves. The intensity of some of these substantially exceeds that of the wanted wave.

VSP results in much improved data quality.

UNWANTED WAVES OBSERVED ON A VERTICAL PROFILE

Unwanted waves observed in VSP may be subdivided into two groups: waves associated with specific conditions for observations in wells, and waves governed by particular features of the wave pattern at interior points of the well. Here we will deal with the first group; the second will be discussed in Chapter 4.

The principal unwanted waves related to the specifics of borehole observations are the cable waves and waves dictated by the geometry of the well. To these waves one also may add waves which propagate along the fluid column enclosed by the well. High-velocity waves, registering ahead of first arrival waves propagating in the formations, are the easiest to study. These waves are responsible for a decrease of accuracy of velocity determination in seismic well shooting. As a rule, they are recorded in the subsequent portion of the record and, therefore, information on their characteristics is still scant and their nature may not always be uniquely established.

Cable waves

The specific conditions for observations in wells result in the following: the oscillations arising in the seismometer-cable system are superposed on the seismic waves propagating in the medium and distort their registration. Moreover, the cable transmits to the seismometer all oscillations pertaining to the surface. The orientation of cable waves on seismograms depends on the interrelationship among wave velocities in the cable and formations. The velocity of cable waves is determined by the cable construction. The velocity value and the effect of the cable wave may be ascertained in each particular case. This is done by recording impacts at the top of the well for a seismometer clamped to the walls of the borehole and for different degrees of cable slack. For multistranded armored cables,[1] the velocity is 2500-3500 m/sec. Therefore, for observations in the upper portion of the cross-section, in which the propagation velocity is low, cable waves may be recorded as first arrivals, thus distorting the data of seismic well shooting. Their pernicious influence was disclosed in full measure during the initial VSP efforts. Reliable contact of the seismometer with the wall of the well and mechanical "decoupling" of the seismometer from the weathered layer by slackening the cable (sometimes amounting to several meters) guarantee the acquisition of a record that is free from the influence of the cable wave over the full interval of recording. It is suitable not only for kinematic but also for dynamic treatment (Berdennikova et al, 1959; Voronin and Zhadin, 1964; Gal'perin and Frolova, 1961; Jolly, 1953; Levin and Lynn, 1958). The effect of the cable wave may be reduced also by various mechanical filters. However, such suppression is not considered adequate when one is confronted with a rigorously quantitative study of the dynamics of seismic waves.

The significance of pressing the seismometer to the wall must be considered

---

[1]Translator's remark: Here, and following, model types and designations pertaining to USSR equipment will be omitted.

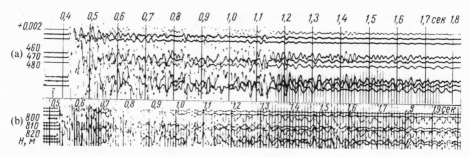

FIG. 4. Seismograms illustrating cable waves (SP 600 m, well no. 2, Staro-Minsk). (a) Upper receiver of the borehole device is not clamped; (b) lower receiver is not clamped.

somewhat more in detail, since lack of it, in the majority of situations, makes the acquired material worthless. Figure 4 illustrates the influence of clamping on the character of recording. Here seismograms are shown for a three-point probe in which one of the seismometers was not clamped to the wall. Comparison of the registrations of the unclamped with the two clamped seismometers indicates that, regardless of which of the seismometers is not pressed to the wall, the record of the loose receiver, prior to the shot, is characterized by a considerably higher level of noise; the rest of the record is, for all practical purposes, completely distorted by unwanted waves. The influence of contact is so pronounced that the lack of clamping can be easily ascertained, without any special check, by the noise background prior to the shot. With some experience, one may reach the same conclusion by visually observing the oscillograph during the process of recording. When the seismometer is properly clamped, the oscillations are rapidly damped after the cable has been given some slack. The clamping of the seismometers may also be checked by swinging the cable up to the pulley of the crown block. For tight contact of seismometers and for a slackened cable, such cable motion is either not sensed at all or is only weakly recorded. When the seismometers are not pressed against the wall, such swinging usually results in a complete disruption of registration. The clamping arrangement may also be checked by an electrical measuring device, wherein the borehole seismometer is switched over to a testing arrangement and the instant at which clamping is established is indicated by a pulse.

The seismometer clamping requirements may differ depending on the problem to be solved. For the acquisition of records primarily utilized for kinematic processing, these requirements are considerably less stringent than for records intended for dynamic treatment. For the latter, the reliability of contact must be checked by a detailed investigation of the oscillation spectra. The equality of contact is usually verified by comparing registrations obtained by identical seismometers placed directly on the surface and pressed to the wall of a shallow borehole or near the top of a deep one.

The specifications for each installation are, to a large degree, determined by the contact of the seismometer. For observations along a vertical profile that crosses layers with different elastic properties, the specifications for the seismometer installation are, in principle, not quite the same as those for surface observations. For VSP, the decisive consideration is the contact of the seismometer with the wall of the borehole, and this contact, basically, is determined by the force of clamping. Under cased well conditions, this force remains invariant. As VSP experience demonstrates, when work is conducted using clamping arrangements, a much better constancy of conditions for the set-up may be achieved than for surface observations.

Thus, reliable contact of the seismometer and its complete decoupling from the surface permit the exclusion of some unwanted waves and a substantial weakening of others. In some special cases, which exhibit sharply defined reflected waves, the latter are evident in the subsequent portion of the record even for unclamped seismometers (Demidenko, 1964, Yacobson, 1956). However, from such records, it is almost impossible to recover information on the dynamics of the event.

**Unwanted waves associated
with the construction of the borehole**

When the clamping mechanism is not controlled from the surface, work in uncased wells is associated with severe risks, i.e., damage to the walls, and the possibility of the device being hung-up at the wall. In this respect it seems much safer to work with cased wells. Moreover, observations in cased wells permit a broadening of the scope and a substantial reduction of operating costs. To that end one may employ standard production wells equipped with tension measuring devices and other types of cased wells. However, the quality of the data substantially depends on the construction of the well.

The adequately cemented casing column does not introduce noticeable distortions into the wave record (in the seismic frequency band). Analogous results have also been obtained abroad (Van Sandt and Levin, 1963). Practically all results of studies of wave fields in actual media discussed in the present book were obtained for observations in cased boreholes. One should, however, keep in mind that for sections of the well for which the casing column is poorly cemented there emerge parasitic oscillations which exist for practically all shotpoint well distances.

For the seismograms (Figure 5a) obtained for the same section of the borehole (1620-1640 m), from SP 1775 and SP 2500 m, the unwanted waves are represented by oscillations with vertical line-ups. Such records are characteristic in this particular well for a depth interval of 1600-1720 m, from any shotpoint. The unwanted waves of this type are associated with vibrations of the uncemented casing. Their intensity sharply increases for observations in wells of cumbersome construction, e.g., those having several strings of pipe, which are not cemented all the way to the top of the well.

Unwanted waves of that type, as a rule, may be observed for the upper portion of the well covered by a surface casing. Here, in the presence of even one string of production casing, observation of useful waves is practically impossible. The influence of the surface casing may be visually illustrated by means of a multichannel seismogram obtained for an interval of the profile which crosses the section in which the surface casing terminates (Figure 5c). In the lower portion of the seismogram which corresponds to the section of the profile beyond the surface casing, the reflected and multiple waves are reliably tracked, the waves being associated with different apparent velocities. For observations within the cased region (H<540 m), the correlation of almost all waves is disrupted and vertical line-ups prevail. Characteristically, these unwanted waves consist principally of oscillations with directions of particle motion near to the vertical. For this reason, while they completely disrupt correlation of longitudinal waves, they do not always interfere with that of converted and transverse waves.

Comparison of seismograms of the Z-component with the three-component symmetrical installation (Figure 5b, I, II), obtained for the very same points at

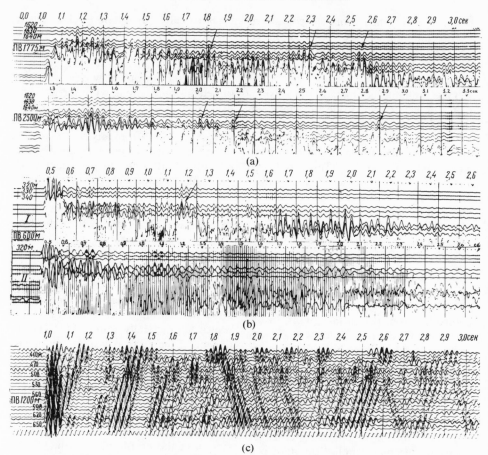

(a)

(b)

(c)

FIG. 5. Unwanted waves associated with borehole construction. (a) Profile section in which the casing is not cemented; (b,c) production casing is not cemented within the jig.

a depth of 320 m within the surface casing, indicates that, while it may be possible to identify some particular waves on the three-component seismogram, this feat is practically impossible for the vertical component.

For VSP, beginning in 1964, the section of vertical profile covered by the surface casing was usually repeated in a shallow well, drilled for the purpose in the vicinity of the main one. Accounting for the complexity of the wave pattern in the upper portion of the cross-section and aware of the importance of continuous tracking capability of waves, up to the very sur-

face, with the goal of correlation of data from vertical and horizontal profiles, the drilling of such auxiliary wells seems expedient. In the future, when exploring borehole sections considered to be of interest for the study of the wave pattern, cementing of all casing strings up to the top of the well should be judiciously provided for during the planning stages of the project.

Pipe waves. — Waves associated with the construction of the well also include pipe waves which cause distortion of the first arrivals. Pipe waves are usually excited by impacts at the edge of the casing column. This wave propagates along the steel pipe (casing) with an approximate velocity of 5.5 km/sec, the latter being almost independent of the velocities of the neighboring formations and of the drilling fluid. The pipe (tube) waves t_T, as a rule, are high-frequency irregular waves. In the upper portion of the cross-section, the intensity of these waves (i.e., of their vertical component) may be relatively high. However, the intensity rapidly decreases with depth (Figure 6) and with the distance of the shotpoint from the top of the investigated well. At depths of approximately 800-1000 m their intensity is usually so low that they practically do not interfere with the registration of waves propagating through the formations. We

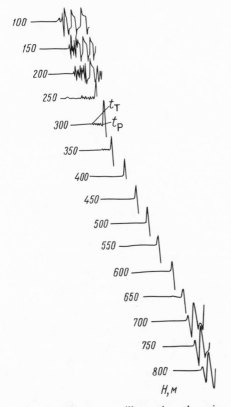

FIG. 6. Seismogram illustrating the pipe wave t_T (SP 100 m, well no. 1, Kletsko-Pochtov, Volgograd district).

shall not elaborate on pipe waves, since they are sufficiently well studied in ordinary seismic well logging (Puzyrev, 1957). For percussion-type excitation, pipe waves do not develop at all, or are inherently of low intensity, thus permitting the registration of first arrivals without distortion.

Waves propagating along the fluid column. — VSP seismograms very often exhibit waves in later portions of the record. These propagate along the fluid column that fills the borehole. We shall designate them by t_{FL} (Sharpe, 1942). These waves strongly interfere with the tracking of reflected waves. The dependence of the velocity of these waves on the constructional particulars of the well, appears to be the reason for delegating them to the category of unwanted waves of the first group. They are distinguished by high intensity which, for practical purposes, does not change with depth. The ratio of the t_{FL} wave to the first wave propagating along the formations, usually increases with depth but decreases with the distance of the shotpoint from the top of the well (for an in-line vertical profile).

The t_{FL} waves have a wide frequency spectrum and may be tracked on seismograms over considerable time intervals. The low values of velocities and the long duration of their registration result in the t_{FL} waves frequently overlapping the interval of registration of transverse waves on vertical profiles. Hence, during the initial experimentation, these waves (Horton, 1943) were identified as transverse waves converted at the bottom of the zone of low velocity (ZLV). In subsequent tests (Sharpe, 1942), the t_{FL} wave and the transverse wave were properly resolved. Usually in VSP one records both incident and reflected t_{FL} waves (i.e., reflected from the bottom of the well). In many instances multiple waves of this type also appear (up to the 6-7th multiplicity). Instances were also observed in which several in-

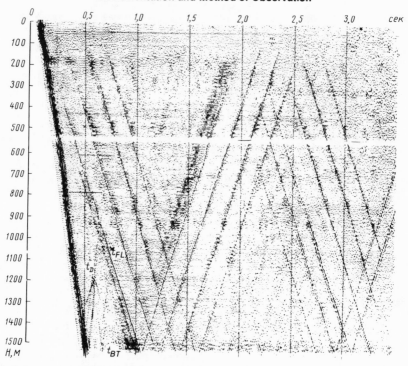

FIG. 7. Seismograms illustrating waves propagating along the fluid column t_{FL} (well no. 1, Kletsko-Pochtov).

cident and reflected waves, following one after the other were recorded (Figure 7). Such waves constitute a serious impediment to tracking useful waves in later portions of the record. In the initial portion of the lower seismograms, and at large depths (Figure 7), one can observe the disruption of correlation of useful waves associated with terrigenous Devonian deposits (t_D) and the crystalline basement (t_{BT}).

The velocities of the t_{FL} waves depend on the elastic parameters of the fluid as well as on those of the borehole walls (White and Sengbush, 1963). Comparison of propagation velocities of t_{FL} waves computed by Lamb's (1898) formula with those acquired from special experiments are in good agreement for uncased wells (Berzon, 1964; Riggs, 1955). The same experiments demonstrate that, for cased wells, a 40-percent increase of

the t_{FL} wave velocity occurs. Cased well velocities of 1430 m/sec were obtained. In such instances, the cable and the construction of the probe no longer influence the velocity of the t_{FL} wave. As the longitudinal waves travel through the cylindrical liquid column, velocity dispersion is observed. Study of this dispersion requires observations over a wide frequency range. Observations in the seismic frequency band (up to 200 hz) indicate that, if the ratio of the wavelength to the diameter of the borehole exceeds 50, the phase and group velocities of the t_{FL} wave are the same and its dispersion is not manifested (Riggs, 1955). The attenuation of the t_{FL} waves is low and there is no reduction of intensity due to spreading (increase of the wavefront). The high-frequency components of this wave are attenuated somewhat more rapidly and, as the number of multiple reflections increases, the low-frequency components become more prevalent.

The t_{FL} waves, in some discrete cases, are excited even from shotpoints located sufficiently far from the top of the borehole. The mechanics of their excitation is inadequately understood. The investigation of the dependence of the time of excitation of the t_{FL} wave on the shotpoint-well separation, for one particular area, demonstrated that the t_{FL} wave is excited by the direct wave propagating with a velocity of 1650 m/sec. In some instances t_{FL} waves were excited by the airborne wave. One may speculate that the intensity of the t_{FL} wave is highly dependent on the density of the fluid: as the density increases, the intensity of the waves decreases.

Occasionally one succeeds in reducing the intensity of these waves by lowering the water or mud level in the well under investigation. The principal means of suppressing the t_{FL} wave are suppression of high frequencies, suppression of low velocities, and an increase of the distance from the source to the vertical profile. Available tests indicate that the intensity of the t_{FL} waves on VSP seismograms decreases as the force of clamping the probe to the borehole wall is increased. The question of conditions of excitation and means of suppressing t_{FL} waves requires specific investigations.

Besides regular unwanted waves, there exists, at interior points of the medium, a background of irregular unwanted waves which likewise encumbers the correlation of waves, especially at large times when the intensity of the wanted waves has rapidly decreased. However, the problem of irregular noise background has not been studied at all. There are no clearly defined concepts either on the nature of the oscillations constituting this background, or on its frequency content and other properties.

Unwanted waves associated with shotholes. — Besides unwanted waves caused by specific conditions of recording, VSP seismograms may register unwanted waves originating in shotholes (Riggs, 1955). Specially planned experiments yielded two types of this noise: waves that are related to the construction of the shothole, and those related to the mechanics of observation. These investigations were examined in detail (Gal'perin, 1965b) and it is sufficient to mention basic conclusions only.

The detailed study of wave fields observed on the surface and at interior points of the medium, for generation of elastic waves in cased and uncased portions of the shothole, indicates that the wave fields may differ substantially, not only by virtue of their different intensity but also by the number of wave types. For shots outside the casing column ($h = 90$ m), for surface seismograms, one observes two waves: the longitudinal t_P and the transverse t_S waves (Figure 8). On seismograms for shots within the cased column ($h = 88$ and 30 m), the wave pattern is considerably more complicated. Not only the intensity of the waves has changed, but new waves have emerged as well. One of these (t_1), recorded by vertical seismometers, is of high intensity and may be correlated with certainty along the profile. The time difference for the arrival of wave t_1 and the direct wave t_P increases as the depth of the probe location decreases. The study of vertical and horizontal traveltime curves and the intensity and trajectories of displacement of particles has shown that this wave is a longitudinal diffracted wave, originating from the lower end of the casing pipe.

In addition to wave t_1, for shots within the casing, there is also wave t_2 which basically registers on horizontal seismometers. Study of the characteristics of this wave did not disclose its exact nature. It is most probable that the t_2 waves are surface waves generated by vibrations

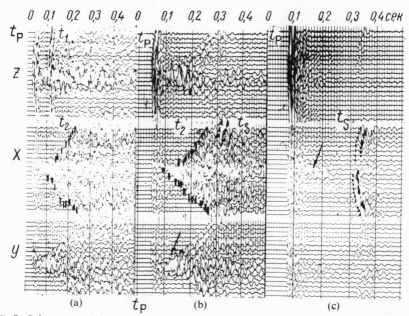

FIG. 8. Seismograms from three-component receivers (X, Y, Z) for a section of a horizontal profile of length 190 m, obtained for the following conditions: (a) Shotpoint in cased shothole at h = 30 m; (b) same for h = 88 m; and (c) uncased shothole at h = 90 m.

of the upper end of the casing, excited by the arrival of the direct wave.

Besides waves t_1 and t_2, associated with the construction of the shothole, other waves appear in the fluid column (Lamb, 1898) that may exhibit high intensity and may register in the immediate vicinity of the top of the shothole (in Figure 8 they are indicated by arrows). The analysis of the velocities of these waves (Berzon, 1964) demonstrates that in the upper portion of the cross-section where the velocity of the transverse waves in the medium is significantly lower than that of longitudinal waves in the fluid, the fluid waves will arrive earlier than the transverse waves, so that identification of the latter near the top of the borehole will be encumbered. At greater distances from the top of the shothole, these waves generally are not recorded. Thus, for torpedoing of boreholes, one should determine wave velocities from records where seismometers are distributed at different distances from the top of the shothole.

INSTRUMENTATION FOR VSP

The parameters and characteristics of VSP instrumentation do not differ essentially from those used in surface observations. Let us examine, separately, the depth (receiving) and the surface (recording) instrumentations.

Depth instrumentation

Up to now no ready-made borehole instrument for VSP has been developed. The question of *channel multiplicity of instrumentation* is of basic significance. Initially, equipment was used that permitted observations involving one seismometer only. Records at different points were obtained from different shots. Under such conditions, a large number of shots (100 and more) were observed at one point. For purposes of preservation of wave correlation, it is necessary to exert a strong control over the conditions of excitation, which is not always easy for a large number of shots.

In 1963 the first three-channel sounding device was developed and applied by the IPE AS USSR. Each of the seismometers was pressed against the wall of the well by means of independent clamps (Gal'perin 1965a). Such a probe permitted the execution of direct registration of one of the components (for example, the vertical component) simultaneously at three points, or the three-component registration at one point. Transition to three-point observations, aside from a reduction in the number of required shots, permits improvement in the correlation of waves in the subsequent portions of the records. In 1963 a large amount of observation was accomplished with the three-point probe. This permitted the formulation of the basic guidelines for VSP, as well as evaluation of its possibilities.

During the last few years a large amount of work was done with a two-point probe operated by a three-conductor cable. In this case the decoupling of the channels is accomplished by symmetric isolation transformers. For high transformer symmetry, cross-talk between channels is practically eliminated. Further increase in channel multiplicity causes considerable technical difficulties. To begin with, there is a shortage of adequate multistranded cables. A substantial increase of cable strands is unlikely in the immediate future. For multichannel registrations, systems that electronically increase the packing density of recording are employed. At present, several systems for increasing density are available. The most widely used system is the one in which frequency packing is employed. Several probes are being tested in which amplitude modulation and frequency discrimination of channels are employed. L. L. Khudzinskyi has worked out a twelve-channel probe based on pulse-width modulation.

Within the next few years, density packing should make it possible to produce multichannel records from deep boreholes.

But experience with VSP shows that quality of the data is not so much dictated by the multiplicity of channels as by the quality of each channel. This primarily involves decoupling seismometers, reliability of seismometer contact with the borehole wall, and frequency characteristic of the channel. Extensive investigation proves it is possible to obtain a stabilized wave pattern if the conditions of excitation remain invariant. In many regions even a single seismometer yields high-quality material. In view of the specific recording required for deep wells and the technical difficulties in creating multichannel probes which accept signals over a high dynamic range (where each seismometer is provided with an independent and reliable clamping arrangement), it becomes unrealistic at present to increase the channel multiplicity beyond twelve.

For the production of multichannel seismograms, it is most convenient to apply magnetic recording and sychronization of shot breaks (Demidenko, 1964). The use of magnetic recording, aside from its convenience, made it possible to analyze vertical seismic data in the manner already available for processing of surface observations; i.e., isolation of useful waves by frequency selectivity, controllable directional reception, and other interference systems of observation.

In the study of dynamic features of the wave field, very low-frequency seismometers are used in order to broaden the frequency characteristic of the channel in the region of low frequencies. This particularly relates to the study of the dynamics of direct waves and the mechanism of their absorption in actual media. Seismometers having a natural frequency of 3-10 hz have been employed. For the study of reflected waves for relatively small distances between shotpoint and borehole under investigation, electrodynamic seismometers having natural frequencies ranging from 18-30 hz are customarily used. Some had small physical dimensions which made it possible to group several per channel in order to increase the sensitivity. For regional investigations, in which vertical profiles were employed in conjunction with shotpoints located at distances of up to 30 km, low-frequency seismometers having natural frequencies of 3-15 hz were used. For the solution of some special problems, e.g., the study of the DSS wave field and the study of the variation of natural noise background with depth, borehole seismometers with a natural frequency of 1 hz were used.

Low-frequency seismometers, as a rule, require delicate handling. Therefore, they were specially adjusted and damped during lowering and lifting operations.

In the study of converted, transverse, and longitudinal waves at large distances (l = 15-30 km), three-component installations were used. The essential portion of the work was done with symmetrical installations which, for observations at interior points of the medium, have substantial advantages over those commonly used (Gal'perin, 1955; 1963a). In these situations, installations without controlled orientation were used, which complicated the correlation of waves.

The importance of reliable clamping of the seismometer to the borehole wall has been mentioned. In contrast to the numerous clampings of the gliding variety employed in production geophysics (in which the force of clamping does not exceed the weight of the probe so that the latter may move freely along the stem of the borehole activated by its own weight), in developing VSP we utilized arrangements for which the force of clamping substantially (2-3 times) exceeded the probe's weight. This was necessary, first, so that the clamped probe would be secured in the borehole and the cable could be slackened (in case of multipoint probes this requirement refers to the upper device of the probe); and, second, in order to avoid record distortions due to various resonance phenomena associated with conditions of the installations (Pasechnik, 1952a,b). The latter applies to all devices of the probe.

For such clamping, the recorded data were satisfactory not only for kinematic but also for careful dynamic treatment. Lately, probes of mixed type are sometimes used; the upper seismometer is hard-clamped, the remaining glide-clamped. Also, probes are being used in which all geophones are equipped with gliding clamps. In such cases various types of mechanical filters are employed for decoupling from the surface. One should mention that distortions caused by gliding clamps have thus far not been investigated. Also, the problem of the required force of clamping cannot be considered solved. This also is the case for the possibility of decoupling of cable waves by means of mechanical filters.

Requirements for clamping in VSP substantially influence the features of the construction of the clamps. Various constructions of clamping arrangements are described in literature, here and abroad (Khalyevich, 1955; Yakovenko, 1966; Jolly, 1953). The arrangements may be subdivided into two groups: those not controlled and those controlled from the surface.

The uncontrolled clamping arrangement which, once activated, (at the bottom of the hole or the lower point of the profile), keeps the probes clamped while it is being shifted along the borehole and allows investigations only during the lifting portion of the operation. Such clamps are only recommended for cased boreholes. At present, uncontrolled clamping is being used, and it is chiefly of the spring-type variety. Some are operated upon command from the surface. In most arrangements, the spring is released mechanically while the probe is being lifted. Also, automatic wedge-type clamps frequently are used, in which the force of clamping is determined by the weight of the geophone. The eccentric clamp is of this type. The clamping force of the eccentric device, prior to its engagement with the wall of the borehole, does not exceed 3-5 kg; other probes have eccentric clamps, wherein each geophone is clamped by removing from it the weight of a deeper geophone. Thus, when the lowest geophone of the probe is clamped, all other geophones are sequentially wedged-in. One should avoid using heavy uncontrolled clamping in deep uncased boreholes because of the threat of well damage. We conducted such observations in relatively shallow wells (up to 500-600 m), specially drilled for VSP. Gliding-type clamps used in VSP are slightly different from arrangements widely employed in production geophysical operations.

Controlled clamping arrangements have the capability of pressing the geophone to the wall and then removing that pressure at any point in the borehole upon command from the surface. This is primarily essential in uncased wells. Controlled clamping arrangements permit observation both during lowering and lifting of the borehole device. Also, should the necessity arise to return to any point of the profile, a repeat measurement may be accomplished.

Controlled clamping arrangements utilize clamps of the hydraulic or electromechanical types. For work in cased wells, magnetic clamps are used. The majority of controlled clamping arrangements used abroad are based on the electromechanical version. The existing controlled systems are complex and, apparently, are not perfected.

At present, three and six point probes are in use with each geophone pressed to the wall of the well by an independent clamping arrangement. The cable connecting all the geophones remains under tension. We have accomplished special experiments with the goal of studying and estimating the degree of acoustic coupling between the points of observation. Comparison of spectra of the direct wave recorded for single point and multipoint observations with those obtained from different geophones of the multipoint probe revealed that even if acoustic coupling does exist, it is insignificant for ordinary observations. However, this problem has not been explored fully and, when studying the dynamics of the waves, it is imperative to pay particular attention to the taut cable connecting the individual geophones.

In planning multipoint controlled systems, it is expedient to allow for possible sequential clamping of each geophone separately, with the interconnecting cable relaxed. When the probe is being lowered by a heavy multistranded cable, it is necessary to be able to check the cable as it moves along the borehole. Otherwise, when working at great depths, it is difficult to check the actual geophone motion, and the possibility exists that an extra cable is in the well. This may cause the cables to tangle, with resultant damage to the cable. It is convenient to check the progress of the geophone by means of a microammeter located in the circuit of the lower geophone of the probe. Alternatively, one may record one of the parameters usually considered in production (commercial) geophysical operations. In the latter case, such a check also permits one to accomplish strict correlation of points of observation with the geologic cross-section, which is required for the study of the wave pattern. This is most essential, since the depth to geophone is not always measured with sufficient accuracy.

Surface instrumentation

The recording of surface oscillations was accomplished by either standard or special stations similar to the standard ones. In order to obtain recordings suitable for dynamic treatment, magnetic tape records were duplicated by oscillographic records without filtering and, simultaneously, for one or two filter settings. Frequency filtering was accomplished basically upon playback of magnetic tapes.

It is particularly difficult to guarantee the required dynamic range for the recording of reflected waves. The dynamic range of standard instrumentation may be inadequate for recording undistorted signals in the time interval from 0 to 4-5 sec (Slutskovskyi, 1958). To obtain such records, careful and painstaking selection of the charge and instrument gain is required. When the wells are available for only a limited time, this is fairly difficult to accomplish. In order to augment the dynamic range of registration intended for dynamic treatment, the recording is usually made on three and sometimes five levels of amplification, differing from one another by a factor of 4 to 5. The signal from each geophone is fed to the inputs of amplifiers in parallel. A voltage-divider precedes the amplifier to avoid over-loading. The output of the amplifier is fed to special voltage dividers connected to two galvanometers.

To study refracted waves, low-frequency stations used in CMRRW were employed. For observations over large distances the dynamic range of the recorded waves is considerably smaller than in MRLW and, as a rule, two levels of amplification are sufficient. Because of the relatively rapid decrease of the noise background with depth in borehole observations, one may realize a substantially higher channel sensitivity than is possible for surface observations. Thus a record containing a large dynamic range is feasible. If for surface observation the useful sensitivity of the recording channel is limited by the background of microseisms, the limit for borehole observation is frequently set by natural electric noise of the amplifier. Therefore, reduction of instrument noise is very important in VSP not only for observation at large distances from the shotpoints, but even for those nearby, and particularly in the study of low intensity waves (e.g., head waves). The reduction of instrument noise for work at great depths under conditions of high temperatures and pressures requires further research.

The amplification of the recording channel is tested by a magnetic generator of constant amplitude or by an ordinary tone generator. In the latter case the output of the generator is recorded by a special galvanometer.

OBSERVATION PROCEDURES

VSP observation methods are similar in many respects to those used for surface observations. We shall restrict ourselves to an examination of specific questions related to VSP only.

Observation system

For VSP, as for surface investigations, the observation system is selected in accordance with the geologic structure of the region and the specifics of the problems to be solved. Thus, systems of observation varying in detail are employed: a single profile, a sequence of unrelated profiles[2] (when observations in one borehole are made from a sequence of shot-

[2]In VSP, when the vertical profile is shot from a sequence of shotpoints located at various distances from the top of the borehole, one obtains, in effect, a family of overlapping traveltime curves for a single profile. However, as a matter of convenience and simplicity of discussion, we shall agree to call such an ensemble of observations a sequence of vertical profiles.

points located along the surface), or a detailed correlation system of observation which guarantees the tracking of waves along vertical and horizontal directions at different depths. For the study of wave fields, systems of vertical profiles were shot from shotpoints located at distances from 0 to 30 km from the top of the well under investigation.

The selection of distances between shotpoints, and their number, are determined by the particulars of the problems. When VSP is conducted under conditions known from surface investigations of the wave field, a well-planned system of observation is possible. In such instances, surface observation reveals the most interesting and difficult locations to interpret, and the wave field is subdivided by vertical profiles located at corresponding distances from the source. If surface observations are lacking, it may be possible to compute a family of theoretical travel-time curves, based on available velocity data, and determine where different wave types will be recorded. VSP observation, depending on the problems to be investigated, may be accomplished either for the complete vertical profile or for separate sections thereof.

The seismometer spacing along the vertical profile is determined, in principle, by the same criteria that govern surface observations. For reliable wave correlation, the phase shift between neighboring points should not exceed about ⅓ wavelength. Since the wave velocities are different at different sections of the vertical profile, equal reliability of correlation is possible for different intervals between observation points. These intervals may be selected beforehand from electric well-log curves and from a general understanding of the cross-section.

Let us examine VSP systems as they apply to MRLW and CMRRW investigations as well as to those of the upper portion of the cross-section.

Systems of observation for MRLW. — The VSP problems most frequently considered in MRLW, stem from the character of the wave pattern on surface seismograms, and may be subdivided into two classes. In cases in which surface seismograms register stable regular waves within the required time interval, the purpose of VSP is to determine their nature and stratigraphic correlation. Most important here is the identification of singly reflected waves among multiple reflections of various types. When it is not possible to track regular waves on surface seismograms, or when such tracking is not considered to be sufficiently stable, VSP attempts to study the reflecting properties of boundaries considered to be of geologic interest. If the reflected waves are identified from observations at the immediate neighborhood of the boundaries, then we must determine why these waves are poorly correlatable on surface seismograms.

In solving all the above problems, with the exception of the last one, observations along the in-line vertical profile[3] are of fundamental importance. This may be explained in various ways. First, most of the MRLW work requires observations in the immediate vicinity of the shotpoint. Second, because of the particular kinematic features of waves for in-line vertical profiles, the region of interference of reflected waves with the direct wave is the shortest, and the waves are optimally time-separated. Third, observations along an in-line profile in a horizontally layered medium, or in a medium with small angles of dip, permit the study of normal incidence waves, where the wave pattern is the simplest and is

[3]We will designate a vertical profile, or horizontal one, as being in-line when the shotpoint is located along the line of the profile (at the top of the borehole, $l = 0$), and being off-line when the shotpoint is displaced from the profile line.

easy to compute. In this respect, the material gained from observation along an in-line vertical profile may be of special interest for dynamic treatment. Usually, in VSP work, the in-line vertical profile is the first to be considered. This yields, in addition to the wave pattern, data on the velocity cross-section and the layer velocities (based on first arrivals) which are necessary for subsequent refinement of the system of observation.

Off-line profiles are indispensable for the study of the intensity of reflected waves as it depends on the angle of incidence or on distance. Since the intensity of reflected waves increases, for incidence angles close to critical, and waves may be tracked up to very considerable distances, off-line vertical profiling provides means to study wave reflections where incidence exceeds the critical angle. This is the more significant, since the indentification of transcritically reflected waves from surface observations and for large distances is fairly difficult to accomplish. Reflected waves, originating from shot-points whose distance exceeds that of the reflecting horizon by a factor of 2 or 3 times, have been successfully tracked.

Systems of observation for the study of the upper portion of the cross-section and associated wave field. — The study of

reasons for the lack of reflected waves on surface seismograms amounts to the study of the wave field associated with the upper portion of the cross-section. Sharp boundaries of separation, low values of velocities, and the large number of waves of different nature forming a complicated interference field cause the complex problem and require highly detailed systems of observation. In the study of the uppermost portion of the cross-section, which is characterized by very low velocity values and by complexity of the wave field, it becomes necessary to decrease the detector spacing to 5 m, and, in the ZLV sometimes to 3 m. For the study of near-surface waves, combined systems of observation were employed. These consisted of a family of vertical profiles at distances which permit one to track the principal wave groups along vertical and horizontal directions on the surface, as well as at different depths (levels). Such systems permit the contouring of regions where groups of waves exist and the construction of time fields. In the majority of the regions investigated, the vertical system covered a zone of about 200 m in depth and 1500-2000 m in length. Such a system of observation required about 400-500 shots.

Figure 9 illustrates a system which sat-

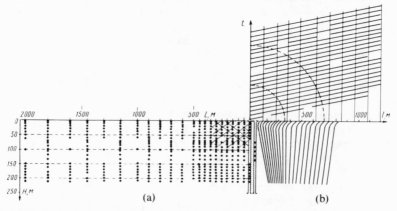

FIG. 9. (a) System of observation in the study of the upper portion of the cross-section. (b) Combination traveltime curves (schematic) for first waves (Dheltmess, Kirghiz SSR).

isfactorily portrayed the complicated wave fields characteristic of broad areas of Mid-Asian platforms (see Chapter 7). Analogous systems of observation were employed in the construction of the velocity cross-section (Gal'perin, 1964c).

The vertical plane observation system could have been accomplished with shots from one shotpoint and records for a sequence of boreholes distributed along a single line (of the profile). However, such a method of shooting the vertical system is difficult in practice. The use of multiple shots with observation in a single borehole is technically easier and economically more profitable. Application of such a system in a vertical plane is acceptable for horizontal layering. This proposition may be checked by studying the vector gradients of the time field for observations from shotpoints distributed at different azimuths in relation to the plane of investigation. An example of an analogous approach applied to the study of the upper portion of the cross-section was described abroad (White, 1965). If the conditions of axial symmetry are not met, the systems of investigation must be of spatial character, i.e., the shotpoints should be distributed at different azimuths with reference to the top of the borehole. The interpretation of observations should then be of spatial character as well. The procedures of such spatial observations of VSP have so far not been worked out. Methods applied in borehole seismic exploration, thus far utilizing only first arrivals, may be regarded as the initial phase in that direction.

Observation system for CMRRW operations. — VSP work according to the method of refracted waves is conducted to determine the nature of the waves and the identification of refracting horizons in the cross-section. Refracted waves, as is known, are observable at some distance from the shotpoint. For this reason, VSP observations are carried out along off-line vertical profiles. When selecting the shotpoint, the same principles as in MRLW operation apply. For the study of the wave pattern associated with the total thickness of sedimentary deposits, VSP was conducted for in-line and for a family of off-line profiles at distances up to 30 km, although some observations were carried out even for considerably larger distances. Such a system of observation permits the study of the characteristics of all waves formed in the medium for the most varied angles of incidence, from normal downward to normal upward, and also the study of laws governing the variations of the wave field with distance. Such systems of observation were carried out from $l = 0$ to $l = 2500$ m (see Figure 22), and up to $l = 14,000$ m (see Figure 118), and $l = 31,000$ m (see Figure 10). The difficulties of operating vertical profiles from shotpoints located at great distances, frequently required the shooting of particular sections of the profile, rather than of the complete profile (see Figure 118). When planning a VSP system of observation with the purpose of studying refracted waves, one should gather very careful information on particular features of the wave field from surface profiles, and the selection of each shotpoint should be adequately substantiated.

Combining systems of horizontal and vertical observations. — The most complete data on the wave field and on the nature of waves registered on surface seismograms, may be acquired by combining observations along a vertical profile with surface observations (along a horizontal profile). Waves recorded in surface observations must be tracked along the vertical profile up to the boundaries with which they are associated. The interrelationship of observations along vertical and horizontal profiles is dictated by the problems to be investigated and by the complexity of the wave pattern. It is ex-

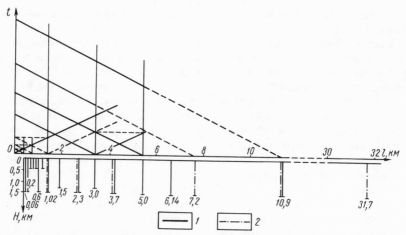

FIG. 10. Combination system of observation (Kletsko-Pochtov). (1) Registration of Z-component; (2) three-component observations.

pedient to use a combined system when the vertical profiles are shot at distances for which the wave pattern along horizontal observations is not wholly comprehensible. The in-line vertical profile, as a rule, is a mandatory phase of such systems.

As an example of combined observations one may consider the system that is schematically indicated in Figure 10. The scope of the study included the complete wave field associated with the thickness of sedimentary deposits and the crystalline basement. The most detailed system of observation was obtained for the study of the upper portion of the cross-section. It consists of 11 shotpoints. The sequence of shotpoints in the interval from 0 to 2300 m is primarily useful for the study of reflected and refracted waves in the thickness of Carbonate deposits. For the study of converted reflected and converted transmitted waves associated with boundaries in the upper portion of the cross-section (400, 800, 1000, 2300 m), three-component observations were carried out. Shotpoints at large distances (3000-7000 m) were utilized for the observation of refracted waves in the immediate vicinity of the deep horizons, as well as waves refracted in Carbonate de-

posits embedded at shallow depths. Records from shotpoints 10,900 and 31,700 m yielded waves which propagate along the crystalline basement, when these waves were registered as first arrivals over the complete vertical profile. In this instance, special significance was attributed to the determination of the nature of the waves forming the initial portion of the record involving the vertical component. From the same shotpoints, converted transmitted waves were recorded, which are associated with deep horizons and the top of the crystalline basement. The described system of observation, involving vertical profiles, was related to a system of observation involving a horizontal profile: it established the nature of the principal waves observed on surface seismograms in the interval from 0 to 31 km. The weight of the charges used during the shooting of the system was subject to wide variations (from 0.1 to 100 kg), and substantially complicated the processing of the records. The amplitudes of the records, obtained for different charges, were normalized to a single charge (Pogonyailo, 1970).

Conditions of excitation

A large volume of VSP work disclosed

the mechanism of the strong influence of the conditions of excitation on the quality of the data in seismic exploration. This influence is contained primarily in the direct wave, which, after all, initiates the whole wave process. The direct wave thus plays a role in the shaping of each particular wave and in the structure of the whole seismogram. In many instances, the conditions of excitation, for all practical purposes, dictate the exploratory possibilities of the observation. Let us examine the specific and basic technical particulars of conditions of excitation as they apply to problems of VSP.[4]

Constancy of conditions of excitation. — For VSP, because of the use of probes containing a low number of channels, and occasionally even single geophones, it is necessary to produce a large number of shots in order to shoot a given profile. Since the form of the direct wave (see Chapter 6) strongly depends on conditions of excitation, the constancy of the latter is mandatory for the acquisition of high-quality data. If the excitation conditions are subject to variation, the form of the first incident wave becomes unstable. Sometimes even insignificant variations in the depth of charge may result in substantial changes in the form of the incident wave and in a disruption of wave correlation along the vertical profile. For shots in sandy-clay formations, the shape of the event usually is firmly established after the first 3 or 4 explosions and is subsequently well-preserved.

In some particular cases, it was possible to produce 30-40 shots in a single shothole. The repeatability of the events is significantly worse for shots in hard media (shales and marls). In such cases, as the weight of the charge increases the

[4]The influence of conditions of excitation on the form of the direct wave is examined in Chapter 6.

stability of excitation conditions rapidly deteriorates. As the sequence of the shots in such a borehole increases, one usually observes a scattering in the amplitude ratios and in the periods of individual phases. Available data indicate that laws governing the variation of form of the record are usually preserved within a given area.

With the goal of studying the invariance of excitation conditions, many repeat shots at different shot depths and with different charge sizes were undertaken. The effects of these shots were recorded at a depth of 200 m by channels having a passband of from 20-400 hz. Analysis of the records indicated that, for relatively small charges (up to 1.2 kg), the duplication of the event is satisfactory (Figure 11a). For larger charges (up to 2.5 kg) one observes a slow increase of the period of first oscillations, as well as of the duration of the impulse with increase of the shot number (Figure 11b). The impulse amplitude is variable and is related to washouts of the shotholes, work interruption, etc. The first 2-3 shots produce, as a rule, a sharply changing amplitude. After that, the amplitude seems to settle down. There is a tendency for the impulse amplitude to increase with repeated shooting. Least stable is the ratio of amplitudes of different phases, particularly the ratio of amplitudes of the first and the third peaks, which may be larger or smaller than unity. As the shot number increases, one observes a gradual weakening of the first peak, after which it increases smoothly. Spectral analysis of impulses indicates that its repeatability is adequate and that scattering is usually attributable to washouts. The shape of the spectrum is less stable for a large charge.

For VSP work, it is important to obtain a simple direct wave of short duration. In so doing, the regions of interference of the direct and secondary waves

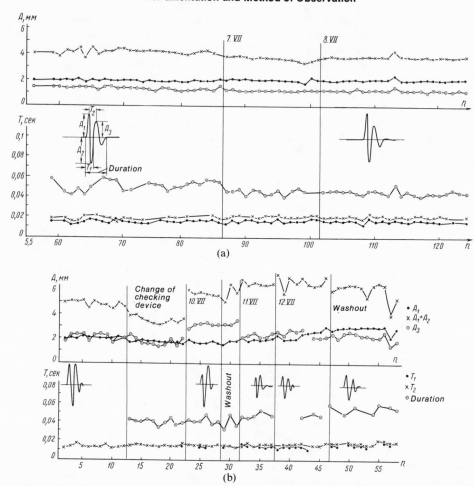

FIG. 11. Graphs illustrating the periods and amplitudes of the first impulse, dependent on the sequential shot number *n* (a) for charges of 1.2 kg, and (b) for charges of 2.5 kg. (h = 125 m, SP 70 m, well no. 4, Kudinov, Volgograd district.)

become less extended, which permits the tracking of reflected waves in the immediate neighborhood of the reflecting boundaries and an increase in the accuracy of stratigraphic correlation of the seismic horizons. Experience demonstrates that, for a relatively simple structure of the ZLV, one practically succeeds in getting rid of ghost-waves, by placing the charge just below the ZLV. In these cases, an increase of charge depth worsens the excitation conditions and complicates the seismogram. When the zone is structurally complex, containing several layers, it is usually not possible to eliminate the ghost-waves entirely. To secure a direct wave of simple form and short duration, it is necessary to separate the ghosts from the direct wave. This is achieved by the effective, although cumbersome, expedient of placing the charge at greater depths. However, this causes the number of waves on the seismograms to increase sharply, and the structure of the seismogram is substantially more complex. For the solution of some geologic problems, it is more advantageous to have a first wave which is of somewhat more complex shape and longer duration, but which would result in records made up of a considerably smaller number of waves. The latter substantially facilitates the interpretation.

Depth of shot. — For a very inhomogeneous upper portion of the cross-section, the depth of charge may exert a strong and, occasionally, a deciding influence on the shape of the incident wave. When the charge depth varies, new ghost-waves may appear and the conditions for their interference with the direct wave may change. As a result, the whole pattern of the incident waves may change, and with it the whole wave field. Moreover, as the charge depth changes, the lithology at shot depth may vary. Experiments demonstrate that variation of shot depths may substantially influence the frequency content of the waves being excited. From the graph of dominant frequencies for an in-line profile (Figure 12) one can see that, even for observations at great depths (from 1500 to 2700 m), the dominant frequency of the first impulse, for explosions at 125 m, is 65-70 hz, for those at 70 m it is 50-55 hz, and for a depth of 16 m, the frequency is about 45 hz. Thus, the depth of charge should be selected in accordance with the problems to be solved.

Charge size. — In VSP the weight of charge is selected from direct observations at great depths. Experience indicates that the form of the incident wave is practically independent of the size of the charge. An increase in the charge weight almost always results in pronounced complications of the wave field from unwanted waves associated with the upper portion of the cross-section. Moreover, as the charge size increases, the duplication of repeat shots deteriorates. Thus, it is expedient to use the smallest possible charges. The high sensitivity of VSP in-

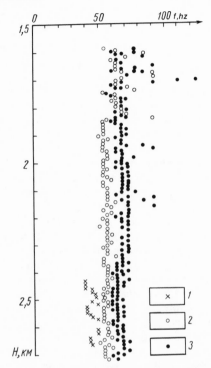

FIG. 12. Graphs of dominant frequencies of direct wave (well no. 90, Kudinov). (1) h = 16 m. (2) h = 70 m. (3) h = 125 m.

strumentation permits, in principle, the use of charges that are substantially smaller than those employed in surface profiling. When comparing records obtained from charges of different weight, one should take into account the possibility of wave field variations.

In the process of development of the VSP method, the following approach was worked out in reference to the selection of conditions of excitation. At several points in the borehole under investigation (below the principal reference horizons of the upper portion of the cross-section, usually in the depth interval of from 1000-2000 m), several shots are recorded, which are produced at different depths (between 5 and 10 m) in the shothole. The operating depth is where the direct wave appears to be the simplest and the shortest. A sequence of shots at that depth then permits the selection of the optimal charge.

Experience with VSP indicates that spectrum control at the source is highly effective. The idea is to excite a spectrum at the source of the impulse which would be compatible with the dominant frequencies of the useful waves; only under such conditions may one fully utilize the energy of the explosion. For control of the frequency content of the impulse, the particulars of the structure of the upper portion of the cross-section should be investigated, since the latter is known to be essential in the formation of the impulse. In some instances, in order to increase the resolving power and to simplify the wave pattern (in particular, to increase the depth of penetration), there arises the necessity to generate a low-frequency source impulse. Experience indicates that for shots in unconsolidated deposits of the ZLV, lower frequency waves are excited than for shots below the zone. A change of the frequency content of the impulse may also be accomplished by utilizing time-delayed explosions or by changing the grouping parameters for group air shots.

Excitation of transverse waves. — Explosions from small charges in shotholes possess definite directional characteristics and excite sufficiently intense transverse waves (Berzon, 1964; Vinogradov et al, 1967; Gal'perin, 1964c). The latter are recorded and utilized in the torpedoing of wells for the study of propagation velocities of transverse waves in the uppermost portion of the cross-section. However, small charge explosions cannot be utilized in the study of transverse wave velocities at large depths. As the charge increases, the directivity of the source deteriorates. Under certain seismological conditions, we learned that large surface charges in prospecting pits and shallow boreholes generated intense transverse waves. These waves propagate downward

to great depths and may be applied to the solution of geologic problems.

In order to classify the cross-section according to the velocities of transverse waves and determine their absorption, direct transverse SH-waves were excited by means of a mobile weight-dropping device mounted on a crane comprising directional features (Anonymous, 1962). If the bottom of the hole is kept in good condition, the repeatability of records resulting from weight-dropping may be better than those from explosions. Moreover, percussion-type excitation yields a much narrower frequency spectrum of the signal in the low-frequency region. For the upper portion of the cross-section, it is often possible to obtain records that are less distorted by unwanted waves than those resulting from explosions. For a 1200 kg weight, falling from a height of 3-4 m, direct transverse waves were registered down to depths of 1300-1500 m.

The excitation of reflected transverse waves was accomplished by a scheme devised under the guidance of N. N. Puzyrev (1967, and Puzyrev et al, 1967). The shots were fired in two shotholes located at either side of a loose-soil zone, created earlier by an explosion in a third hole located between the first two. This permitted directionally opposing (+ and −) interactions. In addition, grouping of directional explosions was also carried out. Observations at interior points of the medium permit an evaluation of the directivity and the effectiveness of the source by means of comparison with an ordinary directional shot. Such a comparison demonstrated that the directivity of an explosive source is highly dependent on the medium in which the explosion occurs. For shots in clayey formations, the directivity of the explosive source is as good as that of a percussive source. However, for shots in sandy formations, the explosive source possesses a considerably lower directivity than the percussive source. In that situation, explosion records compared to percussion records are more complicated, since they contain a considerably larger number of waves and the relative intensity of useful waves is lower.

In the study of "plane wavefront" generation, the vertical profile was shot with lumped charges at shotpoints distributed along the line of the profile.

Checking of conditions of excitation. — Tests indicate that excitation conditions can be checked most effectively by examining the direct wave at interior points of the medium. When testing for these conditions we endeavored to obtain a direct wave that would register an event on the auxiliary checking setup and on the deep setup that would be of similar form. To this end, the checking setup was usually placed below the explosion, in a special borehole at a depth of 150-200 m. Recording was done for low channel sensitivity (and, normally, without amplification) and for a wide-frequency passband (10-300 hz). It was often possible to produce, on auxiliary channels, records that were analogous in form to those from deep borehole geophones. As a further check on the shape of the direct wave, registration of groups of geophones distributed on the surface within a circle having a radius of 70-100 m (with the shotpoint in the center) was occasionally employed. Such averaging also yielded a surface-observed direct wave event that was reasonably similar to the one observed at depth.

Sometimes excitation conditions are checked by overlapping points of observation along the vertical profile. Special instrumentation was employed for observations at large distances from the source when the registration of auxiliary and depth geophones could not be accomplished simultaneously. Under these conditions, each explosion with large charges was produced in a new shothole. The last

are distributed within a circle of radius 20-30 m from the top of the well into which the auxiliary probe was placed. The problem of investigating excitation conditions is not fully solved. To this end, supplementary experimentation is required. Attempts to improve the observed results by introduction of various corrections allowing for the instability of excitation conditions usually degraded the results further.

VSP and torpedoing

It is interesting to compare the procedures of VSP observation with that in which the explosions are produced in a well at different depths, i.e., along the vertical profile (hence the name "torpedoing"). In the latter case, the observations are carried out along a horizontal profile on the surface.[5] Torpedoing is principally used for the study of velocities of direct longitudinal and transverse waves, and, less frequently, for the determination of the nature of waves of different classifications in the uppermost portion of the cross-section and in the ZLV (Berzon, 1964; Gal'perin, 1964c).

In processing of torpedoing data, waves may be identified in two directions: along the horizontal at different depths and along the vertical at different distances from the top of the well. For VSP, correlation along horizontal directions is accomplished by comparing records at the same depth for shots distributed in the neighborhood of the surface at different distances *l*. Vertical correlation is accomplished by data resulting from profile shooting out of a single shotpoint. In torpedoing, correlation along the horizontal is accomplished by multi-channel recordings of a single shot. Correlation along the vertical is done from records

[5]Such observations are sometimes called inverted well shooting, which corresponds more closely to the essence of the method.

obtained from different shots. The quality of correlation, in the above case, substantially depends on conditions of excitation and the details of shooting. In that respect, vertical correlation in torpedoing is analogous to horizontal correlation in VSP. As for vertical correlation in VSP, it might, in principle, be considered analogous to horizontal correlation in torpedoing. However, if multi-channel recording and correlation along the horizontal profile are carried out with care and if difficulties have not been encountered, then, for VSP, because of the particulars of observation at interior points of the medium, tracking of waves along the vertical profile is associated with considerably more pronounced difficulties. In torpedoing, it is often cheaper, and technically easier, to realize a more detailed system of observation than in VSP. Torpedoing is difficult because of the necessity of a deep well which is suitable for explosions. Moreover, in torpedoing, the ability to apply the direction of particle motion to the analysis of the wave pattern is almost completely lost.

Torpedoing in principle, permits the acquisition of a set of observations which, as far as the kinematics of the situation is concerned, is analogous to the set which VSP could yield. All points of excitation are tacitly transposed to the top of the well, whereas all wave arrival times recorded at the surface are ascribed to points of the medium that are located at a depth equal to the depth of the shot, and are at that distance from the top of the well, at which the surface seismometers are located. This is justified under conditions of horizontal layering. Because of the simplicity of field procedures and the ease with which highly detailed data sets can be acquired, torpedoing is usually expedient for the study of the upper portion of the cross-section down to a depth of 100-200 m. In VSP the source is customarily located at some definite depth, while for torpedoing, the seismometers corresponding to that source are located at the surface. This difference must certainly be accounted for when both systems of observation are compared.

Chapter 3
PARTICULAR FEATURES OF WAVE KINEMATICS ON THE VERTICAL PROFILE

The kinematic particulars of various wave types have been studied in sufficient detail for horizontal profiling. Equations for horizontal traveltime curves for a great variety of seismogeologic conditions have been derived and discussed. Kinematic particulars of waves in vertical profiling have been studied much less. Basically, vertical traveltime curves for first arrivals of on-line and off-line vertical profiles were examined. These characteristics were utilized in seismic well shooting by means of incident and refracted waves. Vertical traveltime characteristics for waves registering at later portions of the records were practically ignored until recently. Papers dedicated to the investigation of vertical traveltime curves of different wave types have appeared during the last few years, principally because of the development of VSP. The most complete analysis of vertical traveltime curves has been made by Rudnitskyi (1968) and Demidenko (1964), the results of which we shall use frequently. Experience in interpretation of the wave pattern from VSP demonstrated that the kinematic features of waves arising in vertical profiling may be considerably more significant than those associated with horizontal profiling. Therefore, the study of the kinematics of waves for VSP is of great practical significance. In the present chapter the kinematic particulars of waves in vertical profiling are examined. Only the simplest structures are considered for the medium: homogeneous media and media with a single boundary.

On VSP seismograms, like surface seismograms, the first waves registered on individual sections or along the entire profile are the direct or transmitted waves, refracted and head waves, depending on the geologic structure and the distance between the shot point and the top of the borehole. The subsequent arrivals are associated with reflected and refracted waves (longitudinal, transverse, and converted) as well as multiples. The direct wave on a vertical profile in a homogeneous medium is the first wave with positive apparent velocity. In layered media, this is a transmitted wave. For a continuously varying medium, the wave is by nature a refracted wave. A refraction is understood to be a wave having negative apparent velocity. Depending on the law of velocity variation, this wave may be either a curved-ray refraction or a head wave. In contrast to the curved-ray refraction, a headwave is a wave whose source is diffraction. Near the point of emergence, such a wave appears to be an interferential refracted wave.[1]

In the presence of steeply dipping boundaries, the above signs given to the apparent velocities of direct and refracted waves may, under some circumstances, become reversed in polarity.

For a clearer understanding of the particulars of traveltime curves of various waves and their interrelationship, it is expedient to examine the traveltime characteristics for each medium, and to consider the totality of all wave types. The traveltime curves are investigated in the plane of the raypath, i.e., the plane that is orthogonal to the line of extent of the boundary (Figure 13).

[1]Editor's Note: In keeping with common usage, the term "refracted wave" will be used to designate a wave, other than a reflection, which is returning toward the surface. A refracted wave may have been diffracted at an abrupt velocity interface, called "head wave" in the translation, or may have been bent back toward the surface by travel in a medium whose velocity increases continuously with depth, called "curved-ray refraction" in the translation.

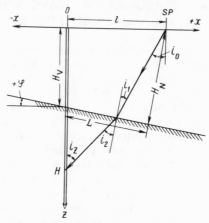

FIG. 13. Derivation of traveltime curves.

KINEMATIC PARTICULARS OF WAVES IN HOMOGENEOUS MEDIA

Let us examine vertical time-distance curves of waves recorded in media with constant velocities and in media with gradational changes in velocities.

Medium with constant velocity

In a homogeneous medium, and for constant velocity, only direct longitudinal and direct transverse incident waves register. For these, the traveltime characteristic is determined by the equation

$$t = \frac{1}{v} \sqrt{H^2 + l^2}$$

which, for the off-line vertical profile ($l \neq 0$), represents a hyperbola, whose axis coincides with the axis of the abscissa. As H increases, the traveltime curve for the off-line vertical profile approaches asymptotically the traveltime of the in-line vertical profile which is represented by the straight line $t = H/v$. The latter formula is the one used to determine the average velocity v_{av} in usual seismic well shooting.

Gradational medium

For actual media, it is characteristic for the velocity to vary continuously with depth, within a single lithologic formation. Discontinuous variation is observed at boundaries between one formation and another. For media with weak velocity differentiation, the velocity gradient normally decreases with depth. For such media, the law of variation of velocity with depth (Berzon et al, 1962; Kondrat'yev and Gamburtsev, 1963; and Puzyrev, 1957), is satisfactorily approximated by the function

$$v(H) = v_0 (1 + \beta H)^{\frac{1}{a}}, \quad 1 \leqslant a \leqslant 3. \tag{1}$$

For $a = 1$ the relationship of velocity and depth is linear and the velocity gradient remains constant.

In continuously-variable layers the first waves registered on seismograms are curved-ray refractions while the subsequent arrivals are multiply refracted waves, i.e., those having been reflected from the surface. In seismic exploration it is common to determine the number of multiplicity according to the number of reflections from the lower boundary. Refracted waves in a homogeneous medium are not subject to reflections. However, for our purposes, it is convenient to establish the convention that the point of maximum penetration of the ray is considered to be a reflection, and to refer to the number of multiplicity to that point. Moreover, for each wave of any given order of multiplicity, there exists a section of the vertical profile where the wave propagates upward with a negative apparent velocity, and downward with a positive velocity, designated $-$ and $+$, respectively, in the formulas.

The equations for the family of rays and vertical traveltime fronts for a gradational medium in parametric form are expressed by (Rudnitskiy, 1968),

$$l = 2k \int_0^{H_r} \frac{pv(H)\,dH}{\sqrt{1 - p^2v^2(H)}} \pm \int_0^{H} \frac{pv(H)\,dH}{\sqrt{1 - p^2v^2(H)}}, \tag{2}$$

$$t = 2k \int_0^{H_r} \frac{dH}{v(H)\sqrt{1 - p^2v^2(H)}} \pm \int_0^{H} \frac{dH}{v(H)\sqrt{1 - p^2v^2(H)}}, \tag{3}$$

where the parameter is

$$p = \frac{\sin i_n}{v(H)} = \frac{1}{v(H_r)}.$$

Considering relationship (1), the equation for the in-line ($l = 0$) vertical traveltime curve of the first wave is determined by the equation (Puzyrev, 1957),

$$t = \frac{a}{\beta v_0(a-1)}\left[(1 + \beta H)^{\frac{a-1}{a}} - 1\right], \tag{4}$$

while the coordinates of the points at which the traveltime curves have a minimum are determined (Rudnitskiy, 1968) from the expressions:

$$l = \frac{1}{\beta}(2k \pm 1)\sqrt{1 + \beta H_{min}}\left(\frac{\sqrt{\beta H_{min}}}{1 + \beta H_{min}} + \arccos\frac{1}{\sqrt{1 + \beta H_{min}}}\right), \quad \text{for } a=2$$

$$t_{min} = \frac{2}{\beta v_0}(2k \pm 1)\sqrt{1 + \beta H_{min}}\arccos\frac{1}{\sqrt{1 + \beta H_{min}}},$$

$$l = \frac{1}{\beta}(2k \pm 1)\left[1 + 2(1 + \beta H_{min})^{2/3}\right]\sqrt{(1 + \beta H_{min})^{2/3} - 1}, \quad \text{for } a=3$$

$$t_{min} = \frac{3}{\beta v_0}(2k \pm 1)(1 + \beta H_{min})^{1/3}\sqrt{(1 + \beta H_{min})^{2/3} - 1}.$$

The presence of two signs in the term $(2k \pm 1)$ accounts for a discontinuous change (of one unit) of the order of multiplicity at these points.

Differentiating (3), one may obtain an expression for the apparent velocity of the first wave ($k = 0$)

$$\frac{dt}{dH} = \frac{\sqrt{1 - p^2v^2(H)}}{v(H)}$$

and the depth of ray penetration $H_{min} = H_r$. Thus, the ordinate of the minimum of traveltime curves corresponds to the depth of maximum ray penetration (for a $\geqslant 1$).

Let us examine, more in detail, the linear law of increase of velocity with depth ($a = 1$), which is the situation most frequently used for approximation of the cross-section.

Linear law of velocity increase

The parametric equations for the traveltime curves of refracted waves in that case have the form (Rudnitskiy, 1968)

$$H = \frac{1}{pv_0\beta} \left\{ \sqrt{1 - \left[(2k \pm 1)\sqrt{1 - p^2v_0^2} - l\beta pv_0 \right]^2} - pv_0 \right\}, \tag{5}$$

$$t \downarrow = \frac{1}{\cdot \beta v_0} \ln \frac{(1 + \beta H)\left(1 + \sqrt{1 - p^2v_0^2}\right)^{2k+1}}{p^{2k}v_0^{2k} [1 + \sqrt{1 - p^2v_0^2} \, (1 + \beta H)^2]}, \tag{6}$$

$$t \uparrow = \frac{1}{\beta v_0} \ln \frac{[1 + \sqrt{1 - p^2v_0^2} \, (1 + \beta H)^2] \left(1 + \sqrt{1 - p^2v_0^2}\right)^{2k-1}}{p^{2k}v_0^{2k}(1 + \beta H)}. \tag{7}$$

Equation of traveltime curves for first waves (zero multiplicity). — This may be obtained from equations (5) and (6) by means of exclusion of parameter p:

$$t = \frac{1}{v_0\beta} \text{ arch} \left[\frac{\beta^2 (l^2 + H^2)}{2 (1 + \beta H)} + 1 \right]. \tag{8}$$

For the particular case of an in-line profile the expression is

$$t = \frac{1}{v_0\beta} \ln (1 + \beta H). \tag{9}$$

Equations (8) and (9) were obtained by Puzyrev (1957). The off-line traveltime (for $l \neq 0$) possesses a minimum, the ordinate of which is determined by expression

$$H_{min} = \frac{1}{\beta} \left(\sqrt{1 + \beta^2 l^2} - 1 \right). \tag{10}$$

As the distance from the source increases, the ordinate of the minimum also increases. The geometric locus of minimum points is determined by the coefficient of velocity increase and may be applied to compute the latter (Gal'perin, 1963b; 1964c). The upper portion of the traveltime curve, which is convex toward the depth axis, corresponds to a negative apparent velocity, the lower portion of that curve, concave toward the depth axis, corresponds to a positive velocity. The particulars of vertical traveltime curves of refracted waves permit the identification of curved-ray refraction even in the case of a medium whose properties vary quite slowly with depth.

Let us examine the horizontal and vertical traveltime curves of first waves computed according to the linear law of velocity increase with depth and for coefficients $\beta = 0.0002$, 0.0004, and 0.0010 m^{-1} (Figure 14). For the first two values of β, the horizontal traveltime characteristic is almost linear. Some curvature in the horizontal traveltime curve is observed only for $\beta = 0.001$ m^{-1}. But the vertical traveltime curves (computed for three values of l) are curved and possess minima whose ordinates increase as rapidly as l and β increase. This is clearly evident from the curves that characterize the variation of the location of the minima of the vertical travel-

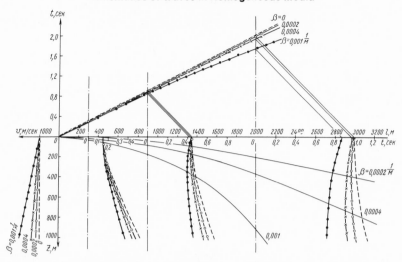

FIG. 14. Computed combination traveltime curves of first head and refracted waves.[2]

time curves for first waves as a function of l and with β as a parameter (thin solid lines). The family of lines of traveltime minima, computed for various coefficients of velocity increase β, may be utilized as a chart for the determination of β based on observed data. Vertical traveltime curves for homogeneous (dotted lines) and gradational media differ from each other in a fairly pronounced manner.

The kinematic particulars of the first refracted waves along the vertical traveltime curve are illustrated by combination traveltime curves (Figure 15). The vertical profile was shot from eight shotpoints at intervals of 170-250 m. The horizontal traveltime curve for first waves is nearly linear. The vertical traveltime characteristics are curved and exhibit minima whose ordinates increase as l increases. The apparent velocities of the upper portion of the traveltime curves are negative; those of the lower portion are positive. The locus of minima (reverse of impingement directions) corresponds to the law of velocity variation with depth having a coefficient $\beta = 0.00048\ m^{-1}$.

Traveltime curves of refracted waves. — In contrast to surface observations, primary and multiple waves registering on vertical profiles differ in directions of approach at profile points, and have correspondingly different signs of their apparent velocities. Waves propagating downward are registered in pure form only on vertical profiles.

For traveltime curves of waves of any order of multiplicity, the point of inflection is characteristic, corresponding to reflection from the surface where $H = 0$. At this point the direction of propagation of the wave changes. Also characteristic is the point of acuteness of first order (Figure 16). At fixed depth, the apparent velocity of waves increases as the order of multiplicity increases. The time values at which the multiple waves arrive at the surface (at the points of inflection on the traveltime

[2]Editor's note: In this figure, the computed traveltimes of the horizontal seismic profile are inconsistent with the computed traveltimes of the vertical seismic profile for zero depth. The horizontal profile traveltimes are approximately twice the vertical profile traveltimes.

curves) may be obtained from equations (5) and (6) by means of substitution into them of the parameter value p for $H = 0$:

$$t = \frac{2k}{\beta v_0} \ln \frac{l\beta + \sqrt{4k^2 + l^2\beta^2}}{2k}.$$ (11)

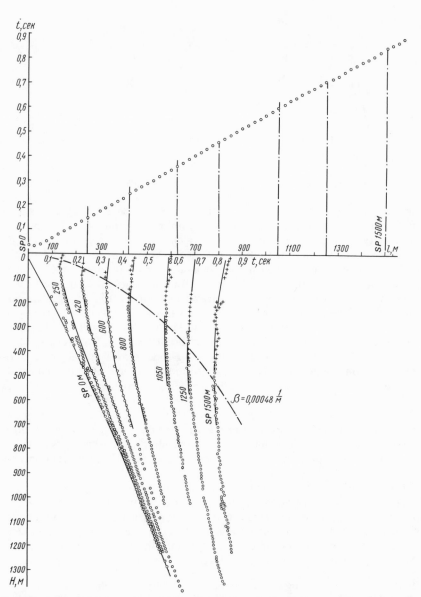

FIG. 15. Observed traveltime curves of first refracted waves. Solid lines indicate theoretical traveltimes computed for the medium using $\beta = 0.0048\ m^{-1}$ (well no. 3, Afip, Krasnodar region).

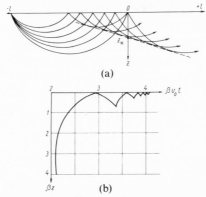

FIG. 16. (a) Raypath schematic for a singly refracted wave. (b) Vertical traveltime curves for multiply refracted waves (generalized system of coordinates). According to Rudnitskiy (1968).

The arrival time increment for multiplicities differing by one unit decreases as the order of multiplicity increases. Multiply refracted waves have a caustic surface where energy is being focused and where the normal intersection of ray bundles is zero (Pomerantseva, 1962). The envelope of the family of multiple-wave rays is the geometric locus of caustic curves H_k and is determined by equation

$$H_k = \frac{1}{\beta} \left[\sqrt{1 + \frac{l^2 \beta^2}{(2k+1)^2 - 1}} - 1 \right]. \tag{12}$$

This envelope is the lower boundary of multiple-wave traveltime curves. As the order of multiplicity increases, the region of existence of multiple waves rapidly diminishes and becomes zero for the limiting case $k \to \infty$ (Figure 16b).

The coordinates of the minima of traveltime curves for multiple waves are determined by the following equations:

$$H_{\text{min}} = \frac{1}{\beta} \left[\sqrt{1 + \left(\frac{l\beta}{2k \pm 1}\right)^2} - 1 \right], \tag{13}$$

$$t_{\text{min}} = \frac{2k \pm 1}{\beta v_0} \times \ln \frac{l\beta + \sqrt{l^2 \beta^2 + (2k \pm 1)^2}}{2k \pm 1} \tag{14}$$

From (12) and (13) it appears that $H_{\text{min}} < H_k$. Neighboring sections of the traveltime curves have curvatures that are oppositely oriented in relation to the depth axis (Figure 16b).

Traveltime curve equation for the exponential law of velocity variation

For the case of a velocity gradient that decreases with depth, $v(H) = v_\infty - (v_\infty - v_0)e^{-aH}$, the equation for the in-line traveltime curve becomes (Kefeli, 1965).

$$t = \frac{H}{v_\infty} + \frac{1}{a v_\infty} \ln \frac{v_\infty - (v_\infty - v_0) e^{-aH}}{v_0}.$$

For the case of increasing velocity gradient, when

$$v(H) = v_0 e^{aH},$$

the in-line traveltime curve takes the form

$$t = \frac{1}{v_0 a}(1 - e^{-aH}),$$

and that of the off-line traveltime curve is expressed by

$$t = \frac{\sqrt{2}}{v_0 a}\ \frac{\sqrt{\cosh aH - \cos al}}{e^{\frac{aH}{2}}}.$$

The ordinate of the minimum of the traveltime curve, in the latter case, is determined by

$$H_{\min} = \frac{1}{a}\ln(\cos al).$$

TRAVELTIME CURVES FOR WAVES IN LAYERED MEDIA

Let us examine vertical traveltime curves of primary and secondary waves in a layered homogeneous medium having a single flat inclined boundary, and those of first waves for a multilayered medium.

Traveltime curves of primary waves above a boundary

The direct wave registers as a first arrival above a boundary for small l. Its traveltime equation is given in the previous section. If velocity v_2 in the second medium exceeds that of the first medium v_1 then, starting with some distance l, one may observe the head wave above the subdividing boundary. Its traveltime curve is represented by a straight line (Puzyrev, 1957) determined by equation

$$t = \frac{1}{v_{P1}}\Big[2H_v \cos i_{cr} \cos \varphi + l \sin (i_{cr} \pm \varphi) - H \cos(i_{cr} \mp \varphi)\Big]. \tag{15}$$

If the boundary is horizontal, this equation takes the form

$$t = \frac{1}{v_{P1}}\Big[(2H_v - H)\cos i_{cr} + l \sin i_{cr}\Big].$$

In equation (15) the upper sign corresponds to the case when the shotpoint is located downdip as related to the top of the borehole. The apparent velocity is expressed by

$$v_a = -\frac{v_{P1}}{\cos (i_{cr} \mp \varphi)}.$$

For a horizontal boundary

$$v_a = \frac{v_{P1}\, v_{P2}}{\sqrt{v_{P2}^2 - v_{P1}^2}} = -\frac{v_{P1}}{\cos i_{cr}}.$$

The minimum value l for which head waves can form is determined by the point of emergence according to the expression

$$l_{\min} = H_v \tan(i_{cr} \pm \varphi).$$

For $\varphi = 0$, $l_{\min} = H_v \tan i_{cr}$.

For l satisfying the inequality $H_v \tan i_{cr} < l < 2H_v \tan i_{cr}$, the head wave does not register on the complete vertical profile but only on the section that is contiguous to

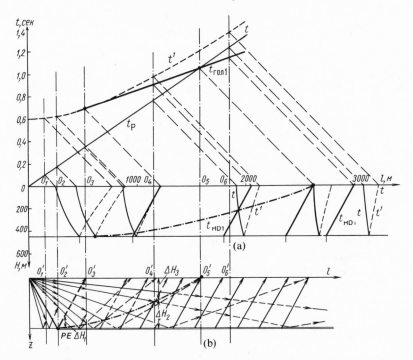

FIG. 17. (a) Combined traveltime curves of direct, head, and reflected waves. (b) Raypath schematic.

the boundary (Figure 17). The length of that section $\triangle H_1$ (from the refracting horizon) is determined by the expression

$$\triangle H_1 = \frac{l - H_v \tan i_{cr}}{\tan i_{cr}} = \frac{l\sqrt{v_{P2}^2 - v_{P1}^2} - H_v v_{P1}}{v_{P1}}.$$

The head wave registers as a first arrival only at a section from the boundary of the cross-section to the point of interference with the direct wave. The length of that section is

$$\triangle H_2 = \frac{1}{v_{P1}^2} \Big[H_v v_{P2}^2 + H_v(v_{P2}^2 - v_{P1}^2) + l v_{P1} \sqrt{v_{P2}^2 - v_{P1}^2}$$
$$- 2v_{P2}\sqrt{H_v} \sqrt{H_v(v_{P2}^2 - v_{P1}^2) + l v_{P1} \sqrt{v_{P2}^2 - v_{P1}^2}} \Big]. \tag{16}$$

Above that section, the first wave observed will be the direct wave, whereas the head wave will appear in later arrivals. The interval $\triangle H_3$ of the vertical profile, in which the head wave registers in subsequent arrivals, may be found for $H_v \tan i_{cr} < l < 2H_v \tan i_{cr}$ as the difference between sectors $\triangle H_1$ and $\triangle H_2$:

$$\triangle H_3 = \frac{2v_{P2}\sqrt{H_v}\left(\sqrt{H_v}\,(v_{P2}^2 - v_{P1}^2) + lv_{P1}\sqrt{v_{P2}^2 - v_{P1}^2} - v_{P2}\sqrt{H_v}\right)}{v_{P1}^2}.$$

Equation (16) can be solved for the minimum distance l_{min} for which a head wave may register as a first arrival, at a point of the vertical profile located at a distance $\triangle H$ from the boundary.

Starting with distance $l = 2H_v \tan i_{cr}$ corresponding to the initial point of the head wave on the horizontal profile, the head wave will register along the entire vertical profile above the boundary. Its first arrivals will register only on the lower portion of the profile section, the value of which is determined by (16). For the horizontal profile ($H=0$) the vertical traveltime curves of reflected and head waves have a common point (Figure 17).

For traveltime curves of primary waves formed by traveltimes of direct, head, and transmitted waves, the existence of two extreme points is characteristic. The largest value t corresponds to the point of conversion of a direct wave to a head wave t_{HD1}, the smallest corresponds to that of conversion of a direct wave to a transmitted wave (Figures 17 and 18). At the first of these points the apparent velocity changes its sign from positive to negative; at the second point, from negative to positive. As the distance l increases, the first point approaches the surface and, at $l = 2H_v\sqrt{\dfrac{v_{P2} + v_{P1}}{v_{P2} - v_{P1}}}$, which for horizontal profiling corresponds to the point of intersection of traveltime curves of head and direct waves, the head wave is registered as first arrivals over the entire vertical profile above the boundary (Figure 17).

Points associated with minimum time values on traveltime curves correspond to the depth to the cross-section boundary. For the particular case of a flat horizon, these points (on traveltimes for different l) are distributed on a straight line. For $H = H_v$ and distances $l > H_v \tan i_{cr}$, the traveltime curves of direct and transmitted waves exhibit a discontinuity of arrival time amounting to

$$\triangle t = \frac{v_{P2}\sqrt{H_v^2 + l^2} - H_v\sqrt{v_{P2}^2 - v_{P1}^2} - lv_{P1}}{v_{P1}v_{P2}}.$$

In some situations of structure of the medium, i.e., for large horizon dips and sharp velocity contrasts, head waves can register as first arrivals either along the entire or along partial sections of the in-line vertical profile (Puzyrev, 1957).[3]

Traveltime curves for secondary waves

When a longitudinal wave impinges on a boundary, two reflected waves (longitudinal and converted) and two transmitted waves (longitudinal and converted) are generated. The traveltime curves of these secondary waves may be obtained from the general equations in parametric form (Rudnitskiy, 1968):

---

[3]Vertical traveltime curves for waves of some particular cases of structure of the medium are examined in Kefeli (1965) and Shmakov (1962).

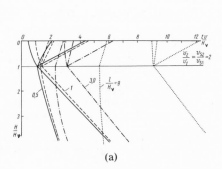

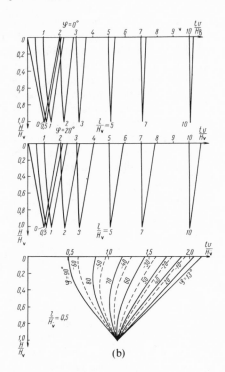

FIG. 18. Theoretical traveltime curves of waves in generalized coordinates. (a) Traveltime curves of direct and secondary waves for four distances corresponding to subcritical and transcritical angles of incidence. Single horizontal boundary. (b) Traveltime curves of direct and reflected waves.

$$H = \frac{1}{\sqrt{1-p^2v_1^2}(pv_2\cos\varphi \pm \sqrt{1-p^2v_2^2}\sin\varphi)}\left[\sqrt{1-p^2v_1^2}(pv_2H_v\right.$$
$$\left. \pm l\sqrt{1-p^2v_2^2}(\cos\varphi \mp pv_1H_N\sqrt{1-p^2v_2^2}\right], \tag{17}$$

$$t = \frac{1}{v_1v_2\sqrt{1-p^2v_1^2}(pv_2\cos\varphi \pm \sqrt{1-p^2v_2^2}\sin\varphi)}\left\{H_N\left[p(v_2^2-v_1^2)\cos\varphi\right.\right.$$
$$\left.\left. \pm v_2\sqrt{1-p^2v_2^2}\sin\varphi\right] + v_1L\sqrt{1-p^2v_1^2}\cos\varphi\right\},$$

where $p = \dfrac{\sin i_1}{v_1} = \dfrac{\sin i_2}{v_2}$. The upper sign corresponds to the transmitted, the lower to the reflected waves.

Investigations of equation (17) in its general form is accomplished in Rudnitskiy (1968). Before describing the particulars of traveltime curves of secondary waves as they follow from the above equations, let us note that for all secondary waves the arrival time at depth H_v of the boundary is determined by the expression

$t = \dfrac{\sqrt{l^2 + H_v^2}}{v_{P1}}$ which is equal to the incidence time of the direct wave on the boundary.

This corresponds to the simultaneous time of incidence on the boundary of the longitudinal wave and the generation of the secondary waves.

Figure 18a indicates that for incidence angles below critical ($l/H_v = 0.5$), the vertical traveltime curves of secondary waves have a common point corresponding to the depth of the boundary. For incidence angles exceeding critical ones, there occurs a break in the transmitted wave and the generation of a head wave. Vertical traveltime curves of the incident, the two reflected (longitudinal and converted) and the transmitted converted waves have a common point at the boundary. As the waves propagate, each of the mentioned waves may, in turn, generate analogous "complexes" of secondary waves at the boundaries. The latter circumstance leads to the formation of multiple waves.

Longitudinal transmitted waves. — The traveltime equation for the transmitted longitudinal wave in parametric form and for $\varphi = 0$ is expressed by

$$H = \frac{(l - H_v \tan i)\sqrt{n^2 - \sin^2 i}}{\sin i} + H_v,$$

$$t = \frac{H_v}{v_{P1} \cos i} + \frac{(H - H_v)n}{v_{P2}\sqrt{n^2 - \sin^2 i}},$$

$$(18)$$

where $n = \dfrac{v_{P1}}{v_{P2}}$. The parameter in these equations is the angle of incidence of the

longitudinal wave upon the boundary. For the in-line vertical traveltime curve, assuming $l = 0$ and $i = 0$, one has

$$t = \frac{H_v}{v_{P1}} + \frac{(H - H_v)}{v_{P2}}.$$

Longitudinal transmitted waves form first arrivals below the boundary.

If $v_{P2} > v_{P1} (n > 1)$, the off-line vertical traveltime curve of transmitted waves possesses a common point (at the boundary of the cross-section) with the off-line traveltime curve of either direct or head waves.

As H increases, the branches of the off-line traveltime curves of transmitted waves approach the branch of the in-line vertical traveltime curve of these waves, the latter branch constituting their asymptote. For cases of small angles of horizon dip (not exceeding 20-30 degrees) and for $l > 0$, a distinct minimum is observed on the vertical traveltime curves in the region of the boundary of the cross-section (the traveltime curve is convex toward the depth axis). For large angles φ, the traveltime curves smooth-out in the neighborhood of the boundaries, they do not possess minima and, as H increases, they remain practically parallel to each other.

If $v_{P2} < v_{P1} (n < 1)$ and for $\varphi = 0$, the traveltime curves indicate less pronounced breaks at the boundary and minima are nonexistent. As φ increases, the shape of the traveltime curves changes insignificantly and it is considerably more difficult to determine the velocity cross-section than for the case $n > 1$.

The apparent velocity of transmitted waves is determined (Rudnitskiy, 1968) from the expression

$$v_a = \frac{v_{P2}}{\sqrt{1 - p^2 v_{P2}^2}\cos\varphi - p v_{P2}\sin\varphi}.$$

$$(19)$$

Analyzing the values of apparent velocities, an analysis that is of great interest in the study of velocity parameters of the medium, one observes that

$$v_a = v_{1r} = v_{P_2} \text{ for } i_2 = -\varphi \text{ or } \varphi = -\arctan \frac{p v_{P_2}}{\sqrt{1 - p^2 v_{P_2}^2}},$$

$$v_a = \infty \text{ for } i_2 = \frac{\pi}{2} - \varphi \text{ or } \varphi = \arctan \frac{\sqrt{1 - p^2 v_{P_2}^2}}{p v_{P_2}}. \tag{20}$$

Consequently, when determining layer velocities v_{1R} according to in-line vertical traveltime curves for transmitted waves, it is necessary to account for the dip angle of the boundary, since otherwise one might obtain values that are too high. For some particular cases, when $v_{P_2} < v_{P_1}$, one might also overlook a layer altogether (Rudnit-skiy, 1968).

Longitudinal reflected waves. — The vertical traveltime equation for reflected waves may be obtained from (17) by elimination of parameter p and introduction of condition $v_{P_1} = v_{P_2}$:

$$t = \frac{1}{v_{P_1}} \sqrt{l^2 + H^2 + 4H_v(H_v - H)\cos\varphi}. \tag{21}$$

The vertical traveltime curve for the reflected wave constitutes a hyperbola. For shotpoint locations within the interval $-H_v \, ctg \, \varphi < l < \infty$, the reflected waves region is located above the boundary of the cross-section. For $l < -H_v \, ctg \, \varphi$, reflected waves would register below the boundary. The latter case is only possible for large angles of dip which, in seismic exploration practice, is seldom encountered.

Traveltime curves of reflected waves may possess a minimum under condition that $0 \leqslant 2H_N \cos\varphi \leqslant H_v$. The coordinates for the minima-points are determined from the following formulas:

$$H_{\min} = 2H_N \cos\varphi,$$

$$t_{\min} = \frac{H_v \sin 2\varphi - l \cos 2\varphi}{v_{P_1}} = \frac{2H_v \sin\varphi - l}{v_{P_1}}. \tag{22}$$

As l increases, the ordinate of the minimum increases. Where this condition is not satisfied, the traveltime curves do not possess extreme points and their slope corresponds to negative or positive apparent velocities depending on the values of the angles φ.

The apparent velocity of the reflected wave at each point H of the vertical profile is

$$v_a = -v_{P_1} \frac{\sqrt{(2H_N \cos\varphi - H)^2 + (2H_N \sin\varphi - l)^2}}{2H_N \cos\varphi - H}$$

$$= -v_{P_1} \frac{\sqrt{l^2 + H^2 + 4H_N(H_v - H)\cos\varphi}}{2H_N \cos\varphi - H}. \tag{23}$$

For the study of kinematic nature of waves it is convenient to use generalized traveltime curves whose coordinates are the relative quantities H/H_v and $v_{P_1} t/H_v$. Figure 18b illustrates traveltime curves of direct and reflected waves for two fixed dip angles ($\varphi = 0$ and 20 degrees), for different values of parameters l/H_v and for a fixed relative distance l/H_v, for various boundary dip angles φ.

For a fixed distance from the source, as the dip angle of the boundary increases, vertical traveltime curves of reflected waves straighten out and for φ values within the interval $\arccos H_v/(2H_N) < \varphi < 90$ degrees they exhibit a minimum. For small angles φ, the apparent velocities of traveltime curves are nearly alike. For traveltime curves of reflected waves possessing minima, v_a is positive for the lower section of the profile and the traveltime curves of reflected waves approach smoothly those of the direct wave. The traveltime curves intersect at the depth of the reflecting horizon. Vertical traveltime curves of waves reflected downward, for the plane of traveltime curves for different φ and for fixed ratio l/H_v, are contained within a narrow strip that widens as the above ratio increases. The region of existence of traveltime curves for $l/H_v = $ const is restricted on one side by the direct wave traveltime curves (for $\varphi = \pm 90$ degrees reflected and direct wave traveltime curves coincide), and on the other side by reflected wave traveltime curves corresponding to the values $\varphi_1 = -\frac{1}{2} \arctan l/H_v$ above the boundary and $\varphi_2 = -\frac{1}{2} \arctan l/H_v + \pi/2$ below the boundary; φ_1 and φ_2 are the values of boundary dips for which the reflection traveltimes have maximal time values.

In VSP practice one often must deal with overlapping reflection traveltime curves obtained for different l values. In those cases where the sources are distributed along the direction of horizon dip, the apparent velocities of reflected waves are negative and are nearly identical. For sources that are distributed up-dip as referred to the boundary, the apparent velocities increase and the traveltime curves exhibit minima (Demidenko, 1964).

Let us examine the level-reduced reflection traveltime curves (obtained for a fixed observation depth and for variable l) which, in many instances, may be utilized for the identification of waves that register from different shotpoints (transpositional correlation). The level-reduced reflection traveltime curve is represented by a hyperbola, the location of whose minimum is determined by the values of the angle φ and the depth H. The abscissa of the minimum is given by the expression

$$l_{\min} = (H - H_v) \sin 2\varphi.$$

For a horizontal boundary of the cross-section, the traveltime curve is determined (Gal'perin and Frolova, 1961; Petkevich, 1957) by the equation

$$t = \frac{\sqrt{l^2 + (2H_v + H)^2}}{v_{P1}}$$

and represents hyperbola having half-axes l/v_{P1} and l, and the center at coordinates $t = 0$ and $H = 2H_v$. The actual hyperbola axis is the straight line that is parallel to the t-axis and has the ordinate $H = 2H_v$. The asymptote of the hyperbola is the straight line $t = \frac{2H_v - H}{v}$ which, for $H < H_v$, represents a reflection traveltime curve for the case of an in-line vertical profile for $\varphi = 0$. If $\varphi \neq 0$, then

$$t = \frac{1}{v_{P1}} \sqrt{H^2 + 4H_v \cos^2 \varphi (H_v - H)}.$$

Comparing equations for direct and reflected waves, it is not difficult to discover that they represent different sections of the same hyperbola. The direct wave traveltime curve is the hyperbola section from the peak to the boundary, and the reflected wave traveltime curve is the hyperbola section from the boundary to the surface.

Therefore, the traveltime curve reflected wave is more linear and, for considerable thickness of the bed relative to the distance l, it nearly coincides with the asymptote of the hyperbola. A difference in curvatures of traveltime curves for direct and reflected waves is more pronounced for small values of l.

The traveltime curve of the longitudinal direct wave easily lends itself to graphical construction. To this end it is sufficient to construct a mirror image with respect to the boundary of the section of the direct wave traveltime curve, corresponding to depths $2H_v > H > H_v$. At each point of the vertical profile, in a homogeneous medium the sum of arrival time of the direct wave, reduced to the in-line profile, and the arrival time of the reflected wave is constant and equal to $2H_v/v_{p_1}$. The difference of traveltime curves for reflected and direct waves is represented by a straight line $H = H_v - \frac{1}{2}v_{p_1}\Delta t$ having a slope $v_{p_1}/2$ which intersects the time axis at a segment $2H_v/v_{p_1}$ and the depth axis at a segment H_v. As l increases, the time difference between arrival times of reflected and direct waves, for fixed depths, decreases. These relationships may be utilized for the determination of the depth of the reflecting horizon when the vertical profile does not cross the reflecting horizon or when the reflected wave could not be tracked along the complete profile, i.e., down to the boundary.

This primarily relates to sections of the profile, contiguous to the reflecting boundary, where the correlation of the reflected wave is disrupted because of interference with the direct wave. Also, this involves profile sections that are contiguous to the surface, where wave correlation is usually severely encumbered (see Chapter 4). With this in mind, one may exploit another property of the vertical traveltime curve of reflected waves. For $\varphi = 0$ and for $l \ll H_v$, the vertical reflected wave traveltime curve is represented by the mirror image of the direct wave traveltime curve which permits the identification of those sections of the reflected wave traveltime curve for which the reflected wave cannot be tracked continuously because of interference, or for any other reason.

If the velocity in the medium increases according to a linear law and the boundary of separation is flat and horizontal, then the equation of the vertical traveltime curve of the longitudinal reflected wave in parametric form is represented by:

$$H = \frac{\sqrt{1 - (2\cos i - \cos i_0 + \beta l \sin i_0)^2} - \sin i_0}{\beta \sin i_0} \, ,$$

$$t = \frac{1}{v_0\beta} \left(\ln \frac{\tan \frac{i}{2}}{\tan \frac{i_0}{2}} + \ln \frac{\tan \frac{i}{2}}{\tan \frac{i_N}{2}} \right), \tag{24}$$

where $\sin i = \sin i_0(1 + \beta H_v)$, $\sin i_N = \sin i_0(1 + \beta H)$.

When the velocity in the overlying medium varies according to a more complicated law, the equation of reflected wave traveltime curve may be written by considering the method of average velocities (Demidenko, 1964):

$$t = \frac{1}{v_{cp}} \sqrt{(2H_N \cos \varphi - H)^2 + (2H_N \sin \varphi - l)^2}$$

$$\times \left[1 - \frac{v_{av\,N} - v_{av}}{v_{av\,N}} \frac{H_v - H}{2H_N \cos \varphi - H + \tan \varphi (2H_N \sin \varphi - l)} \right]. \tag{25}$$

For $v_{av} = v_{av\,N}$, this equation transforms into the equation of the reflected wave traveltime curve for a medium having constant velocity.

Converted reflected and transmitted waves. — Converted reflected waves are characterized by the same laws that govern transmitted waves. The vertical traveltime curve of the converted reflected or transmitted wave, for the case of a horizontal boundary of separation, may be represented by the following equations in parametric form (Gal'perin, 1966).

$$H = H_v \pm \frac{(l - H_v \tan i) \sqrt{1 - n^2 \sin^2 i}}{n \sin i},$$

$$t = \frac{H_v}{v_{P1} \cos i} \pm \frac{H_v - H}{v_s \sqrt{1 - n^2 \sin^2 i}}. \tag{26}$$

The upper sign corresponds to the converted reflected wave, and in that case $v_s = v_{S1}$ and $n = v_{S1}/v_{P1}$. The lower sign applies to the transmitted wave, for which $v_s = v_{S2}$ and $n = v_{S2}/v_{P1}$.

Substituting the value $H = H_v$ into equation (26), one obtains the arrival time of the wave at the depth of the boundary $t = H_v/(v_{P1} \cos i)$ which is equal to the incidence time of the direct wave on the boundary, i.e., the traveltime curves of these waves, at the depth of the boundary, possess a common point.

If $v_{S2} > v_{P1}$, the wavefront of the converted transmitted wave in the second medium, and for $l > H_v \tan(\arcsin v_{P1}/v_{S2})$, overtakes the wavefront of the incident longitudinal wave; thus the converted transmitted traveltime curve no longer intersects (at the boundary) the traveltime curves of incident and transmitted waves at one point. Rather, it overtakes them, while it forms a common point at the boundary with the traveltime curve of the converted head wave associated with the upper layer.

For converted reflected waves ($n < 1$) and for $\varphi = 0$ the shortest arrival times are observed at profile points coinciding with the boundary.

Vertical traveltime curves of converted reflected waves ($n < 1$) for small angles possess asymptotes that are almost parallel to each other, especially for large l. A minimum on traveltime curves only appears for very large values of φ (~ 70 degrees) and it rapidly vanishes as l increases. The apparent velocity increases as the angle φ increases; the traveltime curves for various l remain practically parallel to each other.

For converted transmitted waves ($n < 1$, $\varphi = 0$) vertical traveltime curves do not possess minima and, as the distance from the boundary becomes more remote, the traveltime curves for various l approach each other. For dipping boundaries, the traveltime curve shape is substantially preserved. For $n > 1$ and for $\varphi = 0$, traveltime curves of converted transmitted waves rapidly approach each other as H is increased, tending toward the asymptote which coincides with the in-line traveltime curve of the converted transmitted wave. As φ increases, the traveltime curves become almost parallel to each other.

The construction of theoretical traveltime curves of converted waves (reflected and transmitted), as well as of longitudinal waves, is conveniently accomplished by means of image shotpoints. This permits one to go over from an examination of the trajectory of a converted wave from an actual source to that of trajectories of a wave of a given type from an imaginary shotpoint. Such a method of construction may be simpler and more illustrative than the commonly used method of computations from equations (Figure 19).

For converted waves, each point of a vertical profile corresponds to an image source, out of which the traveltime of the transverse wave at a constant velocity v_s into a corresponding point of the vertical profile is equal to the traveltime of the converted wave into the same point of the profile out of the actual shotpoint. All the image sources for different points of the vertical profile form a line representing the geometric locus of fictitious points determined by the equation

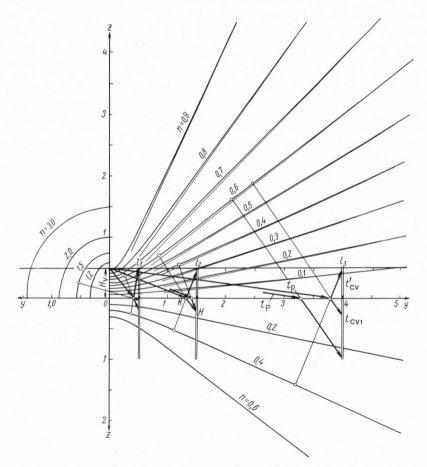

FIG. 19. Lines of virtual sources for different velocity ratios. Positive direction of axis OY for $n < 1$ coincides with the direction of wave propagation; for $n > 1$ the direction of the wave is opposite.

$$\frac{H^2}{n^2 H_v^2} - \frac{y^2}{(1-n^2)\,H_V^2} = 1.$$

For converted reflected waves $n = v_{s_1}/v_{p_1}$, for converted transmitted waves $n = v_{s_2}/v_{p_1}$. This equation shows that, for $n < 1$, the lines of fictitious sources are represented by hyperbolas whose actual axis coincides with the depth axis oz, and this axis also contains the center of the hyperbola (at the depth of the boundary). The foci of the hyperbolas are located at distance H_v from the center. For converted transmitted waves, the hyperbola focus coincides with the source, and the lines of virtual (image) shotpoints are located above the boundary; for converted reflected waves, the focus is located at depth $2H_v$ from the surface and the lines of virtual sources are below the boundary. The depth (see Figure 19) is reckoned from the boundary of conversion: for transmitted waves, upward; for reflected, downward. For $n > 1$ and for converted transmitted waves, the lines of virtual sources are represented by ellipses having their center on the z-axis at the depth H_v from the surface and their focus at the source.

The lines of virtual sources permit the construction of a raypath schematic for any given point on the vertical profile and for a source at any given distance. To this end, it is sufficient to draw a normal from the point of the profile upon the line of virtual shotpoints. This procedure is required for any point where the raypath schematic is to be constructed (e.g., point H in Figure 19). The segment of that normal (HK) from the point of observation H up to the boundary of conversion corresponds to the ray of the converted wave. The straight line connecting the actual source with the point of conversion corresponds to the ray of the incident longitudinal wave. These rays easily lend themselves to the computation of traveltimes and of traveltime curves.

The family of lines (Figure 19) may serve as a general chart, since, as the depth of the conversion boundary changes, neither the form nor the relative disposition of the lines change; the only variation occurs in the scale factor of the axes. The revised annotation of the axes is accomplished by multiplication by a coefficient that is the ratio of boundary depth (on which the construction of the chart was based) to boundary depth corresponding to any particular case.

Multiply reflected waves. — In a layered medium and for a vertical profile, in contrast to a horizontal profile, both upward and downward reflected waves are registered separately. The recording of both wave types is considered to be of great interest. The upward reflected waves permit the identification of prime (fundamental) cross-section boundaries from which the multiple waves originate. The downward-reflected waves permit the determination of the nature and the location of inter-mediate reflecting boundaries in the cross-section. From traveltime curves of downward-reflected waves, the dip angles of the prime as well as the intermediate boundaries of multiples may be determined. Areas of the boundary of separation, "illuminated" by downward multiply reflected waves, are, in fact, a continuation of areas illuminated by upward-reflected waves. The total extent of the area may, for example, exceed the extent of the area illuminated by the upward-reflected waves alone by a factor of $1.5-2$. The total extent of the line segment illuminated by upward- and downward-reflected waves, strongly depends on φ, l, H_v and, in some situations, may exceed the extent of the vertical traveltime curve being investigated.

The qualitative comparison of traveltime curve properties for multiply reflected waves for horizontal and vertical profiles was accomplished (Gal'perin and Frolova,

1961). Let us examine the equations for vertical traveltime curves of multiply reflected waves.

For the case of a single flat boundary, dipping at an angle φ with respect to the horizontal, vertical traveltime curves of reflected waves for any given multiplicity may be represented (Rudnitskiy, 1968) by the equation

$$t=\frac{1}{v_{P1}}\sqrt{l_2+H^2+4H_N\,\frac{\sin k\varphi}{\sin^2\varphi}(H_V\sin k\varphi\cos\mp H\sin\varphi\cos k\varphi)}, \qquad (27)$$

where k is the number of multiplicity. The positive sign corresponds to the wave incident upon the prime boundary, the negative sign corresponds to the reflected wave. The equation for the traveltime curve of a doubly reflected wave for the case of a dipping horizon may be written in the following manner (Demidenko, 1964):

$$t=\frac{1}{v_{P1}}\sqrt{(4H_N\cos\varphi\cos 2\varphi\pm H)^2+(4H_N\cos\varphi\sin 2\varphi-l)^2}.$$

As the number of horizons in the cross-section increases, traveltime curve equations of waves usually become unwieldy, rather than particularly complicated.

According to its parameters, the traveltime curve of a doubly upward-reflected wave corresponds to the traveltime curve of a singly upward-reflected wave, referred to a boundary located at a depth (along the normal to the boundary) $H_N' = 2H_N$ cos φ and dipping with respect to the horizontal at any angle $\varphi' = 2\varphi$.

For the case of a horizontal boundary ($\varphi = 0$) the traveltime curve equation for waves of any given multiplicity has the form

$$t=\frac{1}{v_{P1}}\sqrt{(2H_V k\mp H)^2+l^2}.$$

Traveltime curves for multiple upward- and downward-reflected waves may be described by the discrete expressions:

$$t=\frac{1}{v_{P1}}\sqrt{[(m+1)\,H_V-H]^2+l^2} \qquad \text{for odd } m;$$

$$t=\frac{1}{v_{P1}}\sqrt{(mH_V+H)^2+l^2} \qquad \text{for even } m;$$

where $m = $ total number of reflections that the wave was subjected to from the upper and the lower boundaries. Assuming $m = 0$, one obtains the traveltime curve equation for the direct wave:

$$t^2=\frac{l^2+H^2}{v_{P1}^2}.$$

For $m = 1$, the traveltime curve equation of the singly reflected wave obtains:

$$t^2=\frac{l^2+(2H_V-H)^2}{v_{P1}^2}$$

The apparent velocity of the reflected wave for any given multiplicity is contained in a quasi-periodic function and, at each point of the profile (Rudnitskiy, 1968) is given by

$$v_a=\mp v_{P1}\sqrt{1+\left(\frac{2H_N\sin^2 k\varphi-l\sin\varphi}{H_N\sin 2k\varphi\mp H\sin\varphi}\right)^2}.$$

The apparent velocity of the primary downward-reflected wave (Demidenko, 1964) is:

$$v_a = v_{pl} \sqrt{\frac{(2H_N \cos \varphi + H)^2 + (2H_N \sin \varphi - l)^2}{2H_N \cos \varphi + H}} \,.$$

Independent of the dip of the prime boundary, the above velocity is always positive. For small angles of dip φ, the apparent velocity is close to the velocity of the direct wave.

For $\varphi = 0$ the apparent velocity diminishes as k increases and, in the limit, becomes the layer velocity.

From traveltime curve equations for multiple waves it follows that vertical traveltime curves of waves of different multiplicity constitute sections of a hyperbola. In the case of an in-line vertical profile ($l = 0$), traveltime curves of reflected and multiple waves form a broken line. The apparent velocities of reflected waves of different multiplicity, for $\varphi = 0$, differ not only in values but also in polarities. At the depth corresponding to the boundary, the multiple wave traveltime curve possesses a point of discontinuity.

For off-line vertical profiles ($l \neq 0$), at any given depth as well as at the surface, the time differences between arrival times of waves of neighboring multiplicities increases as the number of multiplicity increases. In the particular case of an in-line vertical profile ($l = 0$), these differences are maximal, constant, and independent of the number of the multiple. As the distance from the source to the top of the well increases, the time increments for arrival times of waves of neighboring multiplicity diminish. If the vertical traveltime curves of a multiply reflected wave is interpreted as a section of a traveltime curve of a singly reflected wave associated with a deeper location of boundary of separation, then the fictitious boundary, thus obtained, is located at a depth that represents a multiple depth of the prime horizon. In order to identify the fictitious boundary it is sufficient to consider the vertical traveltime curve and to convince oneself that at the corresponding depth a reflected wave cannot be generated.

Vertical traveltime curves of reflected waves of any multiplicity may be composed from sections of direct wave traveltime curves constructed from fictitious shotpoints. The traveltime curve of a wave reflected from the surface may be represented by a direct wave traveltime curve out of point 0_2 (Figure 20a) which is the mirror image of point 0_1 referred to the surface. For the construction of the vertical traveltime curve of the doubly reflected wave, it is sufficient to examine the traveltime curve of the direct wave out of fictitious point 0_3 that represents the mirror image of 0_2 referred to the surface. Vertical traveltime curves of waves of any multiplicity may be obtained by analogous constructions.

Thus, vertical traveltime curves of multiply reflected waves may be composed of segments of the hyperbola of the direct wave, a construction that is conveniently done graphically. To this end, the traveltime curve of the direct wave is constructed from SP 0 and is transferred onto tracing cloth. To obtain the vertical traveltime curve of the singly reflected wave, it is sufficient to fold the tracing of the direct wave traveltime curve along the line coinciding with the boundary. For the construction of the vertical traveltime curve of the doubly reflected wave, it is further necessary to again fold the tracing along the line corresponding to the surface. For construction of the traveltime curve of a wave of multiplicity k, the tracing is folded consecutively on the prime and the intermediate (surface) boundaries k times. As a result, the

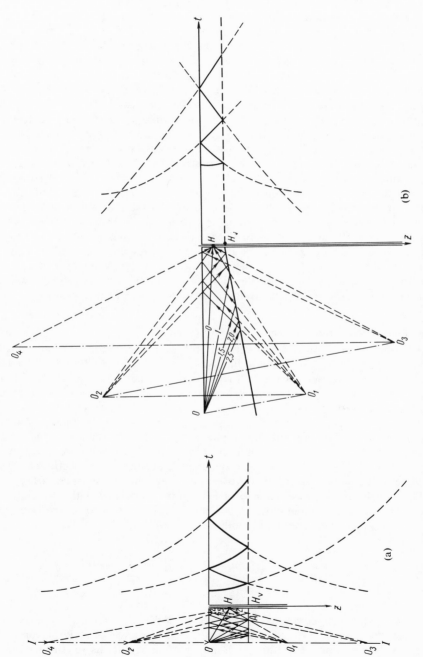

FIG. 20. Construction of vertical traveltime curves of multiply reflected waves. (a) For $\phi = 0$ and (b) for $\phi \neq 0$.

tracing is gathered into an "accordion", each facet of which includes sections of the vertical traveltime curve of the direct wave. which as a whole, comprise vertical traveltime curves of reflected waves of different multiplicity.

The described scheme of construction of a vertical traveltime curve for multiply reflected waves for the case of a flat horizontal boundary may be extended to the case of a flat dipping boundary (Figure 20b). In contrast to the horizontal boundary, for mirror images of fictitious shotpoints, the distances of their projections from the top of the borehole will vary. Therefore, the traveltime curve of a wave incident on a dipping boundary and reflected from the latter is composed of segments of direct-wave traveltime curves which correspond to different distances of the projections of fictitious shotpoints from the well top. The traveltime curves of waves incident on the surface and reflected from it are, just as in the case of a horizontal boundary, contiguous segments of the same traveltime curve of the direct wave.

The examined procedure for the construction of vertical traveltime curves of multiply reflected waves lends itself to an easy determination of the trajectories of these waves as they approach any given point of the vertical profile (e.g., the approach to point H, Figure 20a). The trajectory of the reflected wave is composed of the segment of the direct ray, issuing from the actual point 0, and the segments of rays sequentially directed toward the fictitious shotpoints (0_1, 0_2, 0_3, and 0_4). The raypath schematics for each of the investigated waves are indicated in Figure 20. For a dipping horizon, the raypath schematic permits an estimate of the region of existence, along the vertical profile, of waves of different multiplicity as well as of sections of the boundary of separation that is illuminated by these waves.

Traveltime curves of first waves in multilayered media.

When observing along off-line vertical profiles, and dependent on the value l and the parameters of the cross-section, first waves may consist of either direct and transmitted waves or refracted waves associated with deeper boundaries. The kinematic particulars of head and transmitted longitudinal waves for a medium with several horizontal boundaries, separating layers of considerable thickness (d_1, d_2, . . . , d_n), and having constant velocities ($v_{P1} < v_{P2} < v_{P3}$ . . . $< v_{Pn}$), were examined (Shneyerson, 1959). Sections of the vertical traveltime curve of first waves above the refracting horizons are, starting with definite distances, portions of head wave traveltime curves. Below the refracting horizons the above traveltime curve sections correspond to traveltime curves of transmitted waves. Let us examine these situations separately.

The traveltime curve equation of a head wave associated with the boundary of layers ($n - 1$) and n, when observations are carried out in layer m (the layer parameters are d_m, v_{Pm}), may be written as follows:

$$t = \sum_{k=1}^{n-1} \frac{d_k}{v_{P_k}} \cos i_{kn} + \sum_{k=m+1}^{n-1} \frac{d_k}{v_{P_k}} \cos i_{kn} + \frac{l}{v_{P_n}} - \frac{H - \sum_{k=1}^{m} d_k}{v_{P_m}} \cos i_{mn},$$

where i_{kn} is the angle composed of the raypath of the wave refracted in layer n as it intersects the boundary k, i.e., $i_{kn} = \arcsin v_k/v_n$ is the angle of incidence of the wave upon the kth strip of separation. As a matter of clarity, let us rewrite the equation in the form:

$$t = A \frac{\cos i_{mn}}{v_{P_m}} + c_m,$$

where

$$A = \sum_{k=1}^{m} d_k - H; \quad c_m = \sum_{k=1}^{n-1} \frac{d_k}{v_{P_k}} \cos i_{kn} + \sum_{k=m+1}^{n-1} \frac{d_k}{v_{P_k}} \cos i_{kn} + \frac{l}{v_{P_n}}.$$

Thus, within the limits of the layer, the traveltime curve of the refracted wave is represented by a straight line with the slope equal to $\cos i_{mn}/v_{P_m}$, the latter producing a segment c_m as the intersection of the slope with the time axis.

Since, as one proceeds from layer to layer, only the slope of the straight line and the segment intersected by the time axis change, the traveltime curve of the head wave in horizontally layered media appears to be a broken line with discontinuities at the boundaries of the layers. For a three-layered medium, the minimal l value for which a head wave can be formed at the second interface of separation, is determined by the expression

$$l = \frac{d_1 v_{P1}}{\sqrt{v_{P3}^2 - v_{P1}^2}} + \frac{d_2 v_{P2}}{\sqrt{v_{P3}^2 - v_{P2}^2}}.$$

As l is increased, the region of registration of the head wave in the second layer widens. The interval of registration of that wave, $\triangle H$, in the second layer is:

$$\triangle H = \frac{l - d_1 \tan i_1 - d_2 \tan i_{2cr}}{\tan i_{2cr}}.$$

For

$$l = d_1 \tan \arcsin \frac{v_{P1}}{v_{P3}} + 2d_2 \tan \arcsin \frac{v_{P2}}{v_{P3}}$$

the head wave will register over the complete interval of the second layer d_2, such, that the first arrivals only occur in a region contiguous to the lower interface. For further increase of l, the head wave will register in the region of the profile associated with the first layer as well. For $l = 2d_1 \tan i_1 + 2d_2 tan\, i_{2cr}$, the head wave from the lower layer should register over the complete vertical profile, not everywhere, however, as a first arrival. Only starting with

$$l = \frac{2}{v_{P3} - v_{P1}} \left[d_1 \frac{v_{P3}^2 - 2v_{P1}^2}{\sqrt{v_{P3}^2 - v_{P1}^2}} + \frac{d_2 v_{P1}}{v_{P2}} \frac{(v_{P3}^2 - 2v_{P2}^2)}{\sqrt{v_{P3}^2 - v_{P2}^2}} \right],$$

will the wave, refracted at the lower boundary, be observed as first-arrival events along the entire vertical profile.

For multilayered media containing n layers, the above distance is

$$l = \frac{2}{v_{P_n} - v_{P1}} \left[d_1 \frac{v_{P_n}^2 - 2v_{P1}^2}{\sqrt{v_{P_n}^2 - v_{P1}^2}} + v_{P1} \sum_{i=2}^{n-1} \frac{d_i(v_{P_n}^2 - 2v_{P_i}^2)}{v_{P_i} \sqrt{v_{P_n}^2 - v_{P_i}^2}} \right].$$

Below the lower refracting boundary, the transmitted wave registers as a first arrival. The traveltime curve equation of the transmitted wave in parametric form (Shneyerson, 1959) is expressed by:

$$t = \sum_{k=1}^{n-1} \frac{d_k}{v_{Pk} \sqrt{1 - p^2 v_{Pk}^2}} - \frac{1}{v_{P_n}^2} \sum_{k=1}^{n-1} \frac{d_k v_{Pk}}{\sqrt{1 - p^2 v_{P_n}^2}} + \frac{l}{v_{P_n}^2 p},$$

$$H = \sum_{k=1}^{n-1} d_k + \frac{l\sqrt{1 - p^2 v_{P_n}^2}}{p v_{P_n}} - \frac{\sqrt{1 - p^2 v_{P_n}^2}}{v_{P_n}} \sum_{k=1}^{n-1} \frac{d_k v_{Pk}}{\sqrt{1 - p^2 v^2_k}},$$

where i_k is the angle of incidence of the wave upon the kth interface and

$$p = \frac{\sin i_1}{v_{P1}} = \frac{\sin i_2}{v_{P2}} = \ldots = \frac{\sin i_n}{v_{Pn}} \cdot$$

$$t = \frac{1}{v_{Pn}} H + \sum_{k=1}^{n-1} \left(\frac{d_k}{v_{Pk}} - \frac{d_k}{v_{Pn}} \right).$$

The asymptote of the traveltime curve of the transmitted wave is a smooth curve having its curvature facing the positive time axis and exhibiting a minimum for $p = 1/v_{P_n}$ at coordinate points

$$t = \sum_{k=1}^{n-1} \frac{d_k}{v_{Pk}} \cos i_k + \frac{l}{v_{Pn}}, \quad H = \sum_{k=1}^{n-1} d_k.$$

Traveltime curves of head and transmitted waves possess a common point. The changeover of apparent velocity signs, which correspond to a changeover to traveltime curves of head and transmitted waves, permits the depth determination of the refracting horizon.

For a three-layer medium, the relative distribution of traveltime curves for direct, head, and transmitted waves, and for different l, is illustrated in Figure 21.

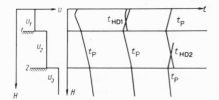

FIG. 21. Relative distribution of traveltime curves for direct, head, and transmitted waves (schematic representation).

From the head wave traveltime curve and from the velocity value $v_{P_n} = v_b$, one may compute the velocity in layer m by means of the formula:

$$v_{P_m} = \frac{1}{\sqrt{\dfrac{\cos^2 i_{mn}}{v_{P_m}^2} + \dfrac{1}{v_{P_n}^2}}} \cdot$$

The relative error associated with this velocity determination is

$$\delta v_{P_m} = \left(\frac{v_{P_m}}{v_b} \right) \delta v_b,$$

where δv_b is the relative error in the determination of the boundary velocity.

For the case of a thick bed the transmitted wave traveltime curve provides the possibility of finding the velocity within it, since the asymptote of the traveltime curve has the direction coefficient $1/v_{P_n}$.

One of the modifications of seismic well shooting, namely logging by means of refracted waves (Ivanov, 1957; Raikher, 1958; Shneyerson, 1959), is based on the study of layer and average velocities according to data provided by refracted waves. The principal advantage of this modification is the exclusion of errors associated with inaccurate time-break registration and with unstable conditions of excitation.

Let us illustrate the kinematic particulars of first waves in multilayered media (previously discussed) by means of an example of vertical traveltime curves of first waves acquired on the Staro-Minsk platform of the Krasnodar region. The velocity cross-section has been studied in detail using a large suite of observations (Berzon, 1967), and the model of the medium has been constructed (Figure 22). For the upper

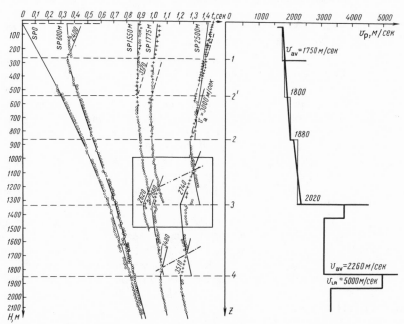

FIG. 22. Traveltime curves of first waves (direct, head, and transmitted) and velocity cross-section constructed from VSP data (well no. 42, Staro-Minsk). Traveltime curves of waves contained within the square are shown enlarged in Figure 109.

portion of the cross-section (down to 1330 m) a weak velocity differentiation, amounting to a monotonic increase of velocity with depth, is characteristic. The cross-section involves three thin layers, the tops of which occur at depths 270 (horizon 1), 1334 (horizon 3), and 1850 m (horizon 4), and they correspond to deposits of Pontian, Paleocene, and chalk, respectively. Let us examine a sequence of first wave traveltime curves obtained in the depth interval of 0 – 2100 m from shotpoints distributed at distances 0, 600, 1550, 1775, and 2500 m. On the in-line vertical profile the direct wave is registered. From SP 600 m the transmitted wave is registered almost over the entire profile. The head wave registers as a first arrival only for a small section of the profile, contiguous to boundary 1.

As the distance increases (SP 1550 m and SP 1775 m), the upper portion of the cross-section is associated with the registration of curved-ray refractions. The corresponding traveltime curves are curved and possess a minimum at a depth of about 650 m. The traveltime curves of head waves computed with the supposition of the existence of a velocity discontinuity, are indicated by dotted lines. The first wave on this section of the profile is the curved-ray refraction, as can be seen from the seismogram (see Figure 30). At great depths, on discrete profile sections, first arrivals are identified as head waves from boundaries 3 and 4. The conversion of direct and head waves is indicated by the dash-dot line that separates the regions of their existence as first arrivals. The region of registration of head waves increases as the source distance increases. The head wave from the weak boundary of separation (H = 860 m) appears in the upper portion of the cross-section only for the most remote shotpoint at 2500 m.

COMBINED HORIZONTAL-VERTICAL TRAVELTIME CURVES

VSP is usually conducted as an overall effort including horizontal observations. It is convenient to represent both horizontal and vertical traveltime curves on one chart (Gal'perin and Frolova, 1963 and 1966). Such a representation, aside from its descriptiveness, provides uninterrupted transition from observations along the horizontal profile to those along the vertical. Vertical and horizontal traveltime curves are linked by time values corresponding to the borehole location at depth zero, since this is the point that is common to both profiles. Uninterrupted tracking of waves for horizontal and vertical profiles, shot for different l-values, permits the determination of the nature of the wave that is registered on the horizontal profile. Since the observation lines for horizontal and vertical profiles are mutually perpendicular, the coordinate system for vertical traveltime curves is shifted by 90 degrees relative to the horizontal traveltime curves.

To illustrate the mutual disposition of vertical and horizontal traveltime curves for various wave types and the capabilities of combined traveltime curves, we shall examine computed traveltime curves of first and subsequent waves for a medium having two boundaries of separation, as well as observed traveltime curves of first waves for a medium having a weak velocity differentiation.

For four distances l, combined traveltime curves of the direct wave t_P and waves identified in Table 1 have been computed.

Table 1

Description of waves	Designation of Waves	
	First boundary	Second boundary
Reflected longitudinal	t^1	t^2
Reflected converted	t^1_{CV}	t^2_{CV}
Reflected multiple	t^{101}	t^{202}
Longitudinal head	t_{HD1}	t_{HD2}

The distances from the shotpoints to the top of the borehole are selected in such a manner that the first arrivals on the vertical profiles would correspond to the direct transmitted wave only (l_1), that the conversion of the direct and the head wave from the first boundary would correspond to the next borehole (l_2), that (l_3) would be associated with the conversion of the transmitted and the head wave from the second boundary, and that the head wave would appear over the entire vertical profile from the farthest shotpoint (l_4). For clarity, the vertical traveltime curves for different l are offset along the vertical.

For l_1, the direct transmitted longitudinal wave registers first arrivals along the entire vertical profile (see Figure 23), while subsequent arrivals principally consist of reflected (t^1, t^2, t^1_{CV}, and t^2_{CV}) and multiple waves (t^{101}, t^{202}). For traveltime curves of reflected waves, points common to the traveltime curve of the direct wave t_P are characteristic. As l increases to l_2, the sections of the vertical profile contiguous to the refracting boundary exhibit first arrivals that are registrations of head waves

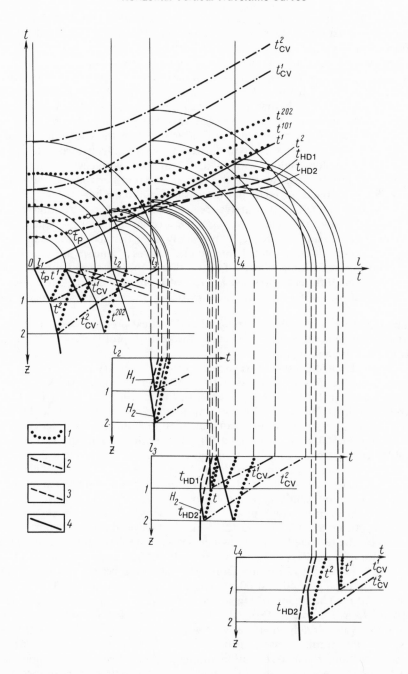

FIG. 23. Theoretical combined traveltime curves (horizontal-vertical) for waves of various types. (1) Waves propagating toward the surface: longitudinal, reflected, and multiple; (2) same, for converted reflected waves; (3) same, head waves; and (4) waves propagating down into the medium. (Horizontal and vertical traveltime curves of the same waves are connected by arcs.)

t_{HD1} and t_{HD2}. The direct wave registering as a first arrival on the horizontal profile for l_2, remains a first-arrival wave on the vertical profile only in the neighborhood of the surface. Starting with some depth (point H_1) and down to boundary 1, it is wave t_{HD1}, associated with horizon 1, that registers as a first arrival. The vertical traveltime curve also indicates that, starting with point H_2 and down to boundary 2, first arrivals of head wave t_{HD2} associated with horizon 2 are observed. For the horizontal profile, waves t_{HD1} and t_{HD2} emerge as first arrivals at distances in excess of l_2. Vertical travel-time curves of longitudinal reflected and head waves are practically parallel.

For l_3, head wave t_{HD1} is trackable as a first arrival over the entire interval of the vertical profile, i.e., from the surface to horizon 1. Waves reflected from the first and second horizons, i.e., longitudinal waves t^1 and t^2, interfere with each other at sections of simultaneous registration. Between the first and second horizons at point H_2, the first arrival involves the changeover of the transmitted into the head wave.

When l becomes large (l_4), first arrival registration over the entire interval of the vertical profile involves the head wave t_{HD2} generated at the lower boundary. On the upper portion of the vertical profile, immediately after the above wave, head wave t_{HD1} registers. Transcritical reflected longitudinal waves t^1 and t^2 are clearly time-resolved, wave t^2 registering ahead of wave t^1. As the distance from the source increases, the time difference between arrivals of waves t^1_{CV} and t^2_{CV} decreases and, subsequently, for the region of their mutual existence, these waves may interfere with each other.

Combining observations along horizontal and vertical profiles, waves recorded on the surface may be continuously tracked on the vertical profile down to boundaries with which they are associated.

Let us now examine combined traveltime curves of primary waves obtained from the structure of the uppermost cross-section and from the entire thickness of sedimentary deposits. In the first case (Figure 24), the maximum distance is 300 m; in the second case it is 3000 m (see Figure 116). Figure 24 indicates that the horizontal traveltime curve of first waves suffers a break at 50 m and then it is practically linear (approximately to 500 m). (See Chapter 7.) To determine the nature of first waves, the profile section from 30 – 330 m was intersected by eleven vertical profiles of approximately 100 m depth each, with intervals of 30 m between profiles. Corresponding points of horizontal and vertical traveltime curves are connected by arcs.

Let us examine the family of vertical traveltime curves of first waves. From SP 30 m and for the entire vertical profile, the first arrival registration constitutes the direct wave t_p. From SPs 60, 90, and 120 m the first wave in the upper portion of the cross-section is the refracted wave[4] t_p associated with the sharp boundary that constitutes the bottom of the ZLV. The thickness of the ZLV is approximately 20 m. The traveltime curve from SP 120 m indicates new first-arrival refracted waves t_{P2} and t_{P3} at approximate depths of 40 and 60 m. Wave t_{P2} registers as a first arrival up to a distance of 210 m. The region of registration of wave t_{P3} on the vertical profile continuously grows as l increases. From the traveltime curve for SP 240 m one observes that the above wave already interferes with wave t_{P2} and that it subsequently emerges as a first arrival. Combined traveltime curves permit the splitting of the upper portion of the cross-section, the determination of the region of wave conversion on the horizontal traveltime curve, the identification of velocity discontinuities in the

---

[4]Because of the thinness of the layers it was not possible to determine the nature of the refracted waves. They shall be tentatively designated as such.

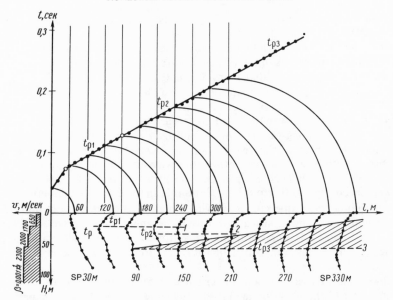

FIG. 24. Observed combined traveltime curves of first waves for a medium having a weak velocity differentiation (Dzheltmess, Kirghiz SSR).

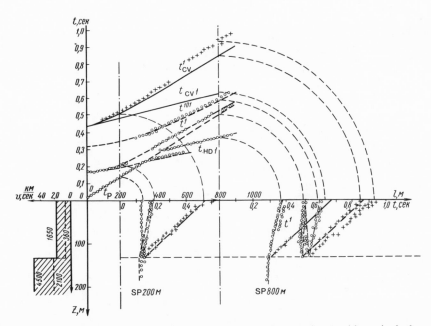

FIG. 25. Observed combined traveltime curves for waves associated with a single boundary of separation (well no. 501, Dmitrovsk, Kuibyshev district).

cross-section, and the construction of a velocity model of the upper portion of the cross-section as indicated at the left.

For the study of the complete sedimentary section, a complicated system of combined traveltime curves was obtained (see Figure 10). From vertical traveltime curves (see Figure 116) one learns that from SPs 600 and 1000 m, refraction takes place directly below the top of carbonate deposits of the Paleozoic ($H = 120 - 130$ m). From SP 1500 m, a wave that is refracted in the bed of carbonate formations of the Lower Carboniferous ($H = 640$ m) is registered. This wave is observed up to 4700 m. The wave refracted along the basement is initially observed from SP 5000 m. Thus, for the horizontal profile, the registration of first arrivals involves three refracted waves that interchange with each other: the wave in the carbonate deposits of the upper portion of the Paleozoic (up to 3.5 km), that in the carbonate bed deposit of the Lower Carboniferous (up to 8.5 km), and that in the crystalline basement.

The combined traveltime curves of waves registered on the initial and the subsequent portions of seismograms and involving a single boundary of separation, are indicated in Figure 25. The combined traveltime curves of waves are particularly convenient in those cases in which observations from a sequence of shotpoints are conducted.

In subsequent discussion. when concerned with the analysis of wave fields, we shall frequently refer to the situation analyzed above and to other kinematic particulars of waves emerging along the vertical profile.

Chapter 4
CORRELATION OF WAVES IN VERTICAL SEISMIC PROFILING

In processing VSP, the accuracy and authenticity of the interpretation effort largely depend on the correct determination of the nature of waves. This determination cannot be accomplished without reliable identification and tracking of waves on VSP seismograms. Therefore, wave correlation is one of the most essential processing operations.

The duplication of the signatures of waves of various types from point-to-point within the medium, with the excitation conditions remaining constant is sufficiently good, as corroborated by field experience. This is substantiated by experimentation, and constitutes the basic premise of wave correlation in VSP. Wave correlation over the vertical profile is possible after removal or substantial suppression of unwanted waves of instrumental nature, i.e., those connected with the specifics of observation in boreholes and examined in Chapter 2. When describing the particulars of wave correlation, it is assumed that the unwanted waves are not present in the seismograms.

DETAILS OF WAVE CORRELATION IN VSP

Spatial wave correlation in VSP is accomplished by means of wave tracking along the vertical profile for a single shot-point. It is based on the same principles that govern surface observations (Berzon et al, 1962; Gamburtsev, 1937 and 1938; Gamburtsev et al, 1952; Gurvich, 1960; Epinat'yeva, 1960; Puzyrev, 1959).

The basic criteria for wave identification are the preservation of the form of the event (the dominant period, duration, amplitude interrelation for different phases) and the line-up of oscillations (Gamburtsev et al, 1952). The specific details of wave correlation in vertical profiling are dictated by the difference between wavefields in surface observations and those observed at interior points of the medium. The principal characteristics that facilitate wave correlation for VSP are the following:

1. The kinematic and dynamic properties of waves along a vertical profile are substantially distinct from similar properties on horizontal profiles. These properties include variation of traveltimes, apparent velocities, amplitudes, frequencies, and regions of existence for various waves.

2. Observations in the immediate proximity of boundaries permit the study of waves associated with these boundaries. These waves register on the initial portion of the seismogram and are, as a rule, less encumbered by regular and irregular noise.

3. Aside from spatial correlation used in surface observations, one may employ polar (azimuth) correlation based on the study of the trajectories of particle motion. The basic feature of a simple wave for polar correlation is the conservation of the polarization law of the wave in time, and this may become a criterion based on strict quantitative evaluations (Gal'-perin, 1955; Gamburtsev, 1952).

4. Records acquired at sufficient depths are free from the influence of the ZLV and the upper portion of the cross-section as well as of low-velocity unwanted waves, including surface waves.

5. For observations at interior points of the medium, the conditions of coupling

exert a much smaller influence on the results than for surface observations, since they are determined principally by clamping methods.

However, correlation conditions for VSP are often more complicated than for surface observations. The reasons are as follows:

1. Among the much larger number of waves registered on VSP records than on surface observations are some which are not observed on the surface at all. Primarily these are multiple waves reflected from boundaries located above the points of observation and converted downward-transmitted waves. Incident waves propagating into the interior of the medium complicate correlation along the vertical profile. In spite of this, it is possible in principle to track waves along the entire propagation path, to decipher the wave pattern, and to understand the nature of many late arriving waves appearing on surface seismograms.

2. Waves approach particular points of the VSP profile from various directions, because of the relative positions of source and receiver and the parameters of the medium. Hence, on seismograms of the same component (vertical, horizontal, or inclined), P- and S-waves may register, but their relative intensity on the record of the particular component may vary substantially along the vertical profile. For correlation of only one component, an erroneous impression of relative intensity between various waves may occur.

3. For a layered medium, the most difficult situations both for observation and interpretation concern wavefields at profile sections that are near layer boundaries, at which one observes discontinuous variations of dynamic wave characteristics and where secondary waves are generated. Aside from this, in the vicinity of boundaries in the interior of the medium, intense low-velocity waves of surface type may emerge. There are particular wave correlation difficulties in the upper portion of the cross-section, especially near the surface. Besides the large number of various waves in the upper portion of the cross-section, the mechanics of VSP generate noise.

The first correlation problem is overcome, to a considerable degree, by apparent velocity selection through the application of interference schemes and, in particular, by controllable directional reception of the second kind, by the method of subtraction, by optical filtering, and by other methods widely used in surface observations.

For the alleviation of the wave-direction problem, correlation of the complete vector motion is required. Such correlation may be achieved by employing the displacement version of CDR of the first kind (see Chapter 5).

A specific characteristic of borehole observations is the lack of uniformity of receiving conditions, since the vertical profile intersects layers with different elastic properties. Thus, the dynamic particulars of records are definitely influenced by the variations in the elastic properties of the medium along the vertical profile. In addition, there are the effects of absorption of oscillatory energy, the spreading of wavefronts, and interference.

In the interior of homogeneous layers the character of the record changes slightly, but for transition across a boundary, the form and the amplitude of oscillations may change sharply. The possibility of variation of amplitude and form, as well as the disruption of the lineup, effects that are associated with layer boundaries must be taken into account in the correlation of waves along a vertical profile. In the zero-order approximation, amplitude variation is principally determined by the behavior of the moduli of coefficients of reflection or refraction and it is only weakly dependent on the behavior of the corresponding arguments. However, the variation of form of a reflected wave, in the case of a thick-layered model of the medium is influenced by the behavior of the argument of the reflection coefficient. The shape of the transmitted wave in the above situation does not vary. For a thin-layered model, the form variations of the wave are controlled by the variation of both the modulus and the argument of the coefficient of reflection and refraction. The influences of the velocity parameters of the medium on the mentioned moduli of various wave types and their variation with distance, as well as the analysis of the arguments and their influence on the form of the recording of these waves, have been examined by many authors (Berzon et al, 1962; Vasil'ev, 1959; Puzyrev, 1959).

The influence of the medium parameters (and simultaneously of the directivity of the wave approach) upon the amplitude of recorded waves is descriptively illustrated by the experimental graphs of intensity of the Z-component of the first longitudinal wave, on sections of the vertical profile crossing layers with sharp contrasts in elastic properties (Figure 26). In layers with increased velocity,

the intensity of the vertical component decays sharply.

The same kinds of interference appear on VSP profiles as in surface observations (Gamburtsev et al, 1952; Kosminskaya, 1956; Puzyrev, 1959): crossover of lineups as the wave is tracked from one side of the interference zone to the other; joining of individual lineups; and superposition of impulses for parallel lineups.

In VSP, the most frequently encountered zones of interference are the intersection of lineups, when reflected and multiply reflected waves, propagating in different directions, interfere with each other. Adjoining lineups are common for regions of interference of incident and secondary waves and are principally observed on profile sections that are contiguous to the boundaries of separation. Superposition of impulses for parallel lineups takes place for interference of a direct wave with ghosts, of reflected and multiple waves propagating in the same direction, and of refracted waves at various boundaries of separation. The latter case of superposition leads to stable and extensive zones of interference and severely encumbers the analysis of the wave pattern. The extent of

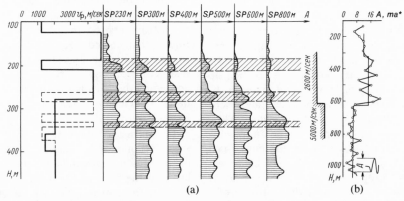

(a)   (b)

FIG. 26. (a) Amplitude graphs of the Z-component of first waves registering for small l-values in the upper portion of the cross-section. (b) Same, for large l-value, $l = 31,700$ m (well no. 1, Kletsko-Pochtov).

*Translator's remark: probably means "amplitude in milliamperes."

such zones of interference is larger, the smaller the difference in apparent wave velocities and the longer the duration of the impulses. VSP seismograms usually involve a combination of various types of interference.

Let us examine the particulars of correlation of different wave types in their first and subsequent arrivals.

DIRECT WAVES

First, let us define more accurately the concept of a direct wave. Direct waves on vertical profiles are not necessarily the same as those on horizontal profiles. In surface observations, a direct wave with a refracted wave propagating primarily in beds underlying the ZLV is considered a direct wave. The traveltime curve for such a wave is almost linear and starts practically at the source (which is how it gets its name). This wave registers as a first arrival for only very small distances from the source (the first tens of meters).

Further on, it is replaced by waves refracted at even deeper layer boundaries. The high intensity of these waves, observed often for later arrivals and for considerable distances from the source, is explained by their interferential character caused by the existence of a velocity gradient below the bottom of the ZLV.

For observations at interior points of a homogeneous medium, we shall tentatively define a direct wave as a wave that arrives first and possesses a positive apparent velocity. In a layered medium this wave is refracted at interfaces and therefore represents a transmitted wave. Along an in-line vertical profile, the direct wave usually registers first for the entire profile. Only in exceptional cases, e.g., when steeply dipping boundaries are present, do discrete sections of the in-line profile have first arrivals that are, in fact, refracted waves (Puzyrev, 1957). These cases may be ignored here. For off-line profiles, the direct wave does not always

produce first arrivals on records. Depending on the velocity cross-section and on the value of l, the direct wave may be observed, section-wise or along the entire vertical profile, in subsequent arrivals, and it also possesses a negative apparent velocity. The traveltime curve of the direct (transmitted) wave may involve discontinuities.

Particulars of direct wave correlation along an in-line vertical profile

For VSP, as in surface observation, wave correlation by first arrivals is the safest way. This is because waves are being observed against a quiescent background, while the background of irregular unwanted waves, caused by the explosion, is still insignificant. Under these conditions, one is able to identify the arrival time of the wavefront on a seismogram, i.e., the instant of transition from a quiescent mode to that of motion. The study of direct wave arrival times for observations along the in-line vertical profile is carried out in conventional seismic well shooting. Much effort has been devoted to these questions and much experience has been accumulated (Puzyrev, 1957; Urupov, 1966). For VSP, when the devices are clamped to the borehole walls and are decoupled from the surface, the useful sensitivity of instrumentation may be considerably higher than for conventional well shooting (see Chapter 2). This yields more distinct recordings of first arrivals, and consequently furnishes more reliable data on velocities than in conventional well shooting.

In contrast to conventional well shooting, VSP offers the interesting possibility of studying not only the instant of arrival, but also the form of the direct wave that initiates the entire wave process. As will be shown later, the form of the direct wave is basically determined by the conditions of interference of the input impulse with waves associated with the upper portion

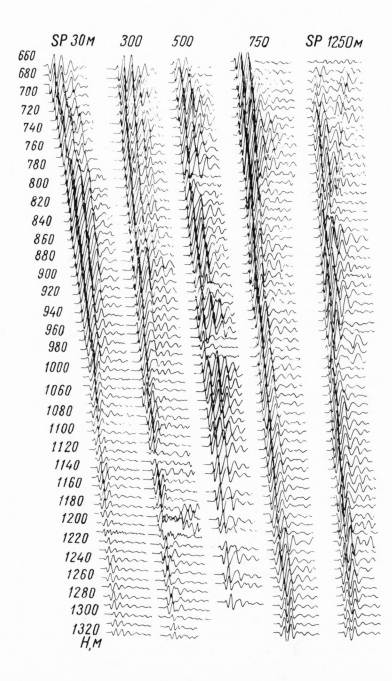

FIG. 27. Composite seismograms of incident waves obtained from a sequence of shotpoints involving unstable conditions of excitation (well no. 15, Chelbass, Krasnodar region).

of the cross-section and primarily with ghosts. For this reason, the direct wave correlation is strongly dependent on the control of the conditions of excitation.

If during observations the excitation conditions have not been strictly preserved (basically this refers to shot depth), then the shape of the event constituting the direct wave is not stable (Figure 27). The number of cycles varies as does the intensity of the wave. For some intervals, one must track an unresolved multiphase oscillation (SP 30 m, $H = 660 - 1000$ m), for other intervals, a relatively short event prevails. This example may serve as a good illustration of low quality observations.

When excitation conditions are kept constant, the form of the direct wave is well-preserved, even though it may be a complicated event created by wave superposition. In most cases one may eliminate ghosts or one may delay them sufficiently by selecting special conditions of excitation. Then one succeeds in obtaining a direct-wave recording that represents a short event consisting of two or three peaks with well preserved form (Figure 28). Phase correlation of such a wave is usually simple. When the direct wave has a simple form, the traveltime curves of various phases are practically parallel to the traveltime curve of first arrivals. Only for large l-values one occasionally notices a "broadening" of the impulse.

For propagation in a thin-layered medium, the waveform of the direct wave continuously changes as do all subsequent waves. However, experience indicates that these changes do not substantially hinder the correlation of waves along a vertical profile.

Disruptions in correlatability of the direct wave represent a local characteristic usually associated with profile sections that are next to boundaries of separation. It is there, because of interference with secondary waves (reflected and transmitted), that the disruption of the direct-

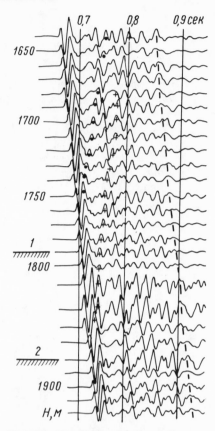

FIG. 28. Disruption of form of direct wave when reflected waves are generated (SP 100 m, well no. 162, Severo-Stavropol).

wave form takes place (Figure 28). The simple, short impulse of that wave is stretched out, new peaks appear which, as the distance from the boundary increases, emerge as independent waves. The possibilities of identifying reflected waves where they interfere with the direct wave shall be examined when the subject of correlation of reflected waves is discussed.

Direct-wave correlation in the upper portion of the cross-section can be complicated because the velocities of unwanted waves (cable and pipe waves) may be larger than those of the direct wave propagating along the formation. In that situation, the unwanted waves superimpose on the direct wave, impeding the correlation of the latter, so that identification of the instant of arrival becomes impossible. Therefore, in well shooting for seismic velocity, the upper portion of the cross-section is usually less amenable to study than the deeper portions of the borehole.

Particulars of direct wave correlation along an off-line profile

As the l-value increases, the direction of approach of the direct wave changes (it approaches the horizontal). Then, the apparent velocity increases, and the relative intensity of its vertical component decreases, while it may increase for other waves (reflected, refracted). Therefore, the resolution of the direct wave on seismograms of the Z-component may be very difficult, even in its first arrivals, against a background of more intense subsequent waves. Sometimes this makes the first arrivals of the direct wave barely perceptible on the record (Figure 29). Against the background of very weak oscillations, caused by the arrival of the direct wave, a considerably more intense refracted wave emerges. In this particular case, the intensity of the horizontal component of the direct wave exceeds that of the vertical component.

For observations in a *continuously varying* medium on off-line vertical profiles, the first waves to appear are the direct refracted waves. The correlation of these waves on seismograms involves a number of specific properties which can be attributed to the kinematic and dynamic particulars of these waves. At the minimum point of the traveltime curve, corresponding to a horizontal approach of the primary wave, a sign inversion takes place. For the profile section located above the minimum, a negative velocity and the corresponding approach of the wave from below are characteristic. For profile sections located deeper than the minimum point, the velocity is positive and the wave approaches from above. In the

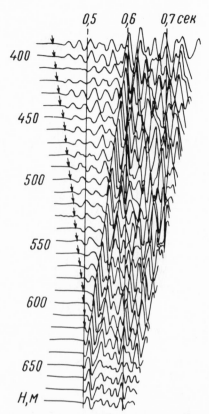

FIG. 29. Influence of direction of approach on intensity of vertical component of direct wave (SP 1500 m, well no. 1, Kletsko-Pochtov).

registration of the vertical component, the recorded amplitude at the minimum is zero while, at either side of this point, the amplitude rises according to a sinusoidal law. Moreover, at relatively small distances from the minimum point, the recorded wave possesses equal amplitudes and identical form, the phase being inverted. However, the value of the full vector observed on three-component geophones remains invariant.

The direct refracted wave in the region of the traveltime curve, i.e., in the depth interval of 510 – 740 m, is indicated in Figure 30. For records with large amplification (lefthand) the sign inversion of first arrivals is evident; this occurs at a depth of about 600 m. For records with

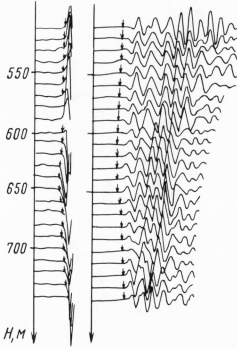

FIG. 30. Seismogram of first refracted wave along an off-line profile (SP 1775 m, well no. 42, Staro-Minsk).

low amplification (righthand), the form of the first wave remains preserved on both sides of the minimum point, keeping phase inversion in mind. Polarity inversion of apparent velocity from negative to positive also occurs for conversion of a head wave or a weakly refracted wave to a transmitted wave in the presence of a velocity jump in the cross-section. This situation will be examined in the next section.

For observations in a *layered medium* the direct wave may register in subsequent arrivals at discrete sections of an off-line vertical profile. The correlatory conditions for the direct wave in that case depend on many factors: primarily, on the intensities of the refracted and the transcritically reflected waves. The first is often determined by the law of velocity variation in the underlying layer.

If a *significant velocity gradient* exists in the layer underlying the boundary of separation, the refracted wave has considerable intensity, and this fact complicates the correlation of the direct wave. As an example, let us examine the correlatory conditions for the direct wave along a vertical profile shot from five shotpoints (Figure 31).

From SP 400 m, the direct wave registers as first arrivals along the entire profile down to the top of the Paleozoic which occurs at a depth of 374 m. The seismogram obtained with high instrument sensitivity (left) shows upward wave arrivals, corresponding to a wave approach from above; also, the increase of amplitudes with depth is evident, which occurs as the direction of the wave approaches the vertical. The seismogram with low amplification (right) indicates the form of the direct wave and its disruption as it interferes with the reflected wave along the profile section that is contiguous to the boundary (340 – 380 m).

From SP 500 m, the wave refracted at the top of the Paleozoic replaces the direct wave at a depth of 330 m, and constitutes a first-arrival wave. This is evident from the change of direction of arrivals and from the laws governing the apparent velocities; this is seen especially on channels having maximum amplification (left). At the profile section that is contiguous to the boundary, the direct wave is within the region of interference with the refracted wave and the transcritically reflected wave, and cannot be resolved. As *l* further increases, the region of registration of the refracted wave as first arrivals increases, and the latter moves out of the zone of interference for a substantial section of the profile. Under these circumstances, the direct wave may occasionally be identified in its subsequent arrivals, and it appears between the refracted and the transcritically reflected waves. Thus for *l* = 750 m, one succeeds in track-

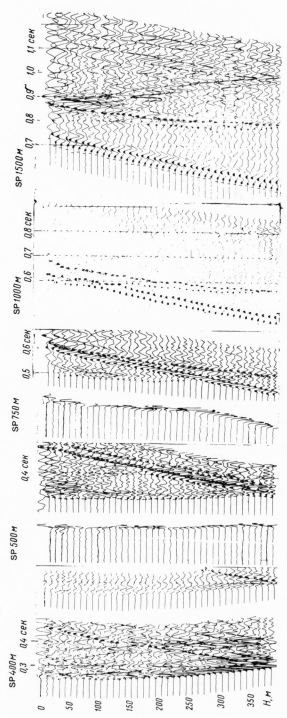

FIG. 31. Seismograms obtained from different shotpoints (well no. 90a, Kudinov).

ing the direct wave down to $H = 200$ m as well as after its interference with the refracted wave, down to its interference with the transcritically reflected wave.

From more remote shotpoints (for example, SP 1500 m), the refracted wave registers beyond the zone of its interference with the direct wave, and it does so over the entire profile interval. However, the correlatory conditions of the direct wave in the subsequent portion of the Z-component deteriorates because of its interference with the transcritically reflected wave and its unfavorable direction of approach. The true interrelation of wave intensities in this situation may only be appraised from records involving a three-component setup (Figure 32), which show that both the direct and the transcritically reflected waves are so much more intense than the first re-

fracted wave that a single level of amplification is insufficient for their simultaneous tracking. From seismograms obtained for low channel amplification it is seen that the direct wave record is readable, whereas the refracted wave is barely visible.

If the *velocity gradient in the underlying layer is absent,* or the thickness of that layer is very small compared to the wavelength, the intensity of the head wave drops sharply. Thus because of the low intensity of the head wave even for a relatively small distance from the point of its emergence, the direct wave is reliably trackable down to the boundary. From Figure 33 one observes that a weak

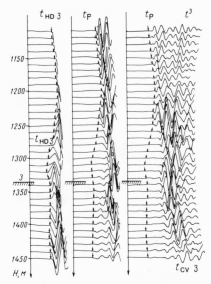

FIG. 33. Composite seismogram of direct, head, and transcritically reflected waves for a section of the borehole traversing boundary 3 (SP 1775 m, well no. 42, Staro-Minsk).

head wave having a negative apparent velocity registers ahead of the direct wave down to depth 1210 m on channels with high amplification. Against the background of the head wave, the direct wave is reliably identified in its subsequent arrivals. On channels having minimum amplification, that wave pro-

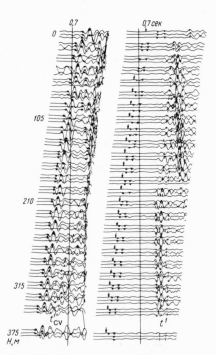

FIG. 32. Seismogram for three-component symmetrical installation (SP 1500 m, well no. 90a, Kudinov).

duces visible first arrivals. As the distance increases, the direct and transcritically reflected waves come closer together and the relative intensity of the direct wave on Z-component seismograms drops off. When that happens, the transcritically reflected wave usually becomes dominant and it is almost impossible to identify the direct wave against the background of the dominant wave on records of the Z-component. In many situations, especially when a large number of horizons are present in the cross-section, subsequent arrivals of direct waves may not emerge at all on records of the vertical component. Then, it appears that the incident wave is absent in the initial portion of the seismogram.

Transmitted wave correlation for grazing incidence

Based on the law of velocity variation with depth in the underlying layer, when the cross-section involves a velocity jump, first arrival registrations above the boundary may consist of refracted waves (head waves or curved-ray refractions). Clarification of the nature of waves above the boundary (and, consequently, on the surface) is accomplished with less effort and with greater reliability by observations relating to the underlying layer than by those relating to layers above the boundary. To a considerable degree, this is where the advantages of VSP lie as compared to surface observation. Let us examine the properties of waves above and below the boundary for two types of medium structure: 1) the velocity in the thick underlying layer is constant ($\beta = 0$); and 2) the velocity increases with depth ($\beta > 0$).

In the first case ($\beta = 0$), diffraction occurs and a head wave registers above the boundary, while on the profile section that crosses the boundary, one observes the transition from head to transmitted wave. Along the traveltime curve at the depth of the boundary a point cor-responding to minimum traveltime exists where the apparent velocity changes discontinuously and where the form of the wave changes sharply (see Figure 112). Immediately below the boundary, linear polarization (which is a characteristic of a head wave) is disrupted and the directions of particle motion no longer coincide with the direction of wave propagation. Disruption of polarization for grazing rays of the transmitted wave attests to the existence of a velocity jump in the cross-section (see Chapter 5). Immediately below the boundary it is better to record the transmitted wave by a three-component installation. The apparent wave velocity below the boundary is close to infinite. For observations from several shotpoints, the geometric locus of points of velocity inversion from negative to infinite values coincides with the boundary.

In the second case ($\beta > 0$), for transition across the boundary, wave shapes practically remain invariant. The reverse of the previous case occurs, i.e., a change of intensity of the vertical component. As the distance from the boundary increases, the intensity first decreases, while the apparent velocity on the profile section adjoining the boundary from below remains negative. Only for a definite distance from the boundary is a minimum observed on the traveltime curve as well as the corresponding changeover of polarities of velocities and direction of motion from negative to positive. The mentioned features are sufficient for the identification of the velocity gradient and the determination of the nature of the wave registering above the boundary.

REFLECTED WAVES

Reflected waves comprise the basic class of waves appearing on later portions of the record. Correlation conditions for reflected waves along vertical profiles are usually more complicated than for surface observations. This is because there are considerably more multiple waves observed at interior points of the medium. Besides, for VSP, the relative intensity of primary waves as compared to multiple waves may be substantially lower than for surface observations since at interior points of the medium one may observe multiple waves which have undergone fewer reflections than have those at the surface.

The correlatibility of reflected waves is governed by their interference with other waves, intensity, and form. It is known that intensity and form of the reflected wavelet are conditioned primarily by the incident direct wave and by the reflection coefficient spectrum.

In a thin-layered medium, the reflection coefficient is a function of frequency and is strongly dependent on the structure of the reflecting boundary element. The form of the reflected wave depends on the frequency content of the incident wave and may differ substantially from the latter. The duration of the reflected wave is greater in comparison to the incident wave. Waves reflected from different elements of the medium may be of different form. The form of the reflected wave, even for invariant impulse and reflecting element structure, may vary with distance (increased angle of incidence), which may encumber the identification of the wave on records acquired from different shotpoints.

As the spectral function of reflection is more selective than that of refraction, the reflected wave changes less for transmission through a thin-layered medium than for reflection. However, here too some stretching of the wavelet is observable.

The particular feature of reflected wave correlation, because of the nature of VSP observations, is that direct and reflected wave traveltime curves possess common points. The waves' mutual interference may be related to a type of convergence. For surface observations such interference occurs for unconformity of bound-aries or for curved boundaries in the region of "loops" of traveltime curves. The extent of the interference zone determines the distance from the reflecting horizon from which tracking of the reflected wave becomes possible and, consequently, at which accurate statigraphic correlation of seismic horizons begins. The extent of the above region of interference is dictated by the duration of the incident wave as well as by the location of the shotpoint. This zone increases as the traveltime curves converge when the shotpoint becomes more remote. Other conditions remaining constant, the interference zone is least extensive for in-line vertical profiles.

Interference of direct and reflected waves may be illustrated by two examples. The seismogram (see Figure 28) obtained over a profile section that crosses two reflecting boundaries, located at depths $H_v = 1790$ and 1880 m, indicates a direct wave of very short duration and consisting of only three peaks. The accompanying ghosts, because of the great depth of explosion ($h = 90$ m), are separated from the direct wave by approximately 0.05 sec. In the neighborhood of the boundaries (at depths $H = 1730$ and 1810 m), the end of the pulse reveals additional peaks which later on leave the interferential zone and are recorded as independent reflected waves, until they interfere with the ghosts. It is typical that the emergence of the reflected wave and the interferential character of the oscillation only become noticeable after a certain distance ($40 - 60$ m) from the boundary. After transit through the boundary the pulse shape of the direct wave is restored.

In the above simplest possible case, the reflected waves were trackable relatively close to the reflecting boundary. However, it is more usual that the duration of the interfering incident wave sharply increases so that it is no longer possible to track the

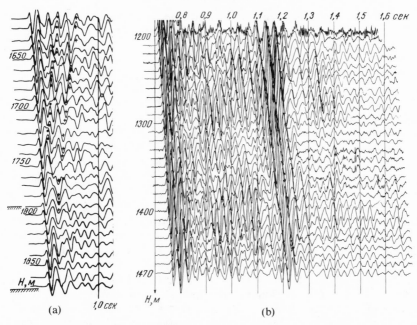

FIG. 34. Deterioration of correlation of reflected waves for a complicated train of incident waves. (a) SP 1200 m (well no. 162, Severo-Stavropol). (b) SP 1000 m (well no. 1, Kletsko-Pochtov).

reflected wave in the vicinity of the boundary, because of superposition of ghosts on the direct wave. The seismogram (Figure 34a) obtained for the same section of the vertical profile as above, indicates that ghosts interfere with the direct wave because of the smaller shot depth ($H = 50$ m) and this complicates tracking capabilities of reflected waves. CDR extends the correlation zone of reflected waves and their tracking almost to the reflecting horizon.

The reliability of VSP seismograms as well as surface seismograms largely depends on the signal-to-noise ratio. As the recording time increases, the useful signal strength decreases while the irregular noise background increases. Therefore, at large time values, the correlatability of reflected waves deteriorates and, beginning with a definite time interval, becomes unreliable.

Interference of singly reflected waves with multiple waves, propagating into the depth of the medium

This is the case most frequently encountered in VSP. Multiple waves from the upper portion of the cross-section form a whole sequence of incident waves that follow the direct wave, and they occupy a substantial interval of the record and propagate into the depth of the medium. For observations at all depths accessible to us, it was impossible to avoid the influence of the upper portion of the cross-section. Records obtained at depths exceeding 3 km indicate that a significant portion of the energy is also associated with multiples propagating from above. High reflection coefficients, characteristic for boundaries in the upper portion of the cross-section and, in particular, for the bottom of the ZLV, dictate the high intensity of these waves; the latter can be considerably higher than the intensity of the singly reflected waves propagating from below (Figure 34b). Multiples possess the highest intensity on the initial portion of the seismogram; they provide good correlatability along the vertical profile and they disrupt the correlatability of singly reflected waves propagating upward from great depths (see Figure 85). Only discrete, strongly dominant reflected waves can be continuously tracked along the vertical profile.

Waves, and occasionally even individual phases, may often be identified on sections before and after the zone of interference with sufficient reliability. This is so because of the practically linear lineups and the relatively short zone of interference. Since the apparent velocities of the interfering waves are of opposite polarity, the extent of the interferential zone is small and it is basically dictated by the duration of the wavelet. Methods of directional reception effectively reestablish the correlation of reflected waves in zones of interference.

Interference of singly-reflected waves with multiple waves propagating upward

In actual media situations frequently arise in which the wave reflected from a deeper boundary and propagating toward the surface reaches the zone of multiple waves, likewise propagating toward the surface, thus producing interference. This has been called parallel superposition of interfering oscillations. For an in-line vertical profile, in the case of a horizontally layered medium, the apparent velocities of these waves are equal. For weakly dipping boundaries, or for off-line profiles, the wave velocities are nearly similar. The resolution of interfering waves under conditions of parallel superposition poses great difficulties. Methods of directional reception are ineffective in these situations as is the analogous case for surface observations.

At the same time, the clarification of such interference zones is often of great practical consequence and is especially important for the solution of whether the wave, in fact, is multiple or single but associated with a deeper boundary.

In order to establish the existence of interference, it is necessary to ascertain that at a depth corresponding to the assumed start of the interference zone a boundary does exist which is associated with a sufficiently intense singly reflected wave. This may be detected from the initial portion of the record. Of substantial help for the clarification of interference are the dynamic properties of waves (sharp variation of intensity and period of oscillations).

HEAD WAVES AND CURVED-RAY REFRACTIONS

Experience with VSP has shown that for actual media the velocity increase with depth is the rule and that curved-path refractions are the waves most prominently recorded. For thin layers where the influence of refraction is not essential, very low intensity head waves[1] may be involved. For the correlation of head and refracted waves, in VSP, in contrast to correlation of reflected waves, one is more frequently dealing with extensive interference zones involving waves of similar or equal apparent velocities. Kinematic schematics of head waves and curved-path refractions are very similar and yet these waves are sharply distinguished by their intensity and thus their correlation is substantially different. Curved-ray refractions, dominant on the initial portion of the record, are safely tracked by their first and subsequent arrivals. Head waves are identified and tracked most reliably in their first arrival.

A comparison of regions where head

[1]In contrast to a curved-path refracted wave, a head wave is understood to be a wave whose mechanism of energy return (to the surface) is diffraction.

waves register on the surface and at interior points of the medium (see Figure 17) has shown that, for surface observations the first arrivals of the head wave may be tracked for a comparatively large distance from the initial point only. Along the vertical profile, first arrivals of the head wave can be tracked immediately at boundary (beginning with the point of emergence). Moreover, for VSP, because of the less pronounced background of seismic noise, a higher useful channel sensitivity is realizable in comparison to surface observations, so that weaker signals may be brought out. For observations at interior points of the medium, head waves, in the majority of situations, cannot be brought out at all. In certain situations only their first arrivals are recognizable down to where they interfere with the incident wave, the polarity inversion of arrivals and the apparent velocities being the criteria. To record the head wave it is essential to have available a channel of large dynamic range. Because of the low intensity of the wave, it is not always possible to establish the first arrival on the record.

Correlation of head waves associated with thin layers

This is the situation that presents most of the difficulties. They are caused by extremely unfavorable relationships of intensities of head, direct, and transcritically reflected waves. On seismograms (see Figure 33) obtained for a section of the vertical profile that is contiguous to the refracting boundary ($H = 1334$ m) and consisting of a packet of thin layers with increased velocity which amounts collectively to a thickness of about 50 m, the first wave, down to a depth of 1210 m, is the intense direct wave. The characteristics for that wave are sharp first arrivals and a positive apparent velocity. A weak arrival emerges at a depth of 1230 m for channels having maximum amplification. As the depth increases, the

time interval between the weak arrival and the intense direct wave increases. At depth 1330 m almost a complete period of oscillation is already perceptible. This is the head wave associated with the thin layer.

The zone of interference of direct and head wave is fairly reliably established on seismograms by the sharp polarity inversion of arrivals and by the intensity of the registration (see Figure 33). It is extremely difficult to evaluate quantitatively the wave intensity and to discuss its form, since the wave is almost at all times located in the zone of interference with the direct wave. It is only possible to say that its first peak is associated with a lower frequency than the direct wave. On seismograms from SP 2500 m (see Figure 111), on which the head wave is tracked as a first wave on the profile interval amounting to almost 200 m, all phases are reliably tracked along the vertical profile all the way to the zone of interference with the direct wave. It is impossible to track the head waves in the region of subsequent arrivals against a background of the intense direct waves. In shooting the vertical profile from different shotpoints, the changeover of direct wave to head wave is usually tracked in a reliable manner.

Thus, the study of head wave correlation and records from a thin layer presents considerable difficulties, since these waves emerge only in the immediate vicinity of the boundary. For surface observations, these waves were altogether unresolved, even after they have been discovered by VSP observations, and in spite of special experiments involving a drastic increase of charges (Epinat'yeva and Karus, 1967).

Correlation of head waves associated with a layer of medium thickness

As the thickness of the refracting layer increases, the intensity of the head wave increases. However, in this case, refraction often exerts a strong influence on intensity. For example, let us examine the correlation of the head wave associated with the refracting boundary (890 m) which is characterized by the velocity jump $V_{P_1} = 0.89$ ($V_{P_1} = 1990$ m/sec, $V_{P_1} = 2250$ m/sec) and the ratio layer thickness to wavelength $H/\lambda = 5.5$ (see Figure 115). The head wave originating from that boundary is replaced by the transmitted wave at a depth of approximately 900 m. Channels having maximum sensitivity indicate first arrivals and show that the head wave possesses a negative apparent velocity and the first motion is downward. Channels with medium sensitivity indicate the complicated form of the head wave: 30 hz oscillations are complicated by a higher frequency component (50 hz). This may be connected with the fact that the cross-section contains two thick layers, subdivided by a thin interstratification (approximately 10 m) with increased velocity. For the transition from head wave to transmitted wave, a sharp disruption of the form of the event as well as a change of its intensity takes place below the boundary. Records taken with minimum sensitivity disclose that the transcritically reflected wave becomes readable in their subsequent arrivals. The head wave here is no longer trackable for all practical purposes.

Correlation of refracted waves associated with a thick layer

In actual media it is very difficult to find thick homogeneous layers with constant velocity. In practically all cases, when the layer thickness permits the reliable determination of the character of its velocity change, a velocity gradient is found. In that situation, the curved-ray refraction is the first to register and it is adequately trackable not only in its first arrivals (see Figure 31, SP 1000 m and SP 1500 m) but also in subsequent arrivals (Figure 31, SP 750 m). The sign of the apparent velocity changes at the boundary for a curved-path refraction, whereas the sign of apparent velocity for head waves does not change.

By reference to a family of traveltime curves of primary waves, obtained for delineating a section of carbonate formations which are interlaced by layers and discrete interstratifications of terrigenous deposits (see Figure 117a), it can be seen that refraction takes place in two limestone beds. The top of the first bed is located at a depth of 125 m, and the second is at a depth of 640 m. Above the level of the second bed, the dotted line indicates the points at which a changeover of direct wave into refracted wave occurs, while inside the bed is shown the line of horizontal motion corresponding to the changeover of polarities of apparent velocities of the refracted wave. This line does not coincide with the boundary. Between the two lines lies the region of negative apparent velocities and directions of approach of the refracted wave from below (this is crosshatched in the figure). The seismogram of the Z-component of the first wave obtained over a profile section that crosses the boundary (see Figure 117b) indicates that the intensity of the refracted wave, as it travels from the lower medium into the upper one, is somewhat increased due to a decrease in velocity as well as due to the approach of the direction of arrival of the wave to the vertical.

Particulars of wave correlation for situations involving several boundaries

This is a situation for which a considerably more complicated wave pattern is observed. On different sections of the vertical profile, refracted waves originating at different boundaries may register so that the inherently simple form of a refracted wave, associated with a deeper horizon interferes with a refracted wave from a shallower boundary, resulting in a complicated interference pattern. The registration intervals of refracted waves, in their first arrivals, are basically identified kin-

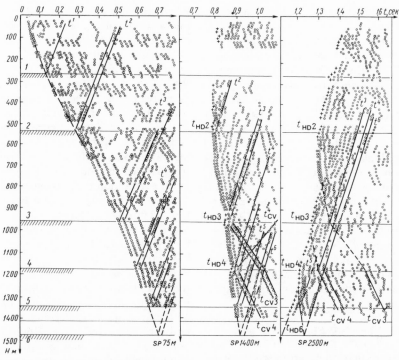

FIG. 35. Composite vertical traveltime curves of waves involving the initial portion of the record (well no. 28, Kushchev, Krasnodar region).

ematically by the negative apparent velocities on the traveltime curves. The region of changeover of discrete waves is difficult or practically impossible to determine from seismogram studies.

Figure 35 illustrates traveltime curves of waves registered in the initial portion of the records from three shotpoints. From SP 1400 m, refracted waves in the immediate neighborhood of boundaries 2, 3, and 4 are registered on three sections contiguous to the above boundaries. The traveltime curve obtained for SP 2500 m indicates more extended regions of registration of these waves. At a large depth the refracted wave from the crystalline basement located at 1480 m (boundary 6) appears as the first arrival.

For a medium with weak velocity differentiation, the regions of registration of refracted waves strongly depend on ve-

locity ratios. When two or more boundaries are present that are located in close proximity to each other in significant regions of simultaneous registration, the arrival-time difference of refracted waves may be very small. In many instances this difference may be smaller than the extent of first-wave registration. As a result, an extensive interference zone is observed.

When registering refracted waves in media with weak velocity differentiation, one observes the most extensive and the most difficult-to-resolve zones of interference. The possibility of resolving interfering wavelets depends to a large degree on their intensity relationships. Only in situations in which the intensity of a wave considerably exceeds that of another, can it can be continuously tracked over the entire — or a substantial region of — the profile. In the remaining situations, separate tracking of waves is practically impossible.

It is of considerable significance for the analysis of wave fields and for the identification of the region of changeover of waves in media with weak velocity differentiation to study the dynamic characteristics of the record: the form amplitudes of various phases, spectra, etc. A large body of work on refracted waves along horizontal profiles for media with weak velocity contrast was done by Epinat'yeva (1960). All correlation characteristics of waves along a horizontal profile apply equally well to vertical profiles. Experience with VSP shows that, in media with weak velocity differentiation, head waves are not present, while what is being basically registered are curved-path refractions (see Figure 15).

TRANSVERSE AND CONVERTED WAVES

Correlation of transverse waves along a vertical profile is much more difficult than that of longitudinal waves. These difficulties may be subdivided into two groups: difficulties of an observational nature, and those due to the nature of shear wave propagation.

Difficulties associated with the procedures of observation

Observation difficulties are caused by the fact that the three-component installation of geophones in a borehole, used for the registration of converted waves, is not oriented with reference to the azimuth. Therefore, records available for wave correlation fail to produce any space-invariant component of motion. Under these circumstances, one may only talk of correlation of the full vector according to all three components of the latter, and this demands special skills and experience. To some degree, full vector correlation reminds one of wave correlation (Gal'perin and Kosminskaya, 1958) for a situation

when tracking does not involve an individual cycle of the event but, rather, a phase group of a given wave.

Correlation difficulties are somewhat compounded by single-point observations. When correlating waves are from single-point recordings, kinematic properties of waves become of primary significance. The utilization of the latter may prove effective by establishing basic boundaries of separation and of quantities v_s computed from known quantities v_p, based as a matter of orientation on previously available data involving longitudinal waves. Therefore, when constructing traveltime curves, the arrival times of converted waves can be approximated by straight lines within the limits of each layer.

Application of multichannel instrumentation with controlled orientation of geophones in the borehole, developed by Vinogradov (1967), permits the correlation of converted waves along the vertical profile as reliably as in the case of longitudinal waves. In the absence of controlled geophone orientation, it is possible to improve the correlation of waves by constructing seismograms of a fixed component by the CDR method of the first kind (CDR-I). Such seismograms may be computed from three-component records for certain simplifying assumptions concerning the medium (see Chapter 9).

Difficulties associated with particulars of the wave field

Among the difficulties arising from the nature of shear wave propagation, difficulties caused by the variation of the direction of wave approach to different points of the vertical profile may be considered basic.

In surface observations, the direction of approach of longitudinal and transverse waves at all points of the horizontal profile is practically invariant and remains close to the vertical, and the longitudinal and transverse waves register separately on records of the vertical and horizontal components. But for observations at interior points of the medium, the direction of wave approach may vary within wide limits as a function of the quantity l and the location of the point of observation along the profile. (This does not refer to the uppermost portion of the upper portion of the cross-section for which the direction of approach of all waves is nearly vertical.) Aside from this, the direction of wave approach substantially depends on the velocity parameters of the medium.

As a result, vertical components of transverse and converted waves may turn out to be commensurable with the vertical component of longitudinal waves (and occasionally to exceed the latter in intensity). Naturally, this applies equally well to longitudinal waves, whose horizontal components may exceed (in intensity) those of the vertical ones under certain conditions (see Figure 130). In Figure 130, the later portion of the seismogram of the Z-component indicates that the low-frequency direct transverse wave S is reliably brought out. For a shotpoint distance of 200 m (from the vertical profile), and for recordings at small depths, the direction of approach of the direct S-wave is close to the horizontal. For that reason the wave just mentioned is satisfactorily registered by vertical geophones. As the observation depth increases and as the direction of approach of that wave approximates the vertical, the intensity of the S-wave from vertical seismometers diminishes, while at the same time, the amplitude of the first longitudinal wave sharply increases. For a second example, consider the records of direct and transcritically reflected longitudinal waves on three-point seismograms (Figure 31) and on three-component seismograms (Figure 32) for $l = 1500$ m. While in Figure 31 the intensities of the direct and transcritically reflected waves do not exceed those of the

first refracted waves, they are considerably more intense on the three-component seismogram. The high intensity of the horizontal component of the direct and transcritically reflected longitudinal waves, as compared to the vertical component, is caused by the direction of wave approach.

The influence of direction of wave approach on intensity of wave components should always be kept in mind. For correlation of converted waves on three-component single-point records, wave amplitudes play a very significant role. From such records it is possible to identify and correlate reliably only the most intense and the most stable converted waves that are trackable over large intervals of the vertical profile. The dependence between direction of approach of waves and correlatability of the record is explained by the fact that waves propagating in directions that are close to the vertical (for observations from very close or very remote shotpoints) are better trackable on records obtained from XYZ installations. At the same time, waves approaching the geophones at appreciable inclinations are better correlated on recordings obtained from three-component symmetrical installations. This rule usually serves as a guideline for the selection of the installation required for the observation.

In a *homogeneous medium,* and for a fixed shotpoint location, the angle of incidence of the direct wave on the boundary of conversion (which controls the coefficients of conversion and consequently the intensity of converted waves) varies within narrow limits. For the registration of converted reflected or transmitted waves along intervals of the vertical profile amounting to $500 - 1000$ m, the angle of incidence of the longitudinal wave varies by not more than $10 - 12$ degrees. For such a small angular variation, the coefficients of reflection and of refraction usually vary smoothly and insignificantly.

Observed data in a layer of constant velocity confirm the gradual and smooth decrease of amplitude of the full vector of motion for converted reflected and transmitted waves as the observation point becomes more remote from the boundary at which the waves are formed.

For variation of the shotpoint location as a function of the ratio l/H_v, the angle of incidence of the longitudinal wave on the boundary of conversion may vary within extremely wide limits. This must surely be considered when selecting a recording system for converted waves of various types.

In *heterogeneous media* the influence of direction of wave approach and of parameters of the medium causes the interrelation of intensities of the Z- and X- components of converted waves to vary a great deal along a vertical profile. In low-velocity layers in which the directions of wave propagation approach the vertical and for which the refraction coefficient of transverse waves increases, the intensity of the horizontal component of transverse waves increases. Moreover these

layers produce a much more complicated wave pattern due to the generation of a large number of multiple converted waves. These layers play the role of waveguides (Figure 36). The correlation of converted transmitted waves, propagating from below, is considerably encumbered in such a situation.

In layers with increased velocity the difficulty of correlation of converted waves is aggravated not so much by the decrease of intensities of these waves as by the fact that, because of the sharp change of direction of approach, the intensity of longitudinal waves for the horizontal component may exceed the intensity of converted waves for the same component by several times. The role of longitudinal and transverse waves in the make-up of the wave field in layers with increased and decreased velocities is illustrated by computerized stacked tapes (Figure 37); see Chapter 9. In terrigenous deposits ($H =$ 320, 470, and 720 m), along with linearly polarized longitudinal oscillations (phase inversion in the neighborhood of 90 degrees and maximum intensities at 0 and

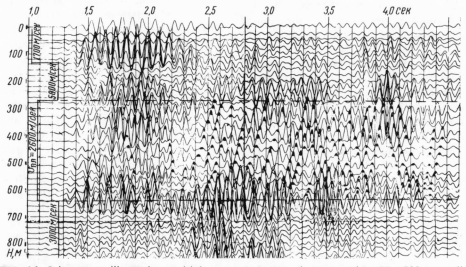

FIG. 36. Seismogram illustrating multiple converted waves in wave guide (SP 3700 m, well no. 1, Kletsko-Pochtov).

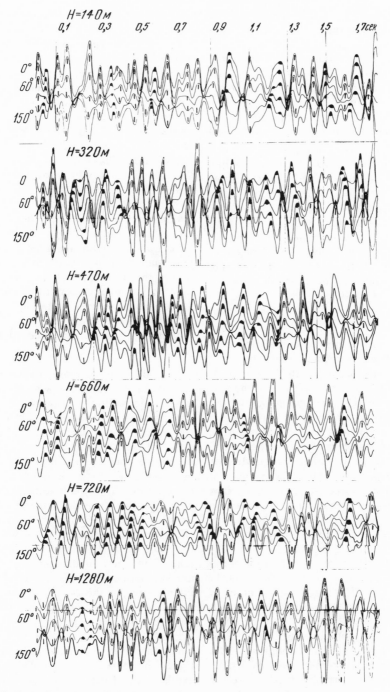

FIG. 37. Summing tapes of CDR-I, computer-processed according to experimental seismograms for $l = 31,700$ m.

180 degrees), linearly polarized transverse oscillations emerge (maximum intensity at 90 degrees, phase inversion at 0 and 180 degrees), as well as nonlinearly polarized oscillations generated as a result of interference of longitudinal and transverse waves. In carbonate deposites (H = 140, 660, 1280 m) linearly polarized longitudinal oscillations are dominant.

Correlation of transverse waves in layers with low velocities is associated with a definite advantage, since regions of interference of P- and S- waves are of shorter duration, and it is easier to resolve the recorded waves. However, in layers with increased velocity, in order to separate the P- and S-waves according to apparent velocities, it is necessary to use large bases of observation (spreads), and in the case of moderately thick layers, the problem becomes insoluble for practical purposes.

Some difficulties in correlating converted waves, and longitudinal reflected waves are associated with the region of their registration. On sections of the vertical profile that are contiguous to the boundaries of conversion, they register on the initial portions of the seismograms, while as one recedes from the boundary, they rapidly go over to the later portion of the records. In the immediate vicinity of the boundary of conversion, there exists an interval of interference between the converted wave and the incident longitudinal wave. Over that profile interval, none of the interfering waves can be identified in its pure form. The duration of the region of interference depends primarily on the ratio of propagation velocities of longitudinal and transverse waves, as well as on the relative locations of the observed sector and the point of excitation. The interference interval may comprise 150 – 200 m. Far away from the boundaries, the disruption of correlation of converted waves is due to interference of waves of different types. In correlation of transverse waves, there also exist difficulties connected with the polarization of these waves. The superposition of SV- and SH-waves, polarized in mutually orthogonal planes, produces trajectories of particle motion in the horizontal plane for small l values which approach ellipses. For observations by means of nonoriented XYZ clusters, it is expedient to accomplish the correlation by recordings of the full vector of oscillation. This is because the record of the component having maximum amplitude is phase-shifted in relation to the full vector in all cases in which the axis of maximum sensitivity of the device does not coincide with the major axis of the ellipse. For correlation along the maximum amplitude, this may incur errors in determining the arrival time of the wave, which may amount to one quarter of the period, and thus brings about scattering of points along the traveltime curve. Such scattering may be more pronounced than for longitudinal waves.

In addition to the above circumstances, correlation of transverse waves may be upset by low-velocity surface-type waves. These waves are associated with boundaries within the medium and are registered on profile sections that are contiguous to the above boundaries. The above waves usually emerge when the source becomes more remote from the investigated borehole. As the distance l increases, the depth at which they appear increases. A characteristic feature of these waves is the rapid decay of intensities as the distance from the boundary increases (Figure 38). Wave t_{st} appears to be the most intense one on the later portion of the record and is easily distinguishable by its low frequency, and it registers at both sides of the boundary (H = 1250 m) with which that wave is associated. Its vertical traveltime curves are parallel to the depth axis and the velocity of its propagation is close to the velocity of transverse waves. The variations of the wave

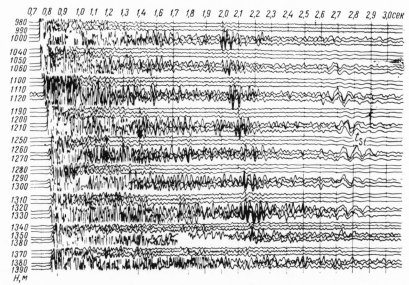

FIG. 38. Low-frequency waves of surface type associated with boundary 3 (H_v = 1250 m, SP 1200 m, well no. 20, Staro-Minsk). Two levels of amplification are used for the registration at each depth.

spectrum, as the distance from the boundary increases, are not detectable since the dominant frequencies (approximately 10 hz) lie outside the passband of the channel. These waves have not been studied specifically. However, they frequently appear in various areas and, according to the enumerated features, may be classified as Stoneley waves.

Correlation of various types of converted waves

Depending on the location of the shotpoint, converted waves of various types may appear along different sections of the vertical profile. From shotpoints located at relatively short distances from the profile, when the primary longitudinal wave propagates into the depth of the medium, converted reflected waves occur above the boundaries of separation, and converted transmitted waves occur below the boundaries. From shotpoints at large distances, when the first arrivals on the vertical profile are due to a wave having a negative apparent velocity, the converted transmitted waves occur above the boundaries and the converted reflected waves below the boundaries. Thus, appropriate VSP systems permit the separate study of converted reflected and upward transmitted waves associated with the same boundary. Let us consider the correlation of converted waves of various types.

Converted reflected waves register on records from inclined or horizontal seismometers, since for upward propagation the direction of approach of the waves more and more approximates the vertical and, consequently, the waves possess a dominant horizontal component of motion.

Correlation of converted reflected waves is often encumbered by their interference with other waves observed at interior points of the medium, particularly in the upper portion of the cross-section. Such disruption of correlation frequently occurs as one approaches the surface where the converted waves which have been formed at the bottom of the ZLV may disturb the correlation of converted waves approaching from below. Figure 39 indicates that converted reflected

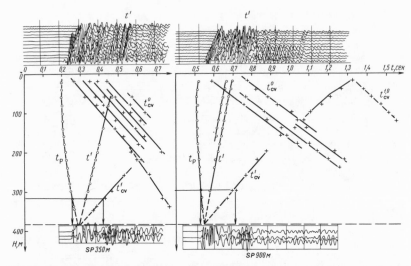

FIG. 39. Disruption of correlation of converted reflected waves (well no. 6, Staro-Minsk).

waves t^0_{cv}, formed when the longitudinal waves are incident on the bottom of the ZLV (shown on surface seismograms), disrupt the correlation of the converted reflected wave t^1_{cv}. The three-component record of the converted reflected wave at a depth of approximately 300 m is shown in the lower portion of Figure 39. The disruption of correlation of converted waves, reflected from deep boundaries of separation, by intense converted transmitted and reflected waves from shallower boundaries, may be observed not only in the near surface but also at great depths. By selecting the distance l, one may improve the conditions of correlation of this or that wave, compressing the interferential regions at the expense of variation of the slope of the vertical traveltime curves of interfering waves. In general, correlation of converted reflected waves is more reliable for the quiescent background of the later portion of the record, removed as it is from the initial portion of the seismogram "violated" by intense longitudinal waves. It is of course understood that the converted wave must be sufficiently intense to be identified at distances remote from the boundary. The

most favorable distances for the observation of converted reflected waves lie in the range of one or two times the depth to the boundary.

Converted downward transmitted waves usually register from shotpoints located at relatively small distances from the top of the borehole, compared to the depths to boundaries of conversion. Experience with numerous observations shows that converted downward transmitted waves possess high intensity and stability. They can be tracked into the depth of the medium far from boundaries at which they are generated. As one recedes from the boundary, depending upon the parameters of the medium, the distribution of intensities of vertical and horizontal components of oscillation of the converted wave may vary substantially (in favor of the vertical component for the case of velocity increase with depth). The most substantial variation of direction of approach of the wave is usually connected not with variation of observation depth, but with variation of velocity along the vertical profile.

For definite angles of incidence of the longitudinal wave upon the boundary,

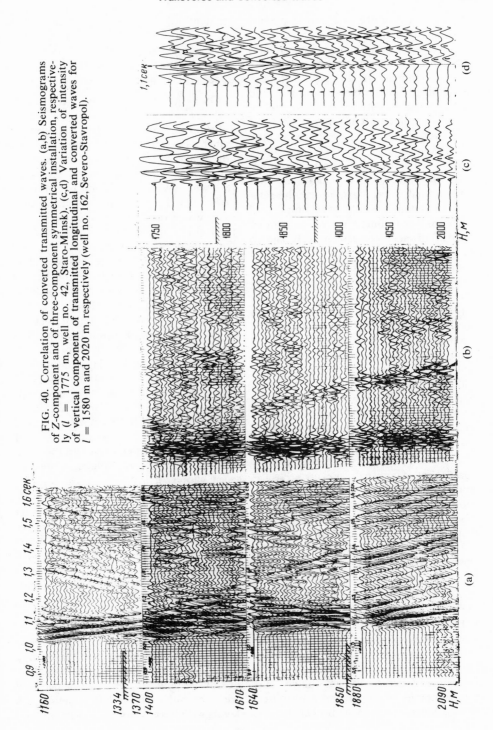

FIG. 40. Correlation of converted transmitted waves. (a,b) Seismograms of Z-component and of three-component symmetrical installation, respectively ($l = 1775$ m, well no. 42, Staro-Minsk). (c,d) Variation of intensity of vertical component of transmitted longitudinal and converted waves for $l = 1580$ m and 2020 m, respectively (well no. 162, Severo-Stavropol).

converted transmitted waves may possess high intensity. The vertical component of converted transmitted waves correlates excellently on records obtained from vertical geophones. It is seen in Figure 40a,b that the converted transmitted wave associated with the boundary $H_v = 1334$ m is well correlated on records from both vertical and inclined geophones. The intensity of converted transmitted waves on records of the vertical component may even exceed that of the first longitudinal wave. Variation of the relation of intensities of longitudinal and converted transmitted waves, as a function of distance, is descriptively shown on composite seismograms of the vertical component for a profile section that crosses the boundaries (Figure 40c,d). Below the boundaries, the transmitted longitudinal and converted waves register on the initial portion of the seismogram. For distance $l = 1580$ m, the intensities of both waves indicated on the seismograms are similar. However, starting with $l = 2020$ m, the relative intensity of the converted transmitted waves sharply increases. The longitudinal refracted wave, because of its low intensity, is hardly visible on the seismograms.

The correlation of an intense vertical component of converted downward transmitted waves on records for vertical seismometers does not differ in any manner from correlation of longitudinal waves. Converted waves frequently distinguished themselves from longitudinal waves by their lowered frequencies, a circumstance that may serve as an additional feature in the correlation on recordings of the Z-component.

Interference with longitudinal and converted waves that propagate upward (primarily these are waves reflected from deeper boundaries and possessing lower intensities) scarcely disturbs the correlation of converted downward transmitted waves. Since these waves propagate into the depth of the medium, they are easily correlatable even in the presence of a large number of unwanted waves associated with the weathered layer and the upper portion of the cross-section.

Converted upward transmitted waves may register for small as well as large l values. For small l the converted upward transmitted waves are for the most part connected with boundaries that are located in the upper part of the cross-section where wave correlation is extremely difficult. It is usually possible to resolve these waves only on the initial portion of the record, i.e., for a small distance from the boundary (see Figure 32). As they approach the surface these waves enter into a complicated zone of interference with numerous waves associated with the upper part of the cross-section.

Of significantly higher exploratory interest are converted upward transmitted waves which are observed for large l values. We first made a large number of specialized VSP observations in 1966. The object was to study converted upward-transmitted waves for large l (up to 31,700 m) in order to estimate the exploratory possibilities of the method of converted transmitted waves in the platform portion of the Volgograd district (see Chapter 9).

In correlating converted upward-transmitted waves in layers with high velocity (> 5000 m/sec), the basic noise appears to involve longitudinal waves that possess an intense horizontal component. In such layers formidable difficulties also arise in the resolution of P- and S-waves according to apparent velocities for relatively small spreads. Under these conditions, the disruption of linear polarization of oscillations connected with interference of longitudinal and converted waves may serve as a criterion for the identification of transverse waves. This can be detected with the aid of the CDR-I method. In layers with lower velocity (<3000 m/sec), the basic difficulty of wave identification consists of interference of transverse (converted) waves having parallel line-ups, as well as of interference with converted and longitudinal downward reflected waves.

From computational data and from experimental observations, it appears that the most intense converted upward transmitted waves are those formed at distinct boundaries of the upper portion of the cross-section. These same waves appear to be the first waves on seismograms of the X-component. For that reason their correlation is the most reliable. In the subsequent portion of the record a large number of transverse waves are registered above abrupt boundaries. Among these waves and converted transmitted waves originating at deep boundaries there are many converted transmitted waves that are generated by secondary longitudinal waves at shallow boundaries. It often becomes practically impossible to bring out converted transmitted waves originating from deep boundaries of separation against the background of the above oscillations.

SOME MEANS OF IMPROVEMENT OF WAVE CORRELATION ALONG THE VERTICAL PROFILE

Wave correlation at interior points of a medium is beset with many difficulties. One of the most effective means of improvement of wave correlation along the vertical profile is the directional reception method.

In profiling as shown by Ryabinkin (1957), the application of various interferential systems (CDR, grouping, etc.) permits the resolution of complicated interferential oscillations into discrete components according to the direction of approach. Such grouping may be termed spatial, or grouping of second kind. For an increase in the effective sensitivity of the instrumentation tailored to the differ-

ent components of motion, methods of directional reception are also applicable. Then summing permits orientation of the directional diagram according to displacements and in contrast to spatial grouping, the above grouping may be termed point-by-point grouping which is referred to as grouping of the first kind. Thus, if grouping of the second kind is related to the directivity of the wave approach, then grouping of the first kind is connected with the directivity of particle motion. The latter, as a supplement to selectivity according to directivity of approach and to frequency, constitutes selectivity according to direction of particle displacement.

CDR based on particle displacements (first kind)

Often in VSP the change from correlating a given component of the record (Z, X, Y) to correlating the full vector motion may substantially improve the conditions of wave tracking. Primarily this occurs in off-line profiles, but also in in-line profiles for dipping boundaries. For such a change, the CDR method according to particle displacement (see Chapter 5) may be employed in VSP. This method permits the achievement of selectivity according to the directions of particle motion (Gal'perin, 1957). The essentials are:

1. The study of the trajectory of particle motion at each point and the enhancement of those oscillation components which best coincide with the full vector. This is accomplished by a summing tape which represents the totality of all records of different components that are specified by a definite spatial orientation.

2. The acquisition of records of given spatial components of motion and the production of composite seismograms of optimal components of motion.

3. The determination of orientation of the three-component cluster in the bore-

hole, for certain simplifying assumptions concerning the medium. For CDR – I, one provides stacking of recordings of geophones that are located at a single point but are spatially oriented in a distinct manner. The variation of the direction of the axis of the directivity diagram, and of its amplitude, is accomplished by an appropriate selection of the parameters of seismometer summations that enter into a given group. The enhancement of waves that are arbitrarily polarized in space, and the presentation of composite seismograms for various components, may substantially improve the correlation on VSP seismograms of any waves that are associated with arbitrarily oriented trajectories of particle motion in space. In contrast to CDR of the second kind (CDR – II), the first kind does not afford the possibility of splitting a complex polarized oscillation (as a result of interference) into its components, since this problem is not uniquely soluble.

CDR according to displacements may be realized either directly in the field (field version) or in subsequent processing (laboratory version). The latter is computer-oriented.

The examined linear variant of CDR – I may prove to be insufficient for the study of complicated wave fields. This refers to complex polarized waves with time-varying axial directions of polarization. In that case it is difficult to filter out the projections of the displacement vector onto a selected axis at those time intervals at which the vector acquires preferential polarization along another axis.

More powerful means of wave selectivity involving polarization exist. They are based on nonlinear transformations and lead not only to changes of orientation of the directivity diagram, but also to changes of its form. One of these procedures in particular is nonlinear spatial filtering (Flinn, 1965). This method,

along with the linear variant of CDR-I, was developed for the study of converted transmitted waves by the VSP method in the Volgograd district (see Chapter 9).

CDR based on the direction of wave propagation (second kind)

Directional reception of the second kind (or selectivity according to apparent velocities) has been developed and successfully employed in surface observations. Its effectiveness is confirmed by observations under various seismogeological conditions (Ryabinkin, 1957), over a period of many years. Wave pattern characteristics for interior points of the medium determined the especially high effectiveness of CDR-II for vertical profiles. Basic are the practical linearity of lineups, especially on in-line vertical profiles (to increase the summation base), and the essential differences in the values of apparent velocities (distinguished by their polarity) of the waves being registered. The presence of basic prevailing directions of wave propagation, involving positive and negative apparent velocities, simplifies the accomplishment of directional reception (Gal'perin, 1965a; 1966c). The correlation method using velocities and dynamic characteristics is oriented toward computer programming and also is closely related to CDR-II.

CDR-II is based on the summation of traces according to lineups with varying inclinations. VSP application of CDR involves nothing new, and the procedures for surface observation are well worked out and sufficiently explained in the literature (Ryabinkin, 1960). Therefore, we shall only illustrate the effectiveness of CDR-II for the enhancement of reflected waves. The composite seismogram (Figure 41) displays many waves with positive and negative apparent velocities. Interference of these waves impedes continuous tracking (over the entire profile) of a single wave.

Analysis of the wave pattern by means

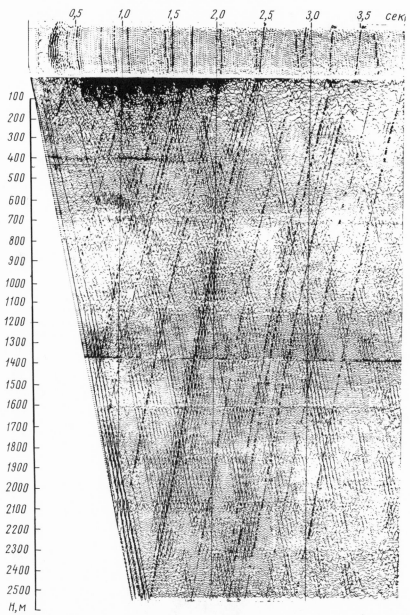

FIG. 41. Seismogram along a vertical profile (SP 100 m, well no. 565, Novodmitriev, Krasnodar region).

of CDR-II permits enhancement of interfering waves and determination of their apparent velocities. For the summing tape involving a 12-channel base, the values of the apparent velocities were determined and the delay times were found. The accomplished summing deleted multiple waves with positive apparent velocities and brought out waves that propagate from below (Figure 42). The parameters of summation, guaranteeing maximum suppression of noise, are determined as a function of the value of velocity. Since the values of apparent velocities usually increase with depth, it is expedient to apply directional summing involving variable baselines. The selection of groups and the computations of summing parameters for VSP are no different from CDR for ordinary surface observations.

For the application of summation over a variable base it is necessary to have contemporary instrumentation that would permit the selection of parameters (including mixing of group-channel aggregates, mixing of channels recorded on

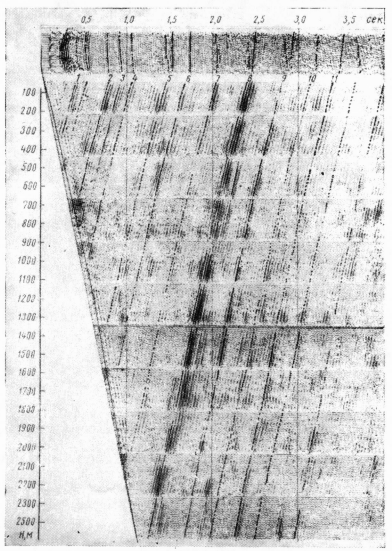

FIG. 42. Seismograms obtained with the aid of directional reception (well no. 565, Novodmitriev).

neighboring tapes). At present, such instrumentation is made available by the industry for the processing of data recorded on the surface. The same kind of instrumentation may be applied to VSP for directional reception of the first and second kinds. Naturally, the use of directional reception for VSP encounters the same difficulties that are characteristic for the surface version of the method.

The most essential problem here is the possibility of false lineups. One of the criteria for the enhancement of regular waves is the fact that they are only brought out when characterized by definite apparent velocities. False waves, on the other hand, may possess different values of apparent velocities and are brought out on seismograms at diverse time delays. In the theory of directional reception, more powerful criteria are known. However, the latter are significantly more unwieldy. Comparison of seismograms for directional reception with initial ones facilitates the identification of regular waves.

In this manner, CDR-I permits enhancement at each point that component of oscillation which is close to the full vector, while CDR-II permits tracking that particular component along the vertical profile. Directional reception in vertical profiling is of special interest for the analysis of complicated wave fields that are primarily associated with the upper portion of the cross-section. The possibilities of enhancement and tracking of waves are substantially aided by the use of computers. At present, CDR-I and CDR-II are programmed and are operational (see Chapter 9).

Selection by combined receivers

Wave selection according to propagation direction substantially improves wave correlation. However, this is accompanied by a loss of resolving power and may lead to the formation of false lineups.

To simplify the wave field observed at interior points of the medium, it is desirable to register at each point of the profile only wanted reflected waves approaching the points of observation from below. This simplifies the wave pattern on seismograms without the loss of resolving capabilities and permits us to track useful waves along the entire profile, practically to the boundary of separation, thus substantially increasing the accuracy and authenticity of the results. Such a receiver may be provided by a combination of pressure transducers and particle velocity transducers.

It is known that the electrodynamic seismometer, in the operating range of frequencies, comprises a transducer of particle velocity and the diagram of its directivity of first kind (according to displacements) in polar coordinates, is represented by two tangential spheres. Therefore, waves of a particular kind (for example compressional) approaching from below and from above register with phase inversion. Hence the direction of wave approach is of no consequence, and waves of a given type are registered in-phase, independent of direction of approach. The diagram of directivity for a pressure transducer is represented by a sphere. This difference in directivity diagrams forms the basis of the combination transducer which possess the required sense of direction; i.e., waves approaching from above are not recorded.

The most intense multiple waves undergo intermediate reflections at boundaries in the upper part of the cross-section and propagate into the depth of the medium. We can select the polarity of the recording channel in such a way that pressure transducers and velocity transducers register useful waves in-phase (upward reflected) independent of the polarity contrast in acoustic impedance at the boundary, while multiple downward reflected waves will register out-of-phase. Summing signals of both transducers suppress multiple waves. The effectiveness of cancellation depends on the identity of waveforms (of amplitudes and of form) resulting from pressure and velocity transducers. The forms of the pulses of pressure and velocity are the same if Hooke's Law is valid. Data from experimental observations indicate that in actual media the wavelet shapes for pressure and particle velocity are similar. They are practically identical when observed by a relatively narrow frequency passband seismic channel. The amplitudes of the waves may easily be adjusted by controlling the amplification of the channel.

For example, suppose we record at point H in the borehole (Figure 43a) the direct t_p, the reflected t^2, and the multiple t^{10} waves, the latter being associated with boundary 1 of the upper part of the cross-section. The direct t_p and the muliple t^{10} waves approach the point of observation H from above with positive apparent velocities. When recording with velocity transducers the reflected compressional wave t^2 is recorded with polarity opposite to that of the direct wave (Figure 43b). However, the multiple t^{10}, although its direction of approach is the same as that of the direct wave, is out-of-phase with the latter, due to the phase inversion for the intermediate reflection. In contrast, when recording with a pressure transducer, the reflected wave t^2 is in-phase with the direct wave t_p, but wave t^{10} is out-of-phase with the latter. If the channel polarity is selected so that the direct wave is recorded out-of-phase on velocity transducers and pressure transducers, then multiples are suppressed when the signals are summed. Examples comparing observed seismograms obtained from combined transducers and from seismometers are shown in Figure 43c which indicate that the wave t^{10} is substantially suppressed.

Summing of signals from both trans-

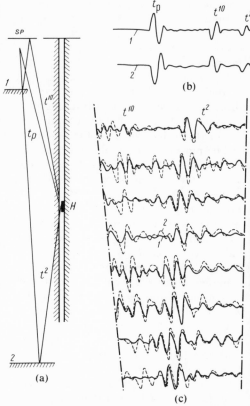

FIG. 43. Selectivity by means of combined transducers. a: Raypath diagrams. b: (1) Records obtained from transducers of velocity displacement (schematic). (2) Records for pressure transducers (schematic). c: Comparison of an observed seismogram section, obtained from (1) combined transducers, (2) velocity transducers.

ducers may be accomplished on the surface subsequent to their separate recording on magnetic tape. This allows rigorous control of channel sensitivities for both transducers and the achievement of very effective recording. To accomplish this, auxiliary strands are required for the cable, which is not always possible. In principle, summing may also be accomplished in the borehole device itself. However, difficulties associated with amplitude equalization for the different channels may arise since the amplitudes of pressure and velocity transducers may vary along the profile.

From an engineering standpoint, the device with combined transducers consists of two interlinked compartments. The upper compartment contains the velocity transducer and is hermetically closed; the lower one, which is essentially a flexible hose, is filled with oil and contains the pressure transducer. The upper compartment also contains the necessary matching arrangement in addition to the seismometer (we have used transformers and emitter followers).

It should be mentioned that the described method is still in the experimental stage. This applies as well to combined transducers, which must be substantially improved. Therefore, there is thus far insufficient experience to justify definite recommendations. Nevertheless, the results available lead us to believe that such selectivity may yet prove to be an effective means of suppression of multiple incident waves in direct observations at each point in a borehole. This should substantially simplify VSP seismograms and thus remove the basic difficulties in the analysis of data. Furthermore, such wave selectivity should facilitate the subsequent analysis of the wave field by the methods of interferential reception.

Frequency selectivity

As in surface observations, frequency selectivity in VSP is of substantial significance in the improvement of correlatability of waves on seismograms. For observations at interior points of the medium, frequency properties of waves may be significantly more representative than they are in surface observations where the absorption properties of the upper portion of the cross-section cause the wave to be considerably smoothed-out. No basic difference exists between VSP and surface investigations for frequency selectivity. Let us only mention that magnetic recording with subsequent

playback permits the full measure of utilization of frequency selectivity and the determination of optimal filtering for the enhancement of the wave of interest. The frequency characteristics of waves from various elements of the cross-section can be studied objectively in VSP investigations. Thus, the effectiveness of frequency selectivity is substantially increased (see Chapter 7). In most cases where the unfiltered record is unreadable (mostly in the upper portion of the cross-section), frequency selectivity significantly improves the correlatability of waves.

Multichannel recording

In the case of a complicated interferential wave pattern, multichannel recording facilitates the correlatability of waves along the vertical profile. In addition to using multichannel probes with independent clamping of each geophone, the possibility of obtaining multichannel seismograms by magnetic recording is of interest in VSP. It is true that for large l, the application of magnetic recording is thus far encumbered by the difficulty of synchronizing the shot break by radio. Magnetic recording has the same advantages as it does for surface observations.

Also, playback from magnetic tapes using variable density recording is characterized by high descriptiveness. For complex wave patterns this permits the tracking of a wave to be accomplished more reliably than by variable-amplitude recordings. From records using variable density, it is possible with a fair degree of reliability, to identify waves and even phases of oscillations up to and beyond the zone of their interference. The application of this playback method resulted in a sharp increase in the number of identified waves (see Chapter 7).

Optical filtering

Records using variable density, besides being descriptive, serve as initial data for optical filtering.

Experience gained in the last few years shows that optical filtering permits the appraisal of the range of apparent velocities by means of two-dimensional spectra and opens up new possibilities for the analysis of the wave field from VSP seismograms. This also applies to information on the frequency composition of waves and, by photometric investigations, information on wave intensities. In particular, wave selectivity based on velocity by means of optical filtering is an effective means of wave enhancement on seismograms.

Augmentation of traveltime curves

In spite of application of the above procedures, continuous tracking of waves along the vertical profile is still impossible in many cases. This is particularly true for sections adjoining the boundaries of separation and the surface. This diminishes the accuracy of stratigraphic identification and correlation of waves along vertical and horizontal profiles. Furthermore, difficulties of phase identification may occur for waves before and after the zone of interference. To overcome these difficulties one may utilize the known kinematic properties of reflected waves on vertical profiles. These properties permit the "extension" or "contraction" of traveltime curves of reflected waves according to the form of the traveltime curve for the first direct wave (Demidenko, 1964).

The in-line vertical traveltime curve of a reflected wave, for small dip angles of the boundary, is symmetric with the traveltime curve of the first wave. This permits one, for shotpoints located at comparatively small distances ($l \ll H_v$) from the profile, to extend the traveltime curve of the reflected wave according to the vertical traveltime curve of the direct wave. For a horizontally layered medium, the traveltime curve of the first direct wave on a vertical profile may be corrected according to the traveltime curve of the reflected wave for the particular section for which the reflected wave is tracked more reliably than the direct wave. As a rule, the first wave correlates much more reliably than do reflected waves, so that the requirement for such correction should seldom occur (for example, for highly intense pipe waves).

For off-line profiles or for the case of dipping horizons, the traveltime curve of the reflected wave no longer constitutes the mirror image of the traveltime curve of the first wave. For comparatively small values of φ and l/H_v, one may utilize the traveltime curve of the first wave that has been "reduced"[2] to the in-line vertical profile to extend the traveltime curve of reflected waves. An estimate of errors indicates that extending the traveltime curve for a reflected wave is permissible over a profile section amounting to $0.10 - 0.15 H_v$ and for the reduced traveltime curve of the first wave, for angles of dip of the reflecting boundaries not exceeding 7 degrees and for shotpoint distances from the vertical profile not exceeding $0.10 H_v$ (Demidenko, 1964).

Straightening of lineups of reflected waves

To improve the correlation of reflected waves, it is recommended in certain situations that the lineups or the traveltime curves should be straightened (Demidenko, 1966). Such straightening may be accomplished if a correction is introduced into the arrival times of reflected waves to account for the variation of the travel path for observations at different points of the vertical profile. It is convenient to reduce the arrival times at each point of the vertical profile to the surface. For reduction to the surface of upward reflected waves, it is sufficient to add to the arrival time along the vertical profile, the traveltime of the direct wave along the in-line vertical profile from the surface to the point of observation. The

[2] The quotes are the translator's.

straightened traveltime curves of reflected waves do not possess external points. For comparatively small angles of dip of the reflecting boundary they are close to the vertical and they cross the surface-reduced traveltime curve of the direct wave at a point that corresponds to the depth of the reflecting boundary.

For reduction to the surface of downward reflected waves, it is sufficient to subtract from the observed arrival time of a wave the arrival time of the direct wave along the in-line vertical profile from the surface to the point of observation. A negative apparent velocity is characteristic for straightened traveltime curves of downward reflected waves. As the number of multiples increases, the slope of the straightened traveltime curves decreases and they approach a vertical line.

The transformation of records to straighten the lineups is conveniently accomplished by analog devices. Straightening lineups improves wave correlation and their stratigraphic correlation. It even permits tracking of waves between observation points that exceed distances usually required for phase correlation. This may be of special significance where observations involving large steps are conducted, as in conventional seismic velocity well shooting.

The effectiveness of the method of straightening lineups substantially deteri-'orates as the shotpoint well separation increases.

One should notice that the effectiveness of all these procedures varies and that the best results may be achieved only by the combined application of various methods.

Transpositional wave correlation in VSP

In a number of cases, it is necessary to identify waves obtained for the same section of the vertical profile but for different l values. In contrast to horizontal profiles, transpositional correlation in VSP cannot be based on reciprocity principle. The waves may be identified according to the system of combined horizontal and vertical observations. In that case, waves registered along vertical profiles and from different shotpoints are identified from horizontal traveltime curves. For correlational systems of observation in the vertical plane when shotpoints are located sufficiently close to each other, waves may also be identified from "levelled" horizontal profiles.

In many cases, wave identification along vertical profiles for different l values may be made from specific characteristics of vertical traveltime curves that are adequate for the determination of the nature of waves from each shotpoint. For reflected waves, this involves the common points with traveltime curves of direct waves. For head waves, points where the direct and head waves interfere must be considered, as well as points at which the head wave is replaced by the transmitted wave. For refracted waves that are registered as first arrivals, minimum points of traveltime curves are involved, etc. General laws governing the disposition of these features at different distances from the sources may be used to identify waves registered on the same vertical profile but from different shotpoints.

Chapter 5
TRAJECTORIES OF PARTICLE MOTION

In the propagation of elastic waves we must examine two groups of parameters and two characteristic directivities, connected with the particle motion in the medium as the wave is transmitted (direction, trajectory), and as the wave propagates in space (direction, velocity) (Gal'perin, 1955; Gamburtsev, 1938). The two directional characteristics will be referred to as the first kind (trajectory) and the second kind (velocity). Different methods of observation must be applied to these two groups of parameters, i.e., the point method and the profile method. The first is based on the study of the full vector of motion of the medium as observed at one point.

Initial efforts to utilize parameters of the first group for the quantitative treatment of seismic data were made by Golitsyn (1909), who proposed a method to determine the direction of the epicenter from the displacement vector of the first wave with the aid of a three-component cluster of seismometers. In seismology, observations are carried out at separate stations which are remote from each other so that wave correlation is encumbered. Therefore, quantitative treatment of trajectories of particle motion was of special interest. The ideas of Golitsyn were implemented in the early stage of the development of seismic exploration. However, the development of the traveltime curve concept and the difficulties of interpreting data obtained from three-component observations contributed to the fact that the study of parameters of particle motion was dropped and the transition was made to the use of parameters of wave propagation.

Because the parameters of both groups supplement each other and should give the most complete information on the medium, over the last 10–15 years we see a tendency toward their joint use for quantitative treatment of data. In seismology, profile methods began to be developed, while in seismic exploration more and more emphasis began to be given to three-component observations at a point. For seismic exploration, it became necessary to determine the trajectories of motion more accurately. To that end, and for a fuller study of seismic wave polarization, Gamburtsev proposed the development of azimuthal observations (Gal'perin, 1955; Gamburtsev, 1952,; Gamburtsev and Gal'perin, 1954) based on the application of correlatory principles to point observations. Azimuthal (or polar) correlation permits a wave, or its separate phases, to be tracked by maximal axial sensitivity of a seismometer as observed at a single point. In contrast to positional correlation, azimuthal correlation uses directional characteristics of the first kind and brings out on seismograms different types of waves according to the character of their polarization. In positional correlation, if one of the basic features of a simple wave is the conservation of the form of the event in space, then, for azimuthal correlation, such a feature is the conservation of the polarization law in time.

In spite of more accurate determination of particle motion trajectories by means of the azimuthal method, the use of these trajectories for quantitative treatment of surface seismic exploration data is very difficult. This is because the upper portion of the cross-section seriously distorts the trajectory of particle motion. Thus, the directions in which the particles move at the surface do not correspond to the directions of their movement at interior points of the medium.

With VSP, the trajectories of particle motion are free from the distorting influence of the upper portion of the cross-section. They correspond to the directions of approach of body waves and may be employed for quantitative treatment.

The possibility of using one of the most sensitive parameters of the wave field — field polarization — represents the specific feature of VSP that distinguishes it favorably from surface observations. The study of trajectories of particle movement provides supplementary data on the nature of waves; enhances regions of their changeover and of their interference; and illustrates such characteristics of the medium as gradient, velocity, anisotropy, and hardness of contact. All of this is not only of theoretical but also of very definite practical interest. Therefore, questions concerning the procedures for the study of wave polarization at the interior points of the medium are relegated to a separate chapter.

We shall examine only the particle-motion trajectory of first waves from the simplest structure of the media. It is advisable to study the polarization of waves registering in later portions of the record and first waves for thin-layered media or for media that are complicated structurally. This, however, requires special procedures and must constitute the subject for future research.

DIRECTION OF THE DISPLACEMENT VECTOR

To determine the trajectory of particle motion in borehole observations, one must use three-component geophone installations.

Three-component installations

For three-component observations in boreholes, one usually employs an arrangement that consists of three mutually perpendicular geophones: two horizontal

(X and Y) and one vertical (Z)[1]. Three-component installations (XYZ) are effective when the directions at which the waves impinge are close to vertical. In that case, longitudinal and transverse waves register from different geophones of the arrangement, and the records are particularly descriptive and simple. These installations are convenient for surface observations; for in-line vertical profiling, especially for well shooting using transverse waves (Berdennikova et al, 1959; Vinogradov, 1967); and for large separations from the source, for example in the registration of converted transmitted waves.

For three-component observations along off-line vertical profiles, the wave approach is not vertical. For that reason, longitudinal and transverse waves are registered by all the receivers. Hence, all components acquire equal status and the XYZ installation loses its basic advantage. Moreover, utilizing XYZ installations to determine trajectories of particle motion makes it difficult to control the identity and sensitivity of horizontal and vertical seismometers under field conditions, not only within the borehole but even on the surface.

It is much more convenient to use a three-component symmetrical installation with inclined geophones (Gal'perin, 1955; Gal'perin and Frolova, 1961; Olhovic, 1964). The axes of the geophones are mutually perpendicular when the inclination of maximal sensitivity of each is $35°20'$ from the horizontal and the azimuthal difference between neighboring devices is 120 degrees. Equal inclination of the axes of all seismometers is significant in two respects: First, a symmetrical installation permits one to control the identity and sensitivity of all seismometers of the installation, not only

[1]There are also multicomponent well installations which are used in observations at shallow depths (Bondaren, 1965).

on the surface, but also in the borehole. This can be accomplished comparatively easily, even under field conditions. Second, one may employ receivers of the same construction. These receivers are thus interchangeable since one is not required to use devices of different types, i.e., horizontal and vertical devices.

On the surface, control of relative sensitivity of channels (seismometer-amplifier-galvanometer) is accomplished by recording signals for parallel orientation of the axes of inclined seismometers (for example by placing them in a common vertical plane, see Figure 44a). Then, prior to dropping the device into the borehole, the seismometers are oriented according to their azimuths into a symmetrical installation. To vary the seismometer azimuths in the installa-

tion, a special adapter is used. The seismometers may be positioned in one plane and then located one above the other at an angle of 35°20' to the horizontal. They may also be positioned so that the azimuths of neighboring seismometers differ by 120 degrees from each other.

In the borehole, identity and sensitivity may be controlled by records of first longitudinal waves arriving at the installation in the vertical direction. If the cross-section does not exhibit steeply dipping horizons, it is possible to check the situation by using records of shots or impacts at the top of the borehole. In that case, the displacement directions in the first longitudinal wave are close to the vertical and are recorded identically by all seismometers.

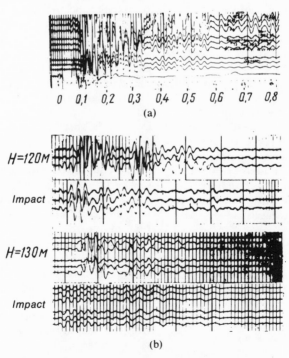

FIG. 44. (a) Monitoring the identity of channels of the three-component installation at the surface. (b) Same, in the borehole from SP 820 m.

Seismograms obtained from SP 820 m for $H = 120 - 130$ m (Figure 44) indicate that records from different receivers show first-wave arrivals have different polarity and amplitudes, since the directions of wave approach are close to horizontal. It is impossible to judge the identity of the channel installation from these recordings. All channels of the installation are identical on records of the direct longitudinal wave excited by an impact at the top of the borehole. The ability to control the identity of channels in a symmetrical installation allows us to determine the direction of motion more accurately than by using a three-component XYZ installation.

Almost all of the three-component observations described hereafter were accomplished using symmetrical installations. The three-component installations used were not oriented in the borehole and permitted only the determination of the value of the full vector of oscillation and of its angle with reference to the vertical. At present, prototypes of preoriented installations based on different principles are available. For work in open wells, installations are oriented by a compass relative to the magnetic field of the earth (Shchepin and Ruchiy, 1963). Gyroscopic arrangements are used for orientation in cased boreholes (Vinogradov, 1967). Orientation of an installation permits the determination of the trajectory of particle motion in space and opens up new possibilities for the study of wave polarization.

The direction sector of the displacement vector

The direction sector of the displacement vector may be determined visually according to the polarities of wave arrivals on records from three-component installations. A chart may be used for this purpose. For a symmetrical three-com-

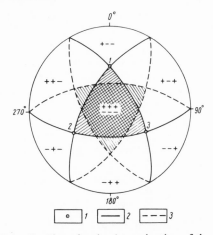

FIG. 45. Chart for the determination of the sector of the direction vector of displacement (stereographic projection). (1) Directions of axes of seismometers in the upper half-space. (2, 3) Planes bounding regions of different polarities for the upper and lower half-spaces. The signs are entered according to the order of seismometer numbers.

ponent installation, a stereographic projection of such a chart is represented in Figure 45. Space is subdivided into eight sectors by the three-mutually perpendicular planes going through the axes of the seismometers. For each sector, the directions of arrivals on the three-component seismogram are distinct as far as their polarity distribution is concerned. Equal polarities on records of all three seismometers of the installation correspond to directions enclosed within the pyramid produced by the axes of the seismometers (crosshatched regions). All other directions differ in their polarity of arrival as shown on records of one of the two other seismic receivers. Knowledge of the particular sector is in many cases sufficient for the determination of the wave type.

Let us examine means of quantitative determination of the direction of particle movement in a medium involving linearly polarized oscillations. Such a determination may be accomplished graphically or analytically (Bondaren and Sivkov, 1963;

Gal'perin, 1955). For a graphic determination it is convenient to use a chart of theoretical diagrams of direction. In orthogonal coordinates, such a chart comprises a family of cosinusoids having different amplitudes. Observed amplitudes are transposed on tracing cloth that is placed over the chart so that one of the theoretical diagrams approximates the observed points. Then the angle of displacement from the vertical ϕ is determined by the formula

$$\frac{A_{max}}{A_{min}} = \frac{\sin(\psi+\varphi)}{\sin(\psi-\varphi)},$$

where A_{max} and A_{min} are the amplitudes at the extreme points of the diagram and ψ is the angle of seismometer inclination to the horizontal.

The azimuth ω of the displacement vector is read from the chart along the maximum of the observed diagram. Angle e_K, which is equal to $(90°-\phi)$, is called the apparent angle of emergence of seismic radiation. For surface observations, this angle differs from the true angle e. The transition from e_K to e is accomplished by the formula $e = e_K - \sigma_e$, where σ_e is the correction that depends on the value of the apparent angle of emergence and on the velocity ratio V_p/V_s in the upper medium (Savarenskiy and Kirnos, 1955).

One of the ways to determine the direction of the displacement vector more accurately is to increase the number of components in the installation, i.e., to go from three-component to azimuthal observations. Computational data to determine the accuracy of a given direction ($\phi = 30°$ and $\omega = 30°$) from three- and four-component symmetrical installations, resulted in the following errors: $|\Delta\phi| \leq 5.0°$, $|\Delta\omega| \leq 14.0°$ (three components); $|\Delta\phi| \leq 2.3°$, $|\Delta\omega| \leq 3.6°$ (four components).

Increasing the number of components for borehole observations is at present impeded by the lack of a multistranded cable. However, one may speculate that, after developing schemes for channel packing, an increase in the number of channels will become feasible and, in certain cases, expedient.

For intricately polarized oscillations, three-component records indicate characteristic phase shifts, differing from 0 or 180 degrees. In that case, all elements of polarization may likewise be determined from three-component records. Let us mention that, in the study of spatial wave polarization, it is convenient to make use of a stereographic net, to each point of which corresponds a direction in space (Razumovskiy, 1932).

VARIATION OF PARTICLE MOTION DIRECTION FOR SEISMIC WAVES TRANSMITTED THROUGH THE ZONE OF LOW VELOCITIES (ZLV)

For surface observations, the heterogeneities of the structure of the uppermost portion of the cross-section exert a significant influence on the directions of particle motion, aside from that caused by reflection of energy from the surface. The presence of one or more layers in the neighborhood of the surface leads to the formation of interference waves and to changes in direction of motion. These variations depend on the velocity ratio of propagation of elastic waves in the particular layer in the underlying half-space, as well as on the ratio of the wavelength λ to the thickness d of the layer.

The dependence of apparent angle of incidence of the wave impinging on the surface on the ratio λ/d, has been computed from theoretical seismograms of interferential waves. When λ/d is small, the direction of particle motion in a longitudinal wave corresponds to the direction of propagation of the wave in the layer, i.e., it is dictated only by the upper layer. For appreciable λ/d, the direction of particle motion corresponds to the direction of wave incidence upon the lower boundary. Thus, the layer does not influence the direction at all. The transition from small λ/d to large ones is initiated for different angles of incidence in the interval $\lambda/d = 2.0 - 4.5$. For a single layer, for $\lambda/d = 10 - 15$, one obtains values that are close to the asymptote. The dependence of the apparent angle of emergence of seismic radiation on frequency, suggested by Gamburtsev, was employed to study the law of velocity variation with depth in the upper portion of the cross-section (Ivanova, 1960).

In developing VSP, it seemed expedient to supplement data on the influence of the ZLV on the direction of particle motion of the medium with experimental investigations. We also checked the correspondence of directions of motion at interior points of the medium with those of wave approach (Gal'perin, 1962). Estimating the influence of the ZLV on the directions of particle motion when a characteristic velocity jump occurs in the ZLV (amounting to $3 - 5$ times) is of particular interest.

Experimental work with that goal in mind was carried out of the Kubyshev district, where the upper portion of the cross-section is a bed consisting of sandy clays approximately 133-m thick overlying carbonate beds. The ZLV is approximately 12-m thick and consists of argillaceous soil and sands. The wave velocity of longitudinal waves in the zone is 1580 m/sec. For surface observations at separations of 240–680 m from the shotpoint, two wave groups are clearly exhibited on the seismograms (Figure 46a). In the region of first arrivals, we can track a refracted wave t_1, from the top of the Kungurian, which has an apparent velocity of approximately 6000 m/sec. In the region of subsequent arrivals, there is an intensive wave group t_2 associated with an apparent velocity of about 1700 m/sec

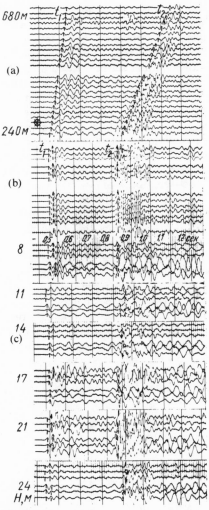

FIG. 46. (a) Positional seismograms. (b) Azimuthal seismograms. (Seismograms obtained at the surface.) (c) Seismograms obtained along the vertical profile (SP 280 m). The star on the positional seismogram indicates the location of the azimuthal installation.

and related to the boundary in the upper portion of the cross-section. The presence of only two groups of oscillations, with sharply different apparent velocities (and, consequently, directions of approach), guaranteed favorable conditions of investigation.

Investigations were made with a 26-channel unit with magnetic recording employing frequency modulation developed by the IPE AS USSR as well as by conventional seismic exploration units. Borehole registration was accomplished with the aid of amplifiers having a passband of 4 – 120 hz. On the surface, the directions of particle motion were determined by means of a 12-component conical azimuthal installation. The angle of inclination of the axes of the seismometers was 45 degrees with respect to the horizontal. The azimuths of neighboring devices differed by 30 degrees. Below the ZLV, the directions of particle motion were determined by a symmetrical three-component installation in the borehole equipped with a clamping arrangement.

Two series of experiments, VSP (for shot and impact excitation) and torpedoing, permitted the study of the direction of particle motion on the surface and below the zone.

Three-component seismograms for VSP, obtained for $l = 280$ m and a station spacing of 3 m (Figure 46c), indicate that wave t_1 possesses vertical lineups as it does on the azimuthal seismogram. For all recordings obtained at a depth exceeding 12 m, wave t_2 is characterized by phase inversions which attests the fact that the direction of particle motion is close to horizontal. Seismograms obtained at depths less than 11 m, including the surface azimuthal record (Figure 46b), indicate in-phase events. Phase inversion occurs sharply at the interval of 11 – 14 m. The directions of particle movement determined for waves t_1 and t_2 (Figure 47a) comprise the following angles to the vertical: 7 degrees in the first and 18 degrees in the second medium for t_1; 20 degrees in the first and 79 degrees in the second medium for t_2.

A velocity of $v_1 = 650$ m/sec for longitudinal waves in the zone was determined from surface-observed emergence angles, apparent velocities, the variations in direction of the waves passing through the lower boundary, and the velocity value $v_2 = 1580$ m/sec below

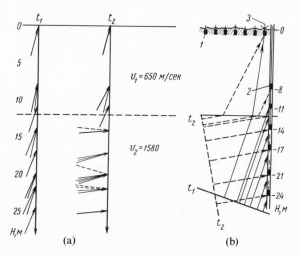

FIG. 47. Vectors of displacement and raypath schematic. a: Observed directions of particle motion. b: Wavefronts and wave rays t_1 and t_2. (1) Positional Z-seismometers, (2) three-component borehole installation, (3) azimuthal installation.

the zone. The directions of motion determined permitted the construction of the raypath schematic (Figure 47b). The schematic indicates the wavefronts for t_1 and t_2 and it shows the sharp variation of particle motion direction for the transition through the zone.

From torpedoing, the directions of particle motion were studied for direct waves. Explosions were produced in the borehole from 0–130 m deep. The directions of motion of the medium were determined on the surface by means of a multicomponent azimuthal installation located at a distance of 40 m from the top of the shothole. The directions were determined for the underlying zone by a three-component XYZ installation located in a special borehole at a depth of 30 m. The well being torpedoed, the borehole containing the three-component installation, and the azimuthal installation were laid out along a line (of length 100 m) on which were deployed 20 three-component XYZ installations of seismic receivers.

Let us examine the first waves on composite seismograms obtained from torpedoing. From three-component records acquired in the borehole below the zone (Figure 48a) it is seen that different polarities of first arrivals are observable in the depth interval of $10-110$ m. Also, wave t_2 which follows the direct wave, is in-phase everywhere.

Azimuthal seismograms, recorded at the surface (Figure 48b), show that first arrivals and arrivals of the t_2 wave are in-phase and are downward directed for shots from all depths. This direction corresponds to the wave approach from below with a direction close to vertical.

Particle motion directions determined at the surface indicate that the directions of the first wave are close to vertical (Figure 49), for practical purposes depend little on charge depth, and are contained within a narrow sector (15

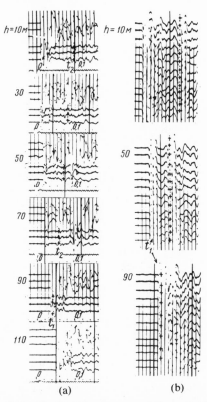

FIG. 48. (a) Seismograms of three-component borehole installations for torpedoing. (b) Seismograms for azimuthal installation on the surface.

degrees). Below the ZLV, the directions of particle motion are in good agreement with the direction oriented toward the source. Comparison of observed and theoretical angles shows that the deviation does not exceed $3-5$ degrees and approaches $7-10$ degrees only at discrete points. This is a measure of experimental errors.

The values of the angles obtained for explosions at a depth section of 130–80 m may be somewhat distorted by refraction at the boundary located at approximately 70 m. As for the accuracy of direction determination, one may note the azimuths observed. The latter should not vary, if the assumption of

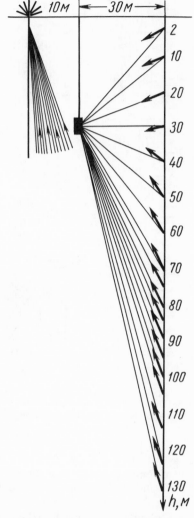

FIG. 49. Directions of particle motion of the
medium in the vertical plane.

from impacts of a weight freely falling from a height of 5 m at a distance of 11 m from the top of the borehole (Figure 50a). On the seismogram for $H = 0$, the amplitudes of first arrivals of the longitudinal wave t_P are about equal to each other and are directed downward, which is close to vertical. This direction is corroborated by the arrival of the direct transverse wave t_s, whose record is likewise characterized by approximately equal amplitudes and by phase inversions. Phase inversion of first arrivals is observed on seismograms for $H =$ 6.5 and 16.5 m, while records of the transverse wave are in-phase. For $H =$ 26.5 m, the records of the direct wave are again in-phase and once more are close to vertical. Phase inversion is observed on the record of the direct transverse wave.

The directions of motion as determined from seismograms satisfactorily correspond to the raypath schematic computed from the velocity cross-section (Figure 50b). For the vertical profile section 26 m in length, a change of direction of motion amounting to almost 180 degrees occurred for both the direct longitudinal and transverse waves.

The simplest structure of the ZLV was represented by a single horizontal layer and the directions of particle motion of the medium changed only in the vertical plane. However, even for the case of comparatively gentle contouring of the bottom of the ZLV and for significant velocity contrasts, the boundary may cause strong azimuthal deviations of the rays (Gal'perin, 1956). Thus, it is practically impossible to utilize the directions of particle motion of the medium as observed at the surface for a quantitative treatment of seismic data. Attempts to account for heterogeneities of the medium and to introduce corrections into the directions of particle motion proved to be unsuccessful because of sharply

axial symmetry is valid. Actually, some scattering of azimuths is observable. This amounts to 10 degrees below the zone (16 directions out of 22 are contained within a limit of 4 degrees) and to approximately 30 degrees at the surface.

The influence of the ZLV on the directions of particle motion may also be illustrated by seismograms obtained

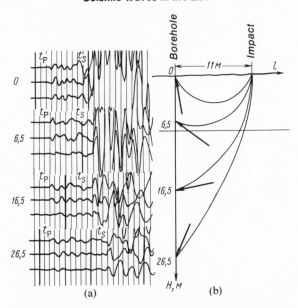

FIG. 50. Variation of direction of particle motion for transition through the ZLV. (a) Seismograms of three-component installation obtained in a borehole for impact excitation. (b) Directions of particle motion and raypath schematic.

varying distortions governed by extremely complicated laws. These conclusions apply to waves within the seismic exploration frequency range. For transition into the region of longer waves, the influence of the upper portion of the cross-section is less pronounced and, for seismological observations, the directions of particle motion in many cases permit the determination of azimuth and angle of emergence.

SOME LAWS GOVERNING THE VARIATION IN DIRECTION OF PARTICLE MOTION ALONG THE VERTICAL PROFILE

Using the trajectories of particle motion for quantitative treatment of VSP data enables us to examine certain laws of variation of direction for propagation of first longitudinal waves along a vertical profile, dependent on the relative positions of source and receiver. In the general case of a heterogeneous, non-

horizontal layered medium, these directions may be different for different azimuths. We shall examine only a few simple cases of an axially symmetrical medium in which the movement of particles occurs only in the vertical plane. These cases are most often encountered in practice and, in diverse combinations, lead to approximations of some actually observed laws of velocity variation with depth.

Medium with constant velocity

The directions of particle motion for $\beta = 0$ for a given depth are functions of l only and do not depend on velocity. The curves of motion directions for three values of l (Figures 51a, b) show that for all distances the lines issue from the origin and are always located in the region of positive angles. As the depth increases, for every l the angle α increases with respect to the horizontal. As l increases, the curve approaches the vertical.

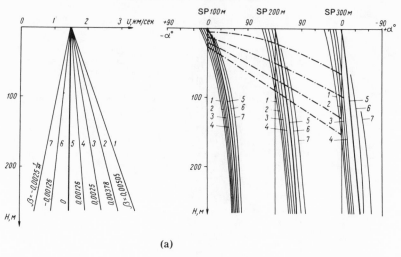

(a)

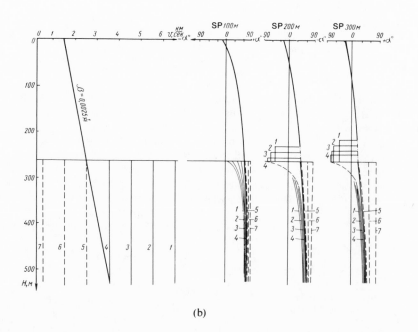

(b)

Gradiented medium

Let us examine a medium in which the velocity increases with depth according to a linear law involving the increment coefficient from -0.0025 to 0.00505 l/m. In Figure 51a, a definite curve of direction of particle motion of the medium corresponds to each value of velocity gradient. In media with positive gradients β (lines 1-4), the motion direction curves for the upper portion of the profile are located in the region of negative values of angles α. This particular region spreads as β or l increase. As

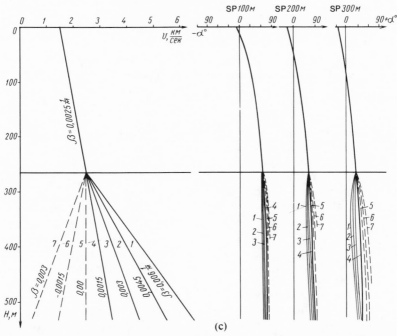

FIG. 51. Curves of directions of particle motion. (a) For medium with linear variation of velocity with depth (dot-dash lines indicate lines of changeover of signs of horizontal displacements). (b) For media with velocity jumps. (c) For medium with gradient jump (for head waves, these are shown schematically).

H increases, the angles become positive. It is characteristic that for $\beta > 0$, these lines originate at the surface. For $\beta < 0$, they originate from a definite depth that depends on the value of the gradient β and the distance l. As l increases for $\beta > 0$, the motion direction curves are displaced to the left. The form of the curves changes little. A chart of this family of curves may be used for simple and rapid determination of the coefficient β of the velocity gradient. To that end, only that section of the curve which corresponds to horizontal displacement is needed. This is reliably indicated by the polarity change of the arrivals from records of the vertical component.

Layered medium

Let us examine a two-layered medium having a boundary of separation of first kind described as follows: in the upper

layer, the velocity varies according to a linear law; in the lower one, it is constant. A velocity contrast occurs at the boundary of the layers (Figure 51b). The curves of direction of particle motion have the following features:

1) The initial portion of the curves corresponds to the particle motion of the refracted wave in the first (upper) layer.

2) A break in the curve occurs (discontinuity of displacement directions) at the boundary. The amount of discontinuity depends on the velocity ratio v_2/v_1 at the boundary of the upper and lower layers. One may determine the particular velocity ratio from the known direction in one of the two contacting media and from the value of the jump of displacement direction. The curves are displaced toward the side having the smaller angel α, for the transition from

the lower velocity to the higher one, and vice versa.

3) For head waves in a homogeneous layer, the curve of particle motion direction is contained in the region of negative α, depends on the velocity ratio v_2/v_1 and, for every fixed ratio v_2/v_1, remains invariant with depth. At the point where direct and head waves merge, the curve becomes disrupted and moves discontinuously into the region of negative values from the region of positive values of angles. For transition of head to transmitted wave, there is a departure from linear polarization. The curves are schematically indicated by dashed lines (Figure 51b).

Gradient discontinuity

The gradient discontinuity boundary is referred to as the boundary of second kind (Figure 51c). The curve of particle motion direction of the medium does not indicate a discontinuity at the boundary. The derivatives of these curves are, however, discontinuous. The curves are displaced to the left for a transition into a medium with a higher gradient, and vice versa. These displacements increase as l and the gradient contrast increase. As l increases, the curve may, partially or fully, go over into the region of negative angles.

Directions of motion for grazing rays of the transmitted wave

Let us examine a homogeneous layer overlying a homogeneous half-space. When the vertical profile crosses the boundary, a change-over of head wave to transmitted wave occurs. The head wave is linearly polarized and the directions of particle motion do not change for various points of the vertical profile. The transmitted wave is elliptically polarized for a direction of propagation that is close to being grazing. Thus, linear polarization is violated when the head wave is replaced by the transmitted one.

As an illustration, let us examine the directions of particle displacement computed for two layers using a formula developed by Podyapolskiy (1959). The calculation is made for three distances equal to 85, 280, and 600 m (from the point of emergence of the head wave), for a depth of the refracting boundary $H_v = 250$ m and for $v_1/v_2 = 0.5$ and 0.9 (Figure 52a, b).

The directions of particle displacement for the head wavefront are indicated on Figure 52a, b at the points at which the vertical profile intersects the refracting boundary. The displacements for the grazing rays of the transmitted wave do not coincide with the direction of wave propagation of the transmitted wave and can be represented by two components: a radial component coinciding with the direction the transmitted wave propagates, and a component near the direction of displacement in the head wave. Immediately below the boundary the first component is extremely small and the ratio of major and minor axes of the displacement ellipse is so large that the phase shift on seismograms does not exceed 0.002 sec and is within the bounds of experimental accuracy. Such elliptic features cannot always be demonstrated in practice. Directly below the boundary, the direction of particle displacement in the transmitted wave remains close to the direction of particle displacement above the boundary in the head wave. As the distance from the boundary increases, the second component gradually approaches the first (the angle between them is reduced), its intensity rapidly decays, and starting with a certain depth, only the first component remains; i.e., the directions of displacement coincide with the direction of propagation of the transmitted wave, which now is linearly polarized.

Comparing the computed directions of

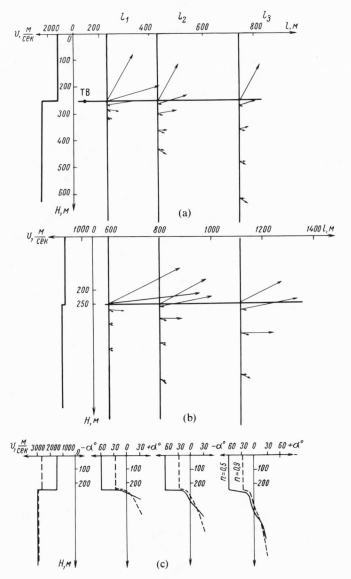

FIG. 52. (a, b) Directions of motion. (c) Curves of direction of particle motion. This refers to grazing rays or transmitted wave. The ratios for the scale factors of l_1, l_2, l_3, are 0.1, 0.5, and 1.0, respectively.

displacement of head and transmitted waves (Figure 52c), one observes that a change occurs for transition of head wave to transmitted wave in the directions of displacement such that the region of negative displacements below the boundary is the more pronounced the larger the velocity contrast at the boundary. Curves for $v_1/v_2 = 0.5$ indicate a more drastic change than curves for $v_1/v_2 = 0.9$. The study of displacement directions in the transmitted wave may aid in the acquisition of more complete data about the formation mechanism of a wave registering above the boundary. This study may also facilitate the acquisition of estimates on hardness of contacts in actual media, which appears to be very significant since the nature of the waves and their intensities substantially depend on this parameter.

Medium with weak velocity differentiation

In media with weak velocity differentiation, it is kinematically difficult to distinguish head waves from refracted waves. This is because the traveltime curves of refracted waves (Alekseyev, 1962) differ little from linear traveltime curves of head waves where there are small velocity gradients. The determination of the character of the velocity cross-section from the directions of mo-

tion is of special interest in these situations.

Let us examine the directivity fields of particle displacement for two laws of velocity variation; a two-layer medium with weak velocity contrast and a gradiented layer with linear increment of velocity (Figure 53). In the first case, the first wave observed near the shotpoint along a horizontal profile is the direct wave. Subsequently, it is replaced by the head wave. In the second case, the first arrivals are due to the refracted wave.

For velocity discontinuities and small l, direct waves approach the points of the vertical profile from above (the direction of approach from above shall be designated by a plus sign). In the region where the head waves registers, it approaches from below (minus sign). Regions of positive and negative motions in first arrivals are separated by the line

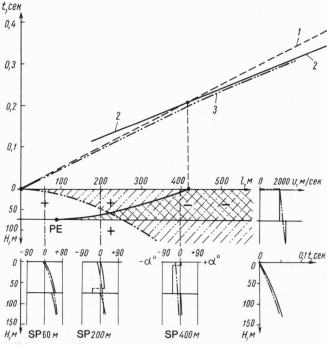

FIG. 53. (1) Traveltime curves of direct wave. (2) Traveltime curves of head wave. (3) Traveltime curves of refracted wave. Regions of different polarities and curves of direction of motion.

of polarity change which represents the geometric locus of points of interference of direct and head waves. This line, at the depth of the boundary, starts at the point of emergence of the head wave (PE) and, at the surface, coincides with the intersection of the horizontal traveltime curves of direct and head waves. To the left of this line the region of positive directions of motion is located. To the right is the region of negative directions.

For linear velocity variation with depth when no change of waves is involved, a polarity change can be seen, nevertheless, which is associated with the curvature of the rays. The time of change in that case starts at the origin of the coordinates and continues into depth as l increases. In addition to regions of different polarities, the cases discussed involve different characteristics of sign change. In the case of the vertical component of a refracted wave, a smooth transition occurs in the curve of directions of motion from negative to positive values of angle α. The line of polarity change corresponds to horizontal displacements. However, in the case of velocity discontinuity, one observes a disruption of the particle-motion-direction curve in the region of transition from direct to head waves.

The above laws may be utilized to determine the nature of waves, the characteristic of cross-section, and the identification of interference regions and wave change. The direction of particle motion is considerably more sensitive to change of a wave type than are the kinematic aspects. It is not always possible to identify the change of waves from the vertical traveltime curve; but, from directions of motion, this is usually done much more easily. For example, for the replacement of a direct wave by a head wave (emergence of head wave into the region of first arrivals), the curve of direction of particle motion goes over discontinuously into the region of negative angles. A sharp change of direction of motion in the interior of the medium (not at the boundary of separation) can indicate interference or changeover of waves.

EXPERIMENTAL STUDY OF DIRECTIONS OF MOTION

Quantitative treatment of trajectories of motion of particles was carried out by us basically for first-arrival waves that are, as a rule, linearly polarized. Waves in the later portion of the record are registered against the background of noise created by interference and are in the majority of cases complexly polarized. It has not been established that these waves can be used for geologic interpretation. Besides, their quantitative study demands research on orientation of the geophone clusters in the borehole.

Directions of particle motion along discrete vertical profiles

Let us compare curves of particle motion directions, vertical traveltime curves of first waves, and the velocity cross-section according to observations on the Russian platform (Kubyshev district). In well no. 501, drilled for VSP, the cross-section is composed of terrigenous beds (sands, clays) of Tertiary age, having a thickness of 133 m. The terrigenous bed is underlain by gypsum and dolomites (133 — 189 m) of Sosnov limestones (189 – 274 m) of Kalinin and gypseous marls (274 – 282 m) of Buguruslan suites. At 283 m, anhydrites and dolomites of the Lower Permian are found.

Investigations were carried out from three shotpoints. From SP 140 m, primarily the direct and transmitted waves were registered. From SP 240 m, the registration involved the replacement of the direct by the refracted wave. SP 800 m was associated with the refracted

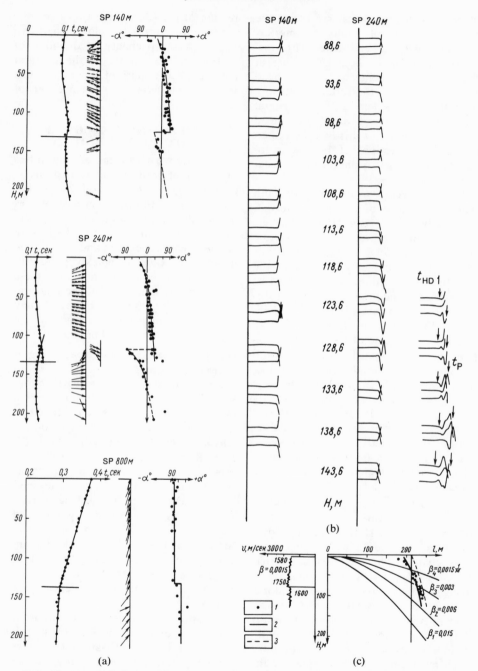

FIG. 54. Observations in well no. 501. a: Vertical traveltime curves, directions and curves of direction of motion for three shotpoints. b: Plots of first arrivals (for SP 240 m two levels of amplification are shown). c: Determination of β from directions of particle motion; (1) observed values; (2, 3) computed curves for $\beta = 0.0015$ and $\beta = 0$, respectively.

wave (Figure 54). Analysis of the wave pattern, accomplished by combined horizontal and vertical profilings, permitted the acquisition of reliable data on the nature of the observed waves.

Direct wave. — The first wave from SP 140 m and SP 240 m is the refracted wave. From SP 140 m, it is trackable as first arrivals to almost the very boundary of separation ($H = 133$ m). From SP 240 m, at a depth of about 115 m, one observes the changeover of direct to refracted wave associated with the Sosnov suite. Vertical traveltime curves of the direct wave from both shotpoints (Figure 54a) are of hyperbolic form. From records of the three-component symmetrical borehole installation, the direct wave is characterized by intense sharp arrivals with phase inversions (Figure 54b). The directions of particle motion in the first wave at the surface approximate the vertical (the wave approaches from below); this is due to the influence of the ZLV (Gal'perin, 1957). At a depth of about 20 m for SP 140 m and at 40 m for SP 240 m, the motions of particles are horizontal; and for further increase of depth, the angle to the horizontal gradually increases (the wave approaches the seismometer from above). The direction curves of particle motion for the direct wave in the upper portion of the profile are within the region of negative angles. Further on, as H increases, the curves smoothly cross the axis of zero values of α and continue into the region of positive angles. The described curves correspond to the curved-path refraction. They permit the determination of coefficients of velocity increment with depth in the upper portion of the cross-section. The observed curve from SP 240 m corresponds to a coefficient $\beta = 0.0015$ m^{-1}, which is in good agreement with data from SWL.

Changeover of direct to refracted waves. — On the vertical traveltime curve obtained from SP 140 m at a depth interval of 123 − 128 m, one notices a section with negative apparent velocity. However, because of the shortness of this section, and the insufficient number of observations, it was difficult to identify the refracted wave from kinematic data. The study of particle motion direction indicated that such a change does take place in the immediate vicinity of the boundary (at a distance of about 10 m from the latter).

The change of direct waves to head waves is identified with increased confidence from SP 240 m. Seismograms for a depth of about 113 m indicate a weak arrival (Figure 54b) approximately 10 − 15 times less intense than the direct wave. This can be established only with very sensitive instrumentation. On three-component seismograms, this wave, in contrast to the direct wave, records in-phase and is actually the refracted wave associated with the Sosnov suite. The change of polarities is well defined on two neighboring seismograms: at a depth of 108 m, the first arrival is the direct wave; at 113 m, it is the refracted wave. Immediately after the arrival of the refracted wave, the intense direct wave arrives. The directions of motion substantiate this arrival. Figure 54b shows the direct wave on records obtained at low amplification. The direction of motion for the direct wave is indicated along the direction for first waves. The change from direct waves to refracted waves is demonstrated clearly by the curve of motion direction. This indicates a discontinuity and passes into the region of negative values of angles.

Refracted waves. — From SP 800 m, the first wave registered over the entire section is the refracted wave connected with the boundary that is not penetrated by the borehole. Below the boundary occurring at 133 m, the direction of motion intersects the horizontal at an angle of about 45 degrees. After refraction at that boundary, the directions of motion approach the vertical at an angle of about 80 degrees to the horizontal. The difference between directions of motion before and after refraction permit the determination of the velocity ratio of longitudinal waves at different sides of the boundary. This ratio is 2.9, which is confirmed by the velocity cross-section.

Changeover of refracted to transmitted waves. — After transition through the boundary of separation, records from SP 140 m and SP 240 m change sharply. Weak in-phase arrivals of the refracted wave become more intense showing phase inversion. The directions of particle motion in the transmitted wave shall be illustrated by means of observations from SP 240 m. From the curve in Figure 54a, it is evident that immediately below the boundary of separation, the directions of motion do not coincide with the direction of the grazing ray and are close to that of the refracted wave. However, in some discrete cases, the directions of particle motion in the grazing ray of the transmitted wave are close to the direction of the grazing ray, where the refracted wave becomes a transmitted wave.

Fields of direction of motion

All the values that permit continuous tracking of directions of motion along the horizontal and the vertical in the vertical plane constitute a field of directions of particle motion. Such a field may be constructed from a single shotpoint with observations from a large number of boreholes. The field may also be constructed from observations in one borehole from a large number of shotpoints distributed along some line on the surface (profile). In that case, all shotpoints are thought to coincide at one point located at the top of the borehole, and the directions of particle motion obtained are transferred to corresponding depths below the shotpoints. Such constructions are valid for axial symmetry of the medium of the section comprising the field.

The first direction fields were obtained in 1961 in certain regions of Middle Asia where, in the investigation of the nature of unwanted waves, the necessity arose for a detailed study of the upper portion of the cross-section and the wavefield associated with it. (Gal'perin, 1964c).

Let us examine the directions field obtained in southern Kirghiz (Figure 55).

The upper portion of the cross-section here is composed of terrigenous deposits with weak velocity differentiation. Three boundaries of separation at depths of 18, 34, and 55 m (Figure 55a) have been identified from the velocity cross-section constructed from well-logging data, velocity well shooting, and horizontal shooting of two boreholes. Deeper, the velocity increases according to a linear law with a coefficient of increment $\beta = 0.001$ m^{-1}. It was not possible to identify the velocity gradient in the comparatively thin upper layers.

The field of directions of motion was obtained from 21 points for $H = 0 - 210$ m and $l = 0 - 2000$ m ("large system"). In order to detail the structure of the medium in the uppermost portion of the cross-section, a "small system" was investigated consisting of 11 shotpoints for $H = 0 - 90$ m and $l = 0 - 330$ m.

From Figure 55b, one sees that for $l = 30$ m, the vectors for the shallowest depths (10 or 14 m) are directed from top to bottom, which corresponds to the arrival of the direct wave. For the same shallow depths, as l increases, the first wave to register is that refracting at the first and deeper boundaries. Where $l >$ 150 m, the first arrival at the surface is the wave refracted at the second boundary. Its existence is indicated by the directions of particle motion at 40 m deep where $l = 120$ m. This wave, refracting at the upper boundary, emerges at the surface. (Refraction is evidenced by the change of direction of motion at depths $20 - 14$ m and for $l = 150$ m.) The point of emer-

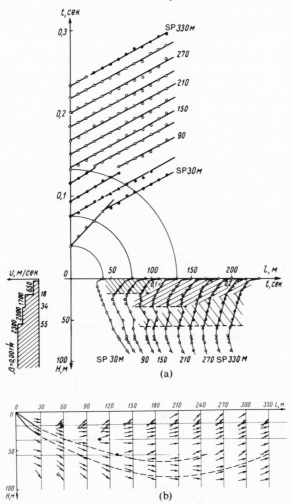

FIG. 55. (a) Family of combined horizontal-vertical traveltime curves. (b) Field of directions of displacement. Regions of registration of curved-ray refracted waves associated with various boundaries of separation are crosshatched. (The velocity cross-section is obtained from data of seismic well logging and from horizontal shooting of the borehole.)

gence of the wave refracted at the third boundary is located at about $l = 130$ m and about 55 m deep. That wave interferes with waves refracted at the upper boundaries and, within the observed field, does not emerge at the surface as first arrivals.

One should notice that a disruption of linear polarization of the first wave is observed for most of the points located at the boundaries of separation. This fact may be of interest in itself. For depths exceeding 55 m, the directions of particle motion form arching lines. Comparison of the direction field with observations of com-

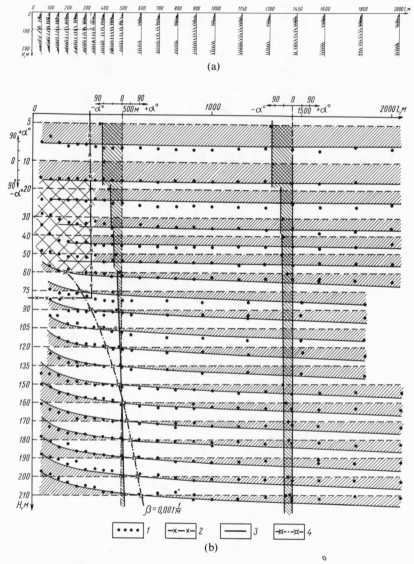

(a)

(b)

FIG. 56. a: Field of directions of particle motion. b: Graphs showing the variation of directions of motion in the vertical plane (the angular scale is indicated at depth of 10m). (1) Observed angular values, (2) contours of the small system, (3) computed curves, (4) line of changeover of polarities of directions.

bined traveltime curves (Figure 55a) confirms the validity of the interpretation of the wave pattern. In Figure 55b, the dashed lines indicate the rays constructed from kinematic data for the sake of descriptiveness.

In order to study the large system (Figure 56a), curves of directions of motion along horizontal lines (Figure 56b) were constructed for different depths. For depths less than 60 m, the curves are wholly in the region of negative angles and are practically parallel to the abscissa axis. Starting at 60 m, and deeper, a region of positive angles is observed in the neighborhood of the shotpoints (the waves impinge from above). This region and the angular values both increase with depth. At greater distances from the borehole, the directions of motion approximate the horizontal and the direction curve goes over into the region of negative angles. Such a characteristic of variation of directions of motion corresponds to a gradiented medium. The observed data are in good agreement with the computed curve corresponding to β = 0.001 l/m (Gal'perin, 1964c). For that same β value, curves of direction variation are computed at different levels along horizontal directions.

Let us examine the characteristics of variation of directions of particle motion along the vertical for l = 500 m and 1450 m (Figure 56b). From the surface down to 20 m, the characteristic for l = 500 m is located in the region of negative angles. The angle to the horizontal is 70 degrees. At the first boundary, the characteristic changes abruptly (by 27 degrees), and it approaches the horizontal axis. At the second (H = 36 m) and third (H = 55 m) boundaries, the directions change abruptly by 9 and 7 degrees. The characteristic is practically parallel to the depth axis at each of the three layers. At 55 m and below, the directions characteristic smoothly approaches the depth axis, crosses it between 150 and 160 m marks, and enters the region of positive angles. At the maximum depth of investigation (210 m), the angle formed with the horizontal does not exceed 10 degrees.

At l = 1450 m, the characteristic likewise is disrupted at the boundaries of separation. However, the jumps are considerably smaller than at l = 500 m. As the depth increases, the characteristic very slowly approaches the axis of horizontal motion. Study of both the small and large systems permitted the establishment of the velocity cross-section of the medium under conditions of weak velocity differentiation.

The above data indicate that quantitative study of laws governing the variation of directions of particle motion permits the acquisition of supplementary data on the nature of waves and details of the velocity cross-section. The study of motion direction not only permits the recognition of a velocity gradient in the medium, but also allows the determination of the value of the coefficient of velocity increment as well as the establishment of the region of wave changeover. Of special interest are situations which disrupt polarization or where the direction of particle motion in the first longitudinal wave does not coincide with the direction of its propagation. Such cases involve downward transmitted waves in profile sections that are contiguous to the refracting boundary (grazing) rays, curved-path refractions and in the section of maximum penetration. In the majority of cases, this disruption is insignificant and may be identified only by special investigations.

These observation systems discussed by us for the study of directions of particle motion may be used to determine the directions of motion in a single vertical plane. For quantitative treatment, such systems are applicable only in the case of a homogeneous or a horizontally layered medium for which conditions of axial symmetry are valid and for which all seismic rays of the incident and secondary waves are contained in a vertical plane.

For the general structural geometry of the medium, seismic rays may not be contained in a single plane. Then, the variation of directions of motion takes place in the vertical plane as well as according to azimuths. Neglecting azimuthal variations of direction of particle motion may lead to substantial errors in the interpretation of data. In addition, the study of directions in space may provide supplementary and independent data on the structure of the medium. Particularly for the simplest structures, procedures have been developed for the determination of stratigraphic details from trajectories of particle motion. These procedures involve the boundary that is intersected by the borehole and are based on the application of stereographic projections (Gal'perin, 1963b). Future improvement of measurement techniques will permit the study of trajectories of particle motion in space and will facilitate their rigorous quantitative treatment. This will be of special interest in the study of generation and propagation of transverse and converted waves. The selection according to directions of motion may be of considerable significance. Such selectivity is accomplished by CDR according to displacements.

CONTROLLABLE DIRECTIONAL RECEPTION ACCORDING TO DISPLACEMENTS (CDR-I)

Let us examine some questions involving the theory of the CDR-I method and, primarily, the equations of the diagram of directivity of a group. It is known (Gamburtsev, 1959) that the diagram of seismometer directivity has one degree of freedom, consists of two tangential spheres, and in polar coordinates, may be written in the form

$$r = K \sin \psi_i \sin \psi_n +$$
$$+ K \cos \psi_i \cos \psi_n \cos(\omega_i - \omega_n),$$

where r is the radius-vector of the directivity diagram determined by coordinates ψ_i, ω_i. Here ψ_i is the angle formed with the horizontal, ω_i is the azimuth. The coordinates ψ_n and ω_n determine the direction of the axis of maximal sensitivity, and the coefficient K determines the sensitivity of the receiver along the axis of the directivity diagram.

The direction of the axis of maximal sensitivity of the seismic receiver coincides with the direction of displacement of its moving part. The diagram of a group of seismometers is determined by the form, the amplitude, and the spatial orientation of the axis of maximal sensitivity. Let us discuss separately the enumerated characteristics of the directivity diagram of a group.

The form and direction of the axis of the directivity diagram of a group.

The plane and space aspects of the problem shall be considered.

Two-dimensional problem. — Let us deduce the basic equations for the seismometer group located in a single vertical plane at various angles with respect to the horizontal (this is called a plane fan-like installation). Let the group consist of m seismometers which form angles ψ_n with the horizontal. The radius-vector of the group's diagram of directivity is written in polar coordinates and it is determined by the formula

$$r = \sin \psi_i \sum_{n=1}^{n=m} K_n \sin \psi_n + \cos \psi_i \sum_{n=1}^{n=m} K_n \cos \psi_n.$$

Expressions $\sum_{n=1}^{n=m} K_n \sin \psi_n$

and $\sum_{n=1}^{n=m} K_n \cos \psi_n,$

in the above equation are constants for a given group.

From these two equations (for the one-dimensional and two-dimensional cases), it follows that the form and direction of the group's directivity diagram coincide with the directivity diagram of a single seismometer. The diagram's axis of maximal sensitivity forms an angle ψ with the horizontal. The angle is determined by

$$\tan \psi = \frac{\sum_{n=1}^{n=m} K_n \sin \psi_n}{\sum_{n=1}^{n=m} K_n \cos \psi_n}.$$

The axis of the directivity diagram of the group remains in that particular vertical plane that contains all seismometers of the group. For this installation in a plane, any selected amplitude and direction for the group directivity may in principle be obtained by changing the sensitivity of a single seismometer in the arrangement. The last equation in that case is conveniently written in the form

$$\tan \psi = \frac{\sum\limits_{n=1}^{n=m-1} K_n \sin \psi_n + K_m \sin \psi_m}{\sum\limits_{n=1}^{n=m-1} K_n \cos \psi_n + K_m \cos \psi_m}.$$

Defining

$$\sum_{n=1}^{n=m-1} K_n \cos \psi_n = A_1;$$

$$\sum_{n=1}^{n=m-1} K_n \sin \psi_n = B_1.$$

one has

$$\tan \psi = \frac{B_1 + K_m \sin \psi_m}{A_1 + K_m \cos \psi_m}.$$

For $K_m = 0$, $\tan\psi = B_1/A_1 = $ const for a given group. For $K_m = \infty$, $\tan\psi = \tan\psi_m$ or $\psi = \psi_m$. If one seismometer of the group is much more sensitive than the others, the direction of the axis of the total directivity diagram approaches the axis of that particular seismometer. When the group consists of one horizontal and one vertical seismometer,[2] $\tan \psi = K_2/K_1$, where K_1 and K_2 are the sensitivities of the horizontal and the vertical seismic receivers, respectively. If $K_1 = $

K_2, the axis of the group directivity diagram forms an angle of 45 degrees with the horizontal.

Three-dimensional problem. — Let the group comprise m seismometers, whose spatial axial directions are determined by the following quantities:

$$\psi_1, \omega_1, \psi_2, \omega_2 \ldots \psi_m, \omega_m.$$

The diagram of directivity of the group in that case is expressed by

$$r = \cos \psi_i \sum_{n=1}^{n=m} K_n \cos \psi_n \cos (\omega_i - \omega_n) +$$
$$+ \sin \psi_i \sum_{n=1}^{n=m} K_n \sin \psi_n,$$

where r is the radius vector in the directions ψ_i, ω_i.

In the above expression, the terms

$$\sum_{n=1}^{n=m} K_n \cos \psi_n \cos \omega_n,$$

$$\sum_{n=1}^{n=m} K_n \cos \psi_n \sin \omega_n, \quad \sum_{n=1}^{n=m} K_n \sin \psi_n$$

are constants for a given group. From this equation, it follows that the formal directivity diagram of the group is equivalent to the directivity diagram of a single seismic receiver. The orientation and the sensitivity of this receiver are determined by the disposition and the sensitivity of the seismometers in the group. In the following, we shall consider such a seismometer to be conditional. The axial direction of the group directivity is determined by

$$\tan \omega = \frac{\sum\limits_{n=1}^{n=m} K_n \cos \psi_n \sin \omega_n}{\sum\limits_{n=1}^{n=m} K_n \cos \psi_n \cos \omega_n},$$

$$\tan \psi = \frac{\sum\limits_{n=1}^{n=m} K_n \sin \psi_n}{\sqrt{\left(\sum\limits_{n=1}^{n=m} K_n \cos \psi_n \sin \omega_n\right)^2 + \left(\sum\limits_{n=1}^{n=m} K_n \cos \psi_n \cos \omega_a\right)^2}}.$$

[2]This particular case is the basis for the procedure suggested by Bereza (1954). It involves tuning out interfering oscillations composed of horizontal and vertical displacements by registration of two seismometers on a single support.

The directivity diagram of the group having an arbitrary orientation may be obtained by varying the sensitivities and the locations of the seismometers in the group. It is convenient to vary the group directivities of the diagram by controlling the sensitivities of the seismometers. Let us examine the manner in which the direction of the axis of group directivity depends on the sensitivity of a single seismometer, i.e., of the mth receiver. The axial direction of the group directivity in this case is determined by the expressions

$$\tan \omega = \frac{A_2 + K_m \cos \psi_m \sin \omega_m}{B_2 + K_m \cos \psi_m \cos \omega_m} = \frac{A_2 + aK_m}{B_2 + bK_m},$$

$$\tan \psi = \frac{C_1 + K_m \sin \psi_m}{\sqrt{(A_2 + K_m \cos \psi_m \sin \omega_m)^2 + (B_2 + K_m \cos \psi_m \cos \omega_m)^2}}$$

$$= \frac{C_1 + cK_m}{\sqrt{(A_2 + aK_m)^2 + (B_2 + bK_m)^2}},$$

where

$$A_2 = \sum_{n=1}^{n=m-1} K_n \cos \psi_n \sin \omega_n,$$

$$B_2 = \sum_{n=1}^{n=m-1} K_n \cos \psi_n \cos \omega_n,$$

$$C_1 = \sum_{n=1}^{n=m-1} K_n \sin \psi_n,$$

for seismometers whose sensitivities are invariant; and where

$$a = \cos \psi_m \sin \omega_m,$$
$$b = \cos \psi_m \cos \omega_m,$$
$$c = \sin \psi_m,$$

for the seismometer with variable sensitivity.

The equation of the plane containing the axial direction of the group directivity diagram may be written in polar coordinates

$$A' \sin \omega + B' \cos \omega + C' \tan \psi = 0.$$

The expressions for $\tan\omega$ and $\tan\psi$ yield

$$\sin \omega = \frac{A_2 + aK_m}{\sqrt{(B_2 + bK_m)^2 + (A_2 + aK_m)^2}};$$

$$\cos \omega = \frac{B_2 + bK_m}{\sqrt{(B_2 + bK_m)^2 + (A_2 + aK_m)^2}}.$$

Substituting the obtained quantities into the equation of the plane, one obtains

$$A'(A_2 + aK_m) + B'(B_2 + bK_m) + C'(C_1 + cK_m) = 0.$$

For another sensitivity value K'_m of the same seismometer, the equation of the plane takes the form

$$A'(A_2 + aK'_m) + B'(B_2 + bK'_m) + C'(C_1 + cK'_m) = 0.$$

The equation of the plane containing two axes of the total diagrams, corresponding to two values of sensitivities of the mth seismometer, becomes

$$(B_2 c - C_1 b)x + (C_1 a - A_2 c)y + (A_2 b - B_2 a)z = 0.$$

The last equation does not contain the quantities K_m and K'_m which determine the variable sensitivity of the mth seismometer. Consequently, the variation of the sensitivity of a single seismometer of the installation amounts to a variation of the axial direction of the group directivity of the diagram within a certain plane. In principle, any spatial directivity diagram may be obtained by varying the sensitivity of two seismometers in the group. Thus, each fixed sensitivity value of one of these seismometers corresponds to a definite spatial position of the axes of the diagram. However, the location of the axis of this plane is determined by the sensitivity of the other seismometer.

Let the sensitivity of all seismometers in the group, except those of the mth and the m-1th be fixed. Also, let the spatial orientation of the axes of all seismometers in the group be fixed. Then, the axial direction of the group directivity is determined by

the group may be carried out by the formulas for lineups and amplitudes derived by Gal'perin (1955) and expressed by parameters of seismometers of the group, i.e., K_n, ψ_n, ω_n as well as parameters of wave polarization. These equations

$$\tan \omega = \frac{A_3 + K_{m-1} \cos \psi_{m-1} \sin \omega_{m-1} + K_m \cos \psi_m \sin \omega_m}{B_3 + K_{m-1} \cos \psi_{m-1} \cos \omega_{m-1} + K_m \cos \psi_m \cos \omega_m},$$

$$\tan \psi = \frac{C_2 + K_{m-1} \sin \psi_{m-1} + K_m \sin \psi_m}{\sqrt{(A_3 + K_{m-1} \cos \psi_{m-1} \sin \omega_{m-1} + K_m \cos \psi_m \sin \omega_m)^2 + (B_3 + K_{m-1} \cos \psi_{m-1} \cos \omega_{m-1} + K_m \cos \psi_m \cos \omega_m)^2}},$$

where

$$A_3 = \sum_{n=1}^{n=m-2} K_n \cos \psi_n \sin \omega_n;$$

$$B_3 = \sum_{n=1}^{n=m-2} K_n \cos \psi_n \cos \omega_n;$$

$$C_2 = \sum_{n=1}^{n=m-2} K_n \sin \psi_n$$

are constants for a given group. As the axial direction of the group directivity varies, so does the sensitivity of the group.

Amplitude sensitivity of the group directivity diagram

The maximal value of the radius-vector of the group directivity diagram $r = A_{max}$ corresponds to the axial direction of the directivity diagram (ψ, ω), i.e., to the condition that $\psi_i = \psi$, $\omega_i = \omega$, and is determined by equation

may also be used to estimate how accurately the sensitivity of the seismic receivers must be adjusted.

The orientation and amplitude of the group diagram may be determined by graphic-analytic means with the help of stereographic nets (Razumovskiy, 1932). Also, the accuracy achieved is sufficient for practical purposes.

Analysis of particular cases

Let us analyze the above equations by means of two cases that are of most interest in practice.

For a three-component installation XYZ, the axial directions of the group directivity diagram are determined by

$$\tan \omega = \frac{K_2}{K_1} \qquad \tan \psi = \frac{1}{\sqrt{K_1^2 + K_2^2}}.$$

The sensitivity of the third seismometer

$$A_{max} = \sqrt{\left(\sum_{n=1}^{n=m} K_n \cos \psi_n \cos \psi_n\right)^2 + \left(\sum_{n=1}^{n=m} K_n \cos \psi_n \sin \omega_n\right)^2 + \left(\sum_{n=1}^{n=m} K_n \sin \psi_n\right)^2}$$

or

$$A_{max} = \frac{\sum_{n=1}^{n=m} K_n \sin \psi_n}{\sin \psi}.$$

The resulting formula permits the computation of the group sensitivity as a function of the sensitivities of the seismometers comprising the group. The calculation of theoretical seismograms for

is assumed to be unity. For this case, the dependence of the axial direction of the group diagram on the sensitivity of the seismometers entering the group is indicated in Figure 57a. The figure shows that in order to obtain the group diagram whose axis may be associated with $\omega = 225$ degrees, $\psi = 29$ degrees, (point A); the rela-

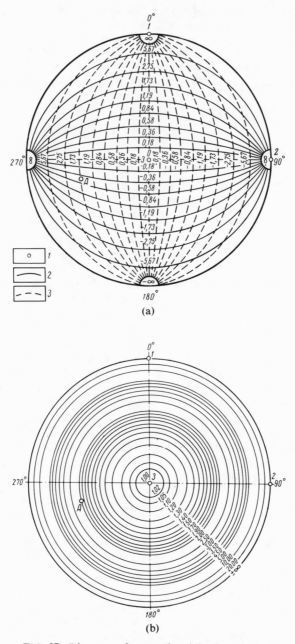

(a)

(b)

FIG. 57. Diagrams of group directivity for a three-component installation XYZ (stereographic projection). a:
Axial directions of the diagram. (1) Axial directions of
seismometers of a three-component installation and their
numbering, (2) lines of sensitivity of seismometer 1, (3)
lines of sensitivity of seismometer 2. b: Dependence of
amplitude of group diagram on the direction of its axis.

tive seismometer sensitivities must be adjusted to $K_1 = -0.44$ and $K_2 = 1.64$. The chart showing the dependence of the diagram amplitude on its axial direction (Figure 57b) indicates that the amplitude of the group diagram (sensitivity) decreases as the angle between the vertical and the axis of the diagram decreases. All group diagrams whose axes are disposed along conical surfaces with respect to the vertical axis possess the same amplitude. The sensitivity of this group (point A) is equal to 2.00. We have discussed the variation of the axial direction of the group diagram as the sensitivity of the two horizontal seismometers is varied.

The axial direction of the diagram may be varied by controlling the sensitivity of the vertical seismometer and one of the horizontal seismometers. In that case, the azimuth of the diagram axis is determined by the ratio of sensitivities of the horizontal seismometers, while its angle to the horizontal follows from

$$\tan \psi = \frac{K_3}{\sqrt{1 + K_2^2}}; \quad K_1 = 1;$$

$$K_2 = 3.73; \quad K_3 = -2.26.$$

For a three-component symmetrical installation, the dependence of the axial direction of the diagram on the sensitivities of two seismometers may be obtained from general equations and is represented graphically in Figure 58. In Figure 58b, the amplitude lines consist of circles of various radii. The centers of the circles are located on the line connecting the center of the projection with the axial direction of the seismometer of the installation. The sensitivity remains invariant. The axis of the group having minimal sensitivity is located on the same line. The plane of infinite sensitivities contains the axial directions of the two seismometers used to control the orientation of the group diagram. The minus sign of the coefficient that determines the sensitivity of the seismometer indicates phase inversion, i.e., the change of the axial direction of the seismometer by 180 degrees.

Procedures for realization of CDR-I

CDR based on displacements is realizable by various means using both analog and computer-oriented procedures performed directly in the field, as illustrated in Figure 59a. This arrangement naturally is not unique and only serves to illustrate the principle of acquisition of summation tapes (films).[3] The instrumentation permits the acquisition of summation tapes and the determination of the character of polarization of waves simultaneously. It might be called a polarized seismic analyzer (PSA). The basic components of a PSA are: (1) a three-component seismic installation, (2) an amplifier, (3) signal dividers, (4) adders, and (5) a multichannel galvanometer bloc. The adder bloc performs the summation (stacking) of signals according to required proportions. The signals are then amplified and transferred to their respective galvanometers. The upper three channels of the seismogram (6) correspond to actual recordings of the three-component installation. The others in this example constitute the summing tape corresponding to all the diagrams whose axes form an angle of 30 degrees with the horizontal. The azimuths of neighboring diagrams differ by 30 degrees. An example of divider adjustment and a sample of the summing tape for CDR-I are shown in Figure 59b and 59c, respectively. The PSA may be implemented in the form of a separate module to work in conjunction with existing seismic units.

In the digital realization of CDR displacements performed by the computer, the program relates the installation to the coordinate system associated with the

---

[3]Translator's remark: It is never clear which is implied.

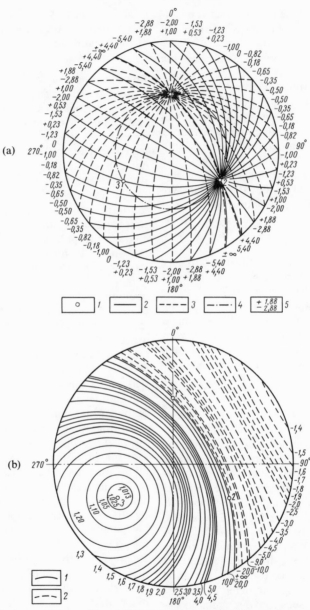

FIG. 58. Diagrams of group directivity of a symmetrical three-component installation of seismometers (stereographic projection). a: Dependence of axial direction of diagram on sensitivity of two seismometers of the group. (1) Directions of axes of seismometers of installation; (2) lines of sensitivity of seismometer 1; (3) lines of sensitivity of seismometer 2; (4) conical surface corresponding to the installation forming an angle of 35 degrees of seismometer inclination with respect to the horizontal; (5) values of sensitivity along corresponding lines: above, sensitivity of first seismometer; below, that of second. b: Dependence of amplitude of diagram on the direction of its axis. (1) Lines of equal positive sensitivities; (2) same, for negative.

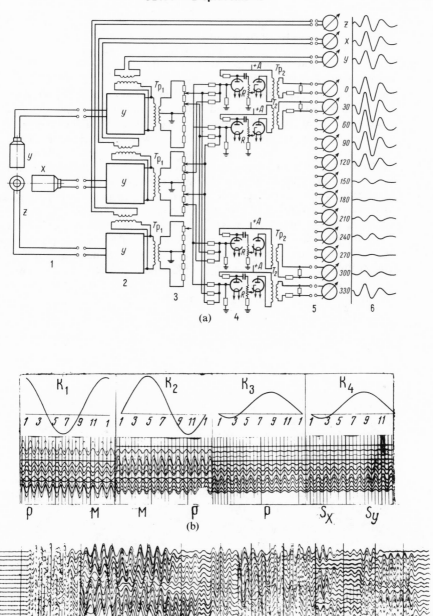

FIG. 59. (a) Block-schematic of a polarized seismic analyzer. (b) Records for the adjustment of dividers of the adder. The numbers identify the devices. (c) Summing tape for various waves: linearly polarized longitudinal (P); transverse (S_X) and (S_Y); polarized (M).

plane of the ray. The original nonoriented three-component borehole installation serves as the input registration, and the computation of the summing tapes is made according to a given step and a given angle in the plane of incidence (see Figure 37). Such a CDR program based on displacements is available in the computing center of the Siberian department of the AS USSR.

For the analysis of complicated polarized oscillations with time-varying axial directions of polarization, more selective systems of directional reception according to displacements may be used. These systems are based on nonlinear transformations and, in particular, on nonlinear spatial filtering (Flinn, 1965).

CDR based on displacements improves the effective instrumentation sensitivity for recording various oscillation components and produces a record of any oscillation component in space. This substantially simplifies the study of wave polarization in space and may be utilized for the determination of directions of motion. This is of particular significance in wave correlation along the vertical profile since it permits the transition from tracking any one component of the record to correlation of the full vector of oscillation. Such correlation was accomplished in the study of converted transmitted waves (see Chapter 9). CDR based on displacement may provide the basis for the development of borehole seismic exploration methods founded on the utilization of kinematic aspects of seismic waves and on the study of trajectories of particle motion.

PART TWO

SEISMIC WAVES IN ACTUAL MEDIA

Let us illustrate the capabilities of VSP by means of data for the study of basic wave types in some media that are structurally different, and let us attempt to estimate the influence of various inhomogeneities of the medium on the wave field. This study must of necessity start with the direct wave which initiates the wave process. Such a discussion will permit the formulation of capabilities of basic methods of seismic exploration and of problems involving further development of VSP.

The basic types of reflected and refracted (longitudinal, transverse, and converted) waves, observed over a broad range of distances are described for two characteristic cross-sections: (1) a terrigenous bed, and (2) a high-velocity carbonate bed with interstratifications of terrigenous deposits. Distinct thin layers with increased velocity are frequently encountered in geologic media, and the study of their influence on the wavefield is of great practical interest. Wavefields for the first type of cross-section are illus-

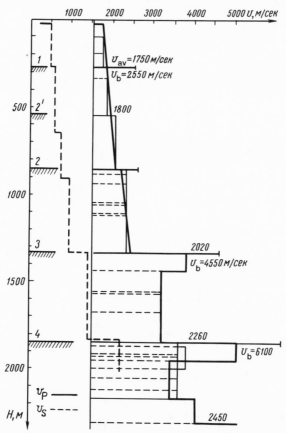

FIG. 60. Velocity cross-section for well no. 42 (Staro-Minsk).

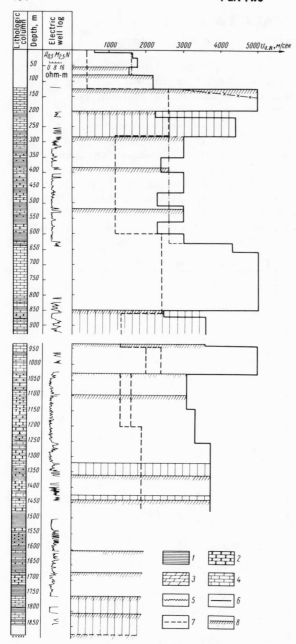

FIG. 61. Velocity cross-section for well no. 1 (Kletsko-
Pochtov). (1) Clay, argyllite, (2) sandstone, (3) marl,
(4) limestone, (5) fault in sedimentation, (6) v_p graph,
(7) v_s graph, (8) reflecting surfaces.

trated by observed data in the northern part of the Krasnodar region. Those for the second are illustrated by data from the platform portion of the Volgograd region along the Volga. Velocity models for the two cross-sections mentioned above are presented in Figures 60 and 61. The models were constructed from detailed VSP investigations using SWL data, velocity well shooting, and directional impacts and shots.

In the first cross-section (Figure 60) the presence of high-velocity layers is characteristic. These layers occur at depths of 270 m, 1334 m, and 1850 m. The boundary at 270 m consists of a sandstone layer with a velocity of 2550 m/sec and a thickness of about 11 m embedded in sandy-clay deposits. In essence, this is a thin layer in a gradiented medium. The velocities below and above the layer are both 1820 m/sec. The boundaries at depths of 1334 and 1850 m are formed by packets of thin layers, the velocities above and below the layers being dif-

ferent. In addition, the cross-section contains a number of less distinct boundaries involving thick layers.[1] The cross-section extends over the platform with sufficient uniformity. The large number of wells investigated (wells no. 2, 6, 20, 42) yield practically identical wave fields.

For the second cross-section (Figure 61), the characteristic features are high-speed carbonate layers that alternate with low-speed terrigenous deposits such that the largest velocity discontinuities of P- and S-waves are associated with limestone layers of different thickness. The limestone layers at depths of 125 – 270 m and 640 – 850 m are characterized by velocity increases which are most abrupt at the top of the layers and less so with depth. The most abrupt velocity horizons of P- and S-waves coincide over the cross-section.

[1]In subsequent discussions of all waves in the cross-section of the Staro-Minsk platform, we shall refer to the numbers of the boundaries in Figure 60.

Chapter 6
DIRECT WAVES EXCITATION AND PROPAGATION

The direct wave is generated near the source and exerts a strong influence on the form of each individual wave and, thus, on the structure of the entire seismogram. This explains the strong dependence of the seismic record on the nature of the source. Understanding the generation of the direct wave and its propagation in actual media is fundamental in determining the capabilities of seismic exploration. Without an experimental study of the direct wave in an actual medium, there is no way to form concepts of the physical model of the absorbing medium. The study of the direct wave is also necessary for the application of dynamic theory to the solution of definite problems and for the development of synthetic seismograms of reflected waves. During the last few years, interest in the direct wave has increased significantly, due to the development of dynamic methods of interpretation. This may also be explained by the fact that, in thin-layered media, the form and intensity of reflected waves substantially depends on the frequency composition of incident waves.

The results of direct wave studies largely depend on the procedures employed in the investigations.

STUDY PROCEDURES

The direct wave is investigated through surface observations as well as by observations at interior points of the medium. A large body of work teaches that the surface-observed direct wave may differ from that observed at the interior. The latter dictates the course of the entire wave field. The basic reasons for these distinctions are: (a) spalling phenomena connected with the free surface, (b) inhomogeneities of the upper portion of the cross-section, and (c) directivity of the source.

Spalling phenomena

The form of the direct wave when it is the first arrival at the surface from a shallow shot may vary substantially. The extent to which it varies depends on the separation from the top of the shothole and the charge size (Gvozdev and Kuznetsov, 1967; Kuznetsov and Gamburtsev, 1967). As the charge size increases, the form of the direct wave becomes more complex and the tail indicates repetitive shocks. The time difference between the initial and the repeat impulses (wavelets) increases with the weight of the charge. The visible form of the initial and repeat wavelets is the same. The spectra of repeat wavelets are narrower and are shifted into the region of lower frequencies. The wavelets indicated on records obtained on the surface near the source were first interpreted as repetitive shocks from explosions in boreholes, and their influence on the shape of reflected waves was not argued. Later is was demonstrated that repetitive wavelets are not connected with the focus of the shot, they do not penetrate into the depth of the medium and, consequently, do not influence the basic wave field. They are the result of a transformation occurring at the receiver, of the dome-shaped displacement within the free surface and the adjacent ZLV. Flocculent soils cause distortions of direct waves by events associated with spalling phenomena even with shots of comparatively light charges. Seismometers on long spikes achieve better contact with the spalled soil and permit acquisition of distortionless records, even when the charges are four to six times larger (Gvozdev and Kuznetsov, 1967). In the immediate vicinity of the top of the shothole, the form of the direct wave may also be influenced by a disruption of consolidation of the medium due to drilling (Kuznetsov and Gamburtsev, 1967).

Inhomogeneities in the upper portion of the cross-section

Inhomogeneities in the upper portion of the cross-section contribute to the generation of various wave types, which may substantially interfere with the direct wave. The existence of boundaries below the shot may lead to intensification of the direct wave observed at the surface and to energy loss by reflection of the direct wave penetrating into depth. Conversely, boundaries above the shot may weaken the direct wave at the surface and change the form and intensity of the wave transmitted into the medium's depth by addition of ghosts. In addition, waves from the ZLV, surface waves excited by Lamb waves, and transverse waves (Berzon, 1964) may interfere with surface observations. If shots occur in cased holes, diffraction at the ends of the casing may influence the form of the direct wave (Berzon, 1964; Gal'perin, 1965b). The filtering properties of the upper portion of the cross-section may also influence the form of the direct wave. This principally affects the high-frequency components of the signal.

Directivity of the source

The effect of the source directivity on seismic observations has scarcely been investigated. Only in the last few years has any data been available relating to this aspect (Vinogradov et al, 1967). Based on considerable experimental evidence, one may assert that the conventional explosion in a hole possesses a natural directivity. However, this question requires specialized research.

In some discrete cases at certain distances from the source, the form of the direct wave on the surface seismogram may still be very similar to its form at interior points of the medium. However, refracted waves, propagating along deeper layers and usually arriving ahead of the direct wave, complicate the observation of the latter in its pure form.

The above circumstances complicate the study of direct waves by means of surface observations. In some cases the effectiveness of this approach even becomes questionable; this primarily refers to problems of excitation and to the process of wave propagation in actual media. VSP permits the study of the direct wave and the influence that is exerted on it by conditions of excitation. Also, VSP permits continuous tracking of the direct wave along the vertical profile. This is extremely important since it contributes to concepts on the form and intensity of the wave as it impinges on the reflecting boundaries. Naturally, characteristics of waves observed on the surface are also dictated by the above parameters.

The direct wave was studied in varying degrees of detail for all regions in which wave fields were investigated by VSP. In some regions, specialized experiments were carried out to study the direct wave. In the following, when describing the direct wave, we shall include not only its first wavelet but the entire train of incident waves that substantially influences the whole wave field.

When developing procedures for VSP studies of the direct wave, one must also formulate the basic instrumentation requirements. Primarily, one must guarantee good contact between receiver and wall of the hole so that the natural frequencies of the receiver-ground system should lie far above the passband of the earth (Pasechnik, 1952a). The operating frequency range must be sufficiently broad. Experience indicates that an upper limit of 150 hz may in some cases prove to be insufficient for spectral studies of the pulses. This is particularly true for high-velocity crystalline formations exhibiting comparatively low absorption.

Here the wavelet may contain high-frequency components even at depths of 2 –
3 km. In these cases, a frequency range
of from 5 – 500 hz is expedient. Dynamic range is of particular significance
since it must guarantee the recording of
the direct wave without nonlinear distortion in the vicinity of the source as well
as at large distances. It is also essential
to ensure stability of the instrumentation.

INFLUENCE OF CONDITIONS OF EXCITATION ON THE DIRECT WAVE

Much work has been devoted to the
study of the shape of the wavelet near
the source including both its theoretical
and experimental aspects (Epinat'yeva et
al, 1963; Kogan, 1961; Anstey, 1958; Aki,
1960; Ricker, 1940; Ricker and Sorge,
1954). These efforts have resulted in the
tentative recognition of three zones in the
vicinity of the shot: zones of shock waves,
zones of plastic deformations, and zones
of elastic deformations. The distances at
which elastic waves begin to register, i.e.,
the start of the elastic deformation zones,
is different for different media. A quantitative estimate of this distance for clayey
beds may be made according to the empirical formula (Aki, 1960) $r = 0.12 \sqrt[3]{Q}$,
where r is the radius of the sphere in
meters and Q the weight of the charge
in grams. As the charge changes from
grams to tens of kilograms, the radius of
the sphere of nonelastic deformation
varies from a fraction of a meter to a few
meters. The elastic deformation zone is
basic for seismic investigations.

In the zone of elastic deformation, as
the distance from the source increases,
the form of the wavelet varies and stabi-
lizes only at a certain distance. From
experimental data in homogeneous
media, this distance approximates 0.75 –
1.0 wavelength. The waveform at the
boundary of this zone has received but
scant consideration. The direct wave
pulse at distances of several wavelengths
has received much more attention. The

analysis of the amplitudes and the spectra
of the direct wave in homogenous media
as it is affected by various parameters
of the shot (Gurvich, 1967; Gurvich et al,
1966), may not always be applicable to
seismic exploration. This is because explosions are produced in the upper portion of the cross-section, which has considerable inhomogeneity and structural
complexity. Under these conditions, the
results obtained in seismic exploration do
not always conform to theory.

The determining influence on the direct waveform is exerted by conditions of
excitation, which are understood to comprise all the factors associated with the
generation of seismic waves. This includes the structure of the medium in the
neighborhood of the explosion (homo-
geneity, lithology, physical properties)
and the parameters of the shot (weight,
shape, disposition of charge). It has been
shown that source conditions may exert
a very strong and occasionally dominant,
influence on the direct wave and the
wavefield. We may speculate that the
study of conditions of excitation comprises one of the basic directions which
one must take to increase the effectiveness of seismic exploration.

Influence of charge weight

VSP basically confirmed the general
laws governing the variations of the
wavelet with weight of the charge [in-
crease of period and duration of wavelet
as the charge increases (Gurvich, 1967)].
VSP permits a more detailed study of
these laws. However, the effect of the
charge weight on the form of the wavelet and the form of the entire initial portion of the seismogram is of most interest.
Let us consider two examples (Figures
62, 63).

In the first example (Figure 62), there
are no sharply defined boundaries and
VSP permits the production of a short
and simple wavelet of the direct wave.
As the charge weight increases over three

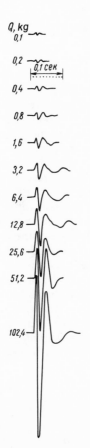

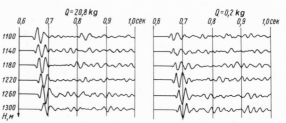

FIG. 63. Comparison of initial portion of seismograms for an increase of charge weight, according to S. V. Klushin (well no. 1, Oktyaber, Byrelorussian SSR).

FIG. 62. Variation of wavelet of direct wave with variation of charge weight, according to E. Ya. Kutsenko ($H = 1000$ m, $h = 20$ m, $l = 40$ m, channel passband 5-130 hz, well no. 17, Kuschev).

orders of magnitude, the form of the record changes slightly, the amplitude of the wavelet increases by about two orders of magnitude, and the period increases by a factor of two.

In the second example (Figure 63), the inhomogeneities in the upper portion of the cross-section cause a somewhat more complex event on the initial portion of the seismogram. However, an increase of charge by a factor of about 100 changes the form of the record somewhat. Strictly speaking, one should not state that, as the charge is increased at the same shot depth, the conditions of excitation remain the same: the form of the charge changes, the packing changes, and blowouts may occur.

Thus, varying the charge weight does not produce a decisive influence on the form of the direct wave and the train of incident waves observed at great depths. On the other hand, varying the charge weight may be of substantial significance for the structure of seismograms observed at the surface. This may be explained by two circumstances. First, as is characteristic for thin-layered media, a pronounced dependency of the form and the intensity of the reflected wave on the incident wave is observed. Second, and equally important, VSP has demonstrated that, as the weight of the charge varies, there occurs a redistribution of energy being transmitted into the depth of the medium and retained in the upper portion of the cross-section. As the charge increases a disproportionate amount of energy may remain in the upper portion of the cross-section, increasing the number and intensity of various unwanted waves which complicates the wavefield and disrupts the correlatability of waves at depth. For observations in the upper portion of the cross-section, the variation of charge is sensed much more acutely than at great depths. This explains to a significant degree the high effectiveness of work accomplished by single small sources in conjunction with stacking.[2]

[2] Translator's note: word used in translation.

Experience with VSP confirms that it is exceedingly expedient to employ charges of least possible weight.

As the charge increases, the directivity of the source may change as well, and a redistribution of energies of longitudinal and transverse waves may also occur. For example, study of the wavefield excited in SWL for observations at great depths, comparatively close to the source, indicates that for explosions in holes, increasing the charge increases the intensity of the transverse wave (Figure 64).

Effect of inhomogeneities near the shot

In seismic exploration, shots are produced in the upper, most heterogeneous, portion of the cross-section. VSP experience indicates that heterogeneities of the cross-section near the shot may considerably influence the form and the intensity of the first wave and the train of incident waves because the work is carried out under the most varied seismic and geologic conditions. These inhomogeneities usually transform the comparatively simple inpulse, generated in the source into a complex train of incident waves. The mechanism of such a transformation is caused by interference of the primary impulse with oscillations of various types generated by the heterogeneities of the upper portion of the cross-section. The form of the incident wave is strongly influenced by the disposition of the charge relative to the heterogeneities. By selection of the charge depth, one may sub-

stantially simplify the form of the direct wave and realize it as a short duration wavelet of simple form. Let us illustrate this by examples of various structural situations of the ZLV.

Figure 65a shows a record of a direct wave obtained in a borehole at 1000 m depth associated with the simplest single-layered ZLV, using instrumentation with a passband of 1 – 130 hz. The record for a shot at $h = 5$ m is very weak. For explosions in the ZLV (10, 15 m), the incident wave consists of three peaks with a small distortion in the tail. For a shot near the bottom of the ZLV ($h = 20$ m) a direct wave of comparatively simple form is obtained. As the charge is lowered below the ZLV, the form of the direct wave sharply deteriorates: the number of phases increases, the event is of interferential character, and the onset of a second wave is evident. The direct wave is most complex for $h = 33$ m. But already starting with $h = 40$ m, the second wave is practically fully formed and, as the depth increases, that wave lags more and more behind the first wave. For $h = 80$ m, the time difference of the wave arrivals amounts to 0.1 sec.

The second wave is a ghost that is reflected from the bottom of the ZLV and its form practically coincides with the form of the direct wave, except for phase inversion. The latter is due to reflection from the boundary of the layer having lower acoustic impedance. The amplitude

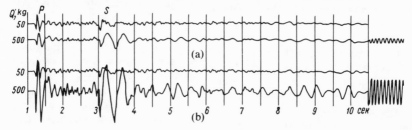

(a)

(b)

FIG. 64. Variation of relative intensities of *P*- and *S*-waves with increase of charge. Record of vertical component obtained at depth of 2000 m by seismometer having a natural frequency of 1 hz for *l* = 2800 m (well no. 10, Alma-Ata). (a) Seismograms with equalized amplitudes for longitudinal waves. (b) Seismograms obtained for equal sensitivities of channels.

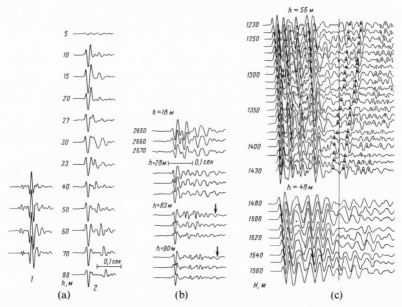

FIG. 65. Variation of form of direct wave as it depends on *h*. a: Under conditions of structural simplicity of the ZLV (1) for *H* = 0, (2) for *H* = 1000 m (*l* = 600 m, *Q* = 0.4 kg, well no. 42, Staro-Minsk). b: Under conditions of multilayered ZLV (*l* = 100 m, *Q* = 0.8 kg, well no. 162, Severo-Stavropol). c: For shots in and below the ZLV (same situation as for b).

of the ghost is 0.6 – 0.7 of that of the direct wave. At *h* = 40 m, the direct wave begins to shrink and is of simple form that changes very little as the depth of the charge increases. As ghosts of the direct wave are not recorded at the surface, the described variation of form of the direct wave is altogether unobservable on surface seismograms. It is for that reason that surface observations cannot be used for rigorous monitoring of the constancy of source conditions (Kaplan, 1962; Shalimov, 1965).

In the more complicated ZLV, the number of ghosts may increase considerably and the conditions of their interference become more complex. Figure 65b shows seismograms acquired through a complicated multilayered zone. For *h* = 18 and 28 m the records exhibit plainly an interferential event of considerable complexity and duration. Only for *h* = 83 and 90 m, the ghosts begin to

separate from the direct wave and the latter is registered in the form of a simple and short wavelet. Following the first wave, a sequence of ghosts is registered. The last weak low-frequency oscillation (denoted by an arrow) represents reflection from the surface.

Sometimes a sharp change of form of incident waves may occur for comparatively small variations of shot depths, particularly when shots are near abrupt boundaries. Here, incident waves of substantially different shapes may be formed at either side of the boundary.

Composite seismograms of different sections of the vertical profile (Figure 65c) obtained from shots at different depths exhibit a noticeable increase in frequency and an improvement of resolving power for a transition from shots within the ZLV (*h* = 48 m) to those below the ZLV (*h* = 56 m).

In this manner, the form of the direct

waves and the sequence of incident waves is influenced by interference with ghosts. The form and the intensity of the ghosts, primarily dictated by the reflecting properties of the ZLV, are of considerable significance. These properties are important in the study of multiples (see Chapter 8) as well.

The spectrum of the incident direct wave with interference by ghost waves is the result of transmission of an impulse through a filter corresponding to a thin layer, assuming that its form is preserved when it is reflected and only the amplitude and phase inversion vary. Under these conditions, it is essential that the source conditions remain constant if the form of reflected waves is to be preserved. If one assumes that the reflection coefficient at the bottom of the ZLV does not change along the profile, one may duplicate the form of the incident wave if one preserves the conditions of interference of the direct waves and ghost waves. In order to do this, it is essential to maintain a constant time shift between direct waves and ghost waves. Thus, it is necessary to study the relief of the basic reflecting boundaries above the shot by means of detailed microseismic well logging.

If the shot depth varies, the form of the direct wave might change. This is caused not only by interference with ghosts but also by the *influence of the properties of the formations* (lithology) in which the shot occurs and on which the frequency composition of the impulse depends. The wave spectrum from hard formations contains more high-frequency components than for shots in plastic formations. As the wave velocity increases in the medium in which the shot is produced, the dominant frequency of the impulse increases while its duration decreases.

The records obtained on the Kuschev platform of the Krasnodar region (Figure 66) are an example of the influence that

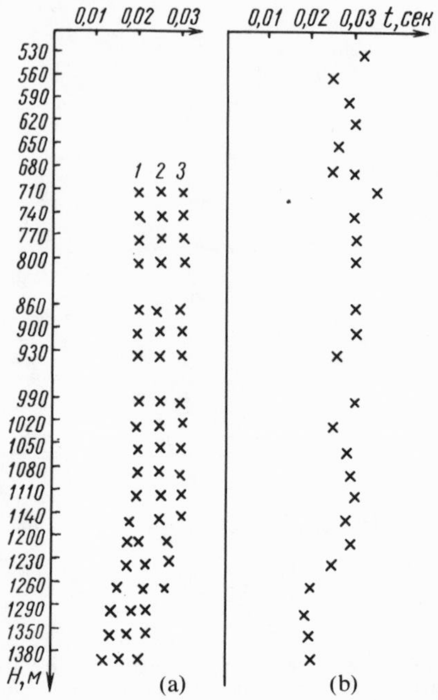

FIG. 66. (a) Dependence of periods of direct wave on depth of shot (well no. 32, Kuschev). (b) Same for wave reflected from crystalline basement.

the shot depth has on the frequency composition of direct and reflected waves. Shots in 'clays at depths of 30 m ($H = 1270 - 1380$ m and for the basement depth $H_v = 1470$ m), produce a first-peak period of 0.013 sec; the subsequent phases of the first-reflected waves and the basement-reflected waves are 0.20 sec. The periods of direct and reflected waves from shots in sand at depth of 18 m ($H = 530 - 1260$ m) increase to 0.02 and 0.03 sec, respectively. The seismograms in Figure 65c may also serve to illustrate the dependence of frequency composition of the record on the properties of formations near the shot.

VSP efforts have shown that the influence of repetitive shocks on direct wave form is often overrated; however, such shocks do occur on occasion. In most cases, one can succeed in simplifying the direct-wave shape by selection of appropriate excitation conditions. This results in a short and simple wavelet. It is equally true, however, that in certain other situations it is impossible to accomplish this feat. This is sometimes caused by repetitive shocks that occur in explosions in boreholes associated with unexpected imperfections or with gaseous cavities. However, repetitive shocks were also observed in holes that do not have a substantial enlargement of the hole. Ricker, (1953) showed that the complex form of the direct wave is the result of interference of three simple impulses which have almost the same typical form separated by nearly equal Δt; each of the subsequent impulses has a smaller amplitude than the preceding one. The series of sequential impulses is analogous to impulses associated with the pulsation of a gaseous bubble in water. It is assumed that the impulses are caused by the elasticity of the shothole. However, because of the small Δt between them, amounting to about 0.0035 sec, it is not possible to resolve them in time.

It is important to emphasize that the form of the direct wave also depends on reception conditions. Since the media in which the observations are conducted are layered as a rule, the variations of the direct-wave form may be connected with its propagation through the medium. However, accumulated observational experience teaches that this variation is insignificant and is of local character associated with the formation of secondary waves on profile sections that are contiguous to the boundaries (see Figure 28). Outside the region of interference with secondary waves, the form of the direct wave again simplifies. At a shot depth of 90 m, the composite seismogram (Figure 67) shows that it was possible to separate the ghosts from the direct wave. The direct wave propagates down in the shape of a simple and short wavelet

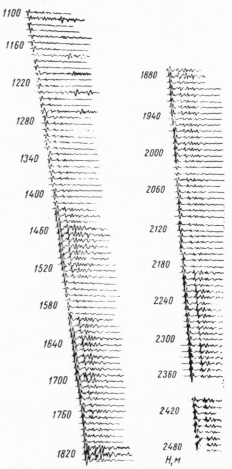

FIG. 67. Seismogram of direct wave and ghosts along vertical profile (well no. 162, Severo-Stavropol).

whose form is well preserved. Only for certain sections above the boundary ($H = 1750$ and 1830 m) does the form of the wave appear to be disrupted by interference with reflected waves. Still, as a whole, waves along the profile vary only slightly. Thus, even for observations at very large depths, it is possible in many cases to obtain a direct wave in the shape of a simple and short wavelet (see Figure 65b).

Occasionally, records with a comparatively simple wave form near the source are much more complex when obtained at great depths. This may be related to lithology near the receivers. Observations were made on the Russian platform in the carbonate bed with a large number of interstratifications of terrigenous deposits. Although the shot depth was moved from 10 m to 170 m and the receiver depth from 1000 m to 2700 m, it was not possible to obtain a simply shaped direct wave and to separate it from its ghosts. In all cases a whole series of incident waves followed the first wave and practically interfered with it. The intensities of these incident waves are near the intensity of the first wave (see Figures 65, 85). The form of this entire series of incident waves remains practically constant as the shot depth is varied over a wide range.

Although the form of the direct wave does depend on the weight of the charge and the properties of the formations near the shot, the heterogeneities of the upper portion of the cross-section are the factors that exert the dominant influence on the direct wave and the entire train of inci-

dent waves. For this reason, it is extremely difficult in heterogeneous media to study the impulse at the source, and it is essential to consider the shot itself, together with the medium, as a complex source. The strong dependence of the direct wave form on source conditions favors the use of that wave for observations at interior points of the medium to monitor the constancy of the source.

The variation of the direct waveform naturally cannot fail to affect the form of reflected waves. Let us illustrate this dependence by showing how the reflected wave is complicated by its ghost. In Figure 68a, the form of a direct wave and that of the wave reflected from the top of the Paleocene ($H_\backslash = 1334$ m) are registered at a depth of 1000 m for various shot depths. For fixed shot depth (Figure 68b) at a profile section above the boundary ($H = 750 - 850$ m), the reflected wave practically duplicates the form of the incident wave. At a profile section immediately adjacent to the boundary ($H = 1240 - 1300$ m), the record

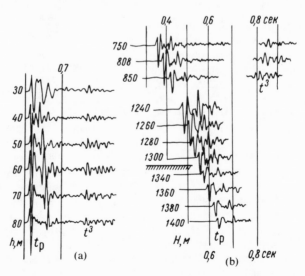

FIG. 68. (a) Variation of form of incident and reflected waves with depth of charge ($H = 1000$ m, $Q = 0.8$ kg, $l = 600$ m). (b) Same for variation of points of reception, well no. 42, Staro-Minsk ($h = 75$ m, $q = 0.4$ kg, $l = 100$ m).

of the incident wave is observed to be substantially more complicated. The original form was restored below the boundary of separation ($H = 1320 - 1380$ m).

THE FORM OF THE DIRECT WAVE

A large body of experimental work involving seismic impulses has been carried out at interior points of the medium (Berdennikova and Limbakh, 1966; McDonal et al, 1958; Jolly, 1953, 1956; Levin and Lynn, 1958; Ricker, 1953) and at the surface (Epinat'yeva et al, 1963; Koryagin, 1966). A considerable amount of data concerning wavelets at distances of several wavelengths from the source were obtained by Ricker. He developed an analytic expression in the 1940's based on the solution of the wave equation in a medium with viscous absorption that was fairly well compatible with the comparatively meager experimental data then available. In subsequent experiments (Ricker, 1953), he obtained short wavelets of comparatively simple form. Registration by means of several levels of amplification over a large range (about four orders of magnitude) demonstrated that the wavelet lacks a sharply defined first arrival. Motion sets in gradually so that the apparent time of pulse arrival on the seismogram depends on the sensitivity of the channel. Experimental data are in good agreement with theory.

One occasionally was able to obtain simple pulses at interior points of the medium that were close to the form of the Ricker wavelet. However, in the majority of cases, they differed by their considerable duration and complexity. In spite of the large number of investigations, the data on first seismic wavelets are still insufficient to establish any general laws whatsoever. As a rule, the upper portion of the cross-section is so complex and its structural composition, even for adjoining sections, may differ to such an extent that the analysis of all possible variants of the direct-wave form is unrealistic. In fact, such an analysis hardly makes any sense. Of considerably more interest is the comparison of the form of the direct wave in those cases for which it is recorded in its simplest and shortest manifestations.

Experience with VSP indicates that it is possible by appropriate selection of source conditions to produce a direct wave of comparatively simple form: It is a short wavelet consisting of two to three peaks. In these cases, the form of the direct wave remains reasonably stable even though it is obtained in different boreholes from completely different areas and from shots in different lithological conditions.

Figure 69 illustrates some of the simplest seismic wavelets which we obtained in the Krasnodar and Stavropol regions with a distortionless setup, and a passband of $15 - 130$ hz. These wavelets are very similar in form to those from other regions (McDonal et al, 1958; Levin and Lynn, 1958; Ricker, 1953). The only difference is in the amplitude ratio of the first and second peaks. In well no. 42 the third peak is less than the first one, while in well no. 162 the reverse is true. Analogous differences may be observed between the Ricker wavelet and those of Levin and Lynn. To appraise this difference, we conducted special experiments in which a sequence consisting of hundreds of shots was repeated for the same charge at the same point. Observations indicate that the amplitude ratio of the first and third peaks is not exceptionally stable and may vary within the course of a single sequence (Figure 69b).

The registered wavelets possess a broad amplitude spectrum. In selecting analytical expressions for the observed wavelets, primary consideration was given to sharpness of onset of the oscillation. This parameter determines the order of the displacement derivative of a

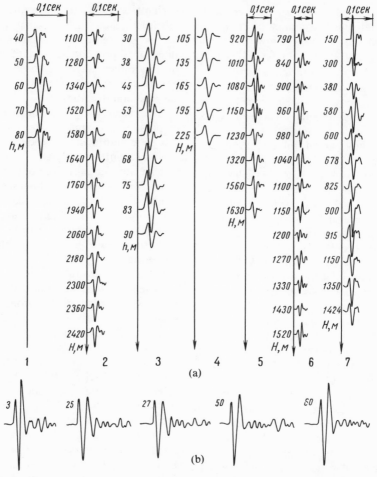

FIG. 69 a: Comparison of form of wavelets of direct waves. (1) $H = 1000$ m (well no. 42, Staro-Minsk); (2) $h = 90$ m (well no. 162, Severo-Stavropol); (3) $H = 247$ m, according to Ricker (1953); (4) same, according to McDonal (1958); (5, 6, 7) same, according to Levin and Lynn (1959). (b) Duplication of wavelet forms (seismograms identify the sequential numbers of the shots).

discontinuity when the transition from quiescence to motion occurs. As the separation from the source increases, the arrivals become less and less abrupt. If in the immediate vicinity of the source the disruption occurs in the displacement or in its first derivative (velocity), then the initial particle velocity is zero at large distances and the discontinuity is caused by either acceleration or higher-order derivatives of displacement.

The wavelet obtained in well no. 162 (Figure 69) is in good agreement with Berlage's (1924) expression

$$U = U_0 t^n e^{-\alpha t} \sin \omega_0 t$$

for $t \geq 0$. For a wavelet of this shape, a discontinuity of nth order is characteristic. Comparison of wavelets observed in various media with computed ones indicates that the agreement is close. For example, both wavelets fully coincide in three peaks and three transitions through zero (Figure 70b). The wavelet recorded in well no. 42 is very close to the Ricker wavelet (Figure 70a). All derivatives of

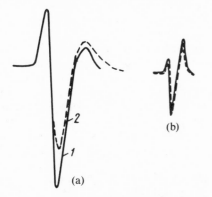

FIG. 70. Observed (1) and computed (2) impulse wavelets.

the theoretical Ricker wavelet are continuous and its amplitudes rapidly decay in time (because of the exponential term). For that reason, its duration is limited. Puzyrev (1959) has discussed a wavelet whose shape is close to the above.

The constancy of the form of the direct wave when the source conditions are maintained (especially that of the depth of charge) permits the monitoring of the depth to which the charge is lowered. The stability of the form of the direct wave and its ghosts can be seen on the seismogram (see Figure 67) obtained at a depth interval of 1100 to 2480 m. Up to a depth of 1880 m, the cross-section has alternating layers of sandy clay deposits. From 1880 m down to the hole bottom ($H = 2880$ m), a strongly metamorphosed high-velocity layer is embedded.

The requirements demanded of the direct wave are dictated by the investigated problems. It is essential to generate a direct wave which has a short duration and a broad spectrum in order to learn the nature of dynamics of direct waves and how they propagate in actual media.

This is so important that it may justify specialized experiments in each particular case. However, for other investigations, it is more expedient and more economical to obtain the incident wave in a somewhat more complicated form but without ghosts (see Figure 65a for $h = 15$ m, 20 m, 27 m, and Figure 68 for $h = 30$ m). In such situations the form of each discrete wave on the seismogram is relatively more complex than would be true for a simple direct wavelet, but the structure of the entire seismogram appears to be considerably simpler due to the substantially reduced number of waves that comprise the seismogram.

PROPAGATION OF THE SEISMIC IMPULSE IN ACTUAL MEDIA

The seismic impulse, propagating in the actual nonideally elastic medium, gradually broadens and contains pronounced low-frequency components. This is dictated by the variation of its amplitude and phase spectra as a function of distance. Amplitude distortion is caused by the spectrum of the absorption coefficient. Phase distortion is caused by dispersion. Actual media are not only not ideally elastic but also usually thin layered, and the latter dictates the filtering action of the medium. Thus, the basic factors contributing to intensity and form of the wavelet, as it propagates through the medium are: absorption and dispersion caused by nonideal elasticity, phenomena of reflection and refraction (at the boundaries of separation) which generate secondary waves, and scattering of energy at various fine heterogeneities.

Absorption

Absorption is one of the basic parameters which characterize the medium (Gamburtsev and Deryagin, 1934; Gurevich, 1955; Deryagin, 1931; Kogan, 1961 a, b; Ogurtsov and Ozerov, 1959; Shan'gin, 1958; Futterman, 1962; Lamb, 1962; Wuenschel, 1965). The study of absorption has considerable practical and theoretical meaning. The practical significance is absorption permits us to estimate the intensities of various waves at different sections of the line of observation. In particular, for VSP, it permits the appraisal of wave intensities on the surface from observations at the boundaries of separation, or it permits the calculation of intensities of various types of multiples. The theoretical significance has to do with the study of the mechanism of absorption.

The two efforts (applied and theoretical) demand different levels of accuracy. The crux of the matter is that if the absorption coefficient α is linearly related to frequency f the amplitude of the wavelet must decrease with distance but it does not do so according to the exponential law that governs its monochromatic components (Kogan, 1961a). Thus, α values calculated from the decrease of peak amplitudes as a function of distance are not highly accurate.

The most complete information on the value of the absorption coefficient and its dependence on frequency may be acquired by comparing spectra of one wave at several points of a homogeneous medium. Though, for applied purposes in discrete situations, one may be satisfied by effective α values of some kind that characterize the general decay of amplitudes. Then, for theoretical purposes it is essential to study the spectra themselves. Thus, the determination of the absorption coefficient is based on two procedures: the amplitude and the spectral approaches (Ogurtsov and Ozerov, 1959). Naturally, α values resulting from these procedures may not agree with each other. Up to now, no rigorous discrimination of these data has been undertaken. Perhaps it is because of this that reliable data on the dependence of the absorption coefficient on frequency are not as yet available. This situation is explained,

on the one hand, by the difficulty of obtaining experimental data of required quality and, on the other by the difficulty of excluding the effect of amplitude decay in the analogous ideally elastic medium from the observed decay of amplitudes, since heterogeneities of actual media may considerably complicate the wavefront geometry.

Absorption properties of hard media have been studied under laboratory conditions on rock samples (Karus, 1958) and on artificial materials (Bokanenko, 1967; Kolsky, 1956). However, in spite of the large number of such investigations, basic significance is attached to experiments on rocks in situ (Vasil'ev, 1962; Gurvich and Gil'bershteyn, 1961; Karus and Pasechnik, 1954; Nersesov, 1960; Nikolayev, 1965; Ogurtsov and Ozerov, 1959; Collins and Lee, 1956; McDonal et al, 1958). As the dynamic interpretation of waves is further developed, the amount of such experimentation increases each year.

Many procedures have been developed for the determination of α. The majority of them are based on the utilization of various wave types (reflected and refracted) registering in surface observations. Let us only mention that the basic difficulties lie in determining the nature of the wave, making certain assumptions on the structure of the medium. Procedures have also been developed for the determination of average values of $\alpha(f)$ from surface observations in conjunction with spectra of direct and reflected waves, surface recorded by one receiver (Kuznetsov, 1967). The direct wave serves as a reference which corrects for the influence of the shot's spectrum, the conditions of reception, and of the heterogeneities of the upper portion of the cross-section. This procedure provides somewhat better possibilities than is the case when only reflected waves are being used. However, here too one has to make many assumptions. In particular, the medium is assumed to be homogeneous and isotropic and the form of the direct wave is assumed to be identical on the surface and in the interior of the medium.

More complete absorption data can be acquired for observations in the interior of the medium where the spectrum of the same wave at many points of the profile may be studied (Berdennikova et al, 1959; Berdennikova and Limbakh, 1966; Zhadin, 1960). The majority of the cited references are investigations of direct longitudinal and transverse waves that are generated by direction-oriented impacts. Unfortunately, such a source has a narrow band low-frequency spectrum which prohibits the study of $\alpha(f)$ in its full broad-frequency range. Thus the α obtained relates to the dominant frequency of the wavelet. In addition, the impact source restricts the depth of peneration. This is perhaps the reason that the basic body of determinations is conducted for the upper portion of the cross-section, i.e., down to 1000 – 1200 m.

The dependence of $\alpha(f)$ can be determined along vertical and inclined rays. Technically, the first procedure is simpler since the seismometer is positioned along the borehole. However, when a small number of channels are used, it is difficult to preserve constant excitation conditions. The application of a large number of channels will permit us to avoid these difficulties and to improve the accuracy of the results.

The method employing vertical rays is applicable for the study of absorption of direct P- and S-waves. Observations of inclined rays require the simultaneous registration in two boreholes and therefore are restricted to work at shallow depths. Such observations permit the use of any kind of source and thus the study of spatial waves of all types within a wide range of frequencies. Since oscillations are excited by a single shot, one may

dispense with the source monitor and still secure more accurate data. To do this, however, it is essential to have adequate knowledge of the ray geometry.

Experience indicates it is very difficult to determine absorption in actual media because of the heterogeneous and thin-layered structure of the media. The data characterize the general decay of amplitudes and involve so-called "effective absorption".

It is possible to obtain the absorption coefficient in some discrete cases in the presence of a thick homogeneous bed. However, carefully executed experiments are then required. Of basic significance is the registration of the same wave and maintaining a constant amplitude spectrum of the source. The spectrum must be monitored over a wide frequency range. Still more difficult is the determination of the dependence of the absorption coefficient on frequency. In order to do this, it is necessary to register the events over a sufficiently wide frequency range (for example, from 5 – 500 hz) and to procure high-quality data that would guarantee the possibility of statistical treatment. Unless these demands are met, attempts to obtain the $\alpha(f)$ relationship hardly makes sense.

Dispersion

The variation of the form of the seismic impulse is not only dictated by the dependence of absorption on frequency but also on the dependence of the phase velocity $c(f)$ of spatial waves on frequency. The absorbing medium is associated with dispersion. For observations in thin-layered media, velocity dispersion may result from interference of waves of different multiplicity. This type of dispersion must be distinguished from dispersion caused by nonideal elasticity in homogeneous and isotropic media. However, absorption properties of actual media have been studied considerably more successfully than dispersion. Only by studying absorption and dispersion together is it possible to develop the theory of absorption of waves in non-ideally elastic media and to obtain compatibility between computed and observed data. Such a study of absorption $\alpha(f)$ and dispersion of velocity $c(f)$ was carried out on rock samples in the laboratory under natural field conditions, and on artificial materials. Let us discuss some of the results.

Zhadin's (1960) observations of direct and transverse waves in boreholes obtained in sandstone indicated a linear dependence $\alpha(f)$ and the absorption decrement $\gamma = 0.25$ over a frequency range of $25 - 100$ hz, whereas he observed practically no dispersion. About the same results were obtained earlier for longitudinal waves in sandstones in the frequency range of $100 - 900$ hz. Wuenschel (1965), using experimental data from Mc-Donal (1958) in clayey shales in the frequency range of $25 - 500$ hz, established a linear dependence $\alpha(f)$ and showed that phase velocities increase with frequency by 2 percent (from 2205 m/sec for 25 hz to 2251 m/sec for 400 hz), i.e., anomalous dispersion of phase velocities takes place. He demonstrated the feasibility of calculating wave dispersion from the known dependence of absorption coefficient on frequency and the availability of the wavelet at a fixed point. Analogous results were obtained by Kolsky (1956). Futterman (1962) made such calculations possible. He derived an analytic formula that related dispersion to absorption for known parameters of wave propagation and amplitudes of the wavelet at one point.

In addition to waves produced by shots, $\alpha(f)$ and $c(f)$ of Rayleigh waves for excitation of stationary oscillations by electromagnetic radiators were studied. Karus and Pasechnik (1954) obtained the dependence $\alpha(f)$ in the frequency range of $80 - 5000$ hz tnat proved to be close to linear for various samples having $\gamma = 0.20$ (jergellites[3]), 0.25 (ferrous cherts), 0.12 (sylvinite), 0.66 (argillaceous soil), and 0.48 (glacierous ice).

Numerous measurements have been made of $\alpha(f)$ and $c(f)$ on artificial materials, metals, and plastics. Bokanenko (1967) studied absorption and dispersion of transverse waves in two media: in weakly absorptive plexiglass ($\gamma = 0.064$) and in highly absorptive vinyl plastic ($\gamma = 0.14$). By carefully conducted experiments, Bokanenko showed that the with frequency, that velocity dispersion indicates anomalous characteristics, and that the relation $c(f)$ increases as the decrement of absorption increases within a fixed frequency interval ($12 - 140$ hz). In the frequency interval of $14 - 140$ khz, in plexiglass, $c(f)$ increases by 1.7 percent, while in vinyl plastic, for which γ is 2.2 times larger than in plexiglass, $c(f)$ increases by 3.2 percent.

In the study of dispersion in vertical profiling, phase velocities may be determined by the direct method which utilizes the spectra of direct waves that are registered along the vertical profile. Phase spectra may be used to construct vertical traveltime curves of phases that easily yield phase velocities.

Thus absorption becomes the decisive factor influencing the form of the wavelet. Data on wave dispersion and its relation to the coefficient of absorption in rock formations are extremely scant and occasionally contradictory. Nonetheless, the majority of authors assume that even if dispersion exists, it is not very pronounced (not more than a few percent for a frequency variation of $10 - 12$ times) and its character is anomalous. As to the quantitative relation of dispersion to the value of the amplitude coefficient, or to the decrement of absorption, data are as yet almost nonexistent.

[3]Transliterated from the Russian.

Chapter 7
LONGITUDINAL REFLECTED AND MULTIPLE WAVES

When the method of reflected waves (MRLW) was developed, it became fundamental in the suite of geophysical methods of exploration for oil and gas. At present, the MRLW is essentially the only procedure used preparatory to the drilling of structures. Most seismic parties in the USSR and abroad use the reflection method. However, as penetration increases and as one proceeds to more complex regions, effectiveness of the method is substantially reduced. One limit of the exploratory capability of the MRLW is the registration of multiples and in many cases it is impossible to identify reflected waves from deep boundaries. Otherwise, multiples may lead to erroneous interpretations of seismic data. Therefore, an appraisal of the exploratory capabilities of the MRLW cannot be accomplished without the study of multiples.

During the past 20 years, a great amount of experimental and theoretical investigation of multiples[1] (Nauka, 1964) was made. And, despite this, multiples still restrict the inherent possibilities of the MRLW. This is because the exploration depth is continuously being increased, so that the relative intensity of singly reflected waves is reduced and becomes commensurable with (and in many regions is even less than) the intensities of multiples associated with major boundaries in the upper portion of the cross-section.

Three aspects comprise the problem of multiples: the study of their kinematic and dynamic characteristics, their identification on seismograms, and their suppression. Application of procedures of interferential reception in particular common-depth-point stacking, and com-

[1]A list of works devoted to the study of multiples contains more than 100 references.

puter-treatment of data, may lead to broadening of the MRLW capabilities. However, the effectiveness of all methods of suppression of multiples depends to a considerable degree on the knowledge of the parameters — the nature, and the mechanism of multiple generation.

Difficulties in the study of multiply reflected waves arise from the kinematic and dynamic characteristics of primary and multiply reflected waves. Observations along the horizontal profile are almost the same, while the regions of registration coincide (Gal'perin, 1965a). For surface observations, as a rule, the multiples can be identified on the seismograms, while it is not always possible to determine the nature, the parameters (primarily, the relative intensities), and the boundaries of the cross-section with which they are associated. In this respect, VSP is of particular interest.

The study of reflected and multiple waves by observation at interior points of the medium (Gal'perin and Frolova, 1961) shows that the regions where reflected and multiple waves exist are sharply separated. The kinematics of these waves are also substantially different (see Chapter 3). Along the vertical profile, upward reflected waves and downward reflected multiples propagating into the depth of the medium are registered separately. VSP permits the observations and study of the process of formation and propagation of reflected and multiple waves, and appraisal of the influence that various elements of the cross-section have on the formation of the field of reflected and multiple waves.

1. Reflected and multiple waves are wave types that register on the later portion of seismograms along vertical and horizontal profiles. The dominant reflected and multiple waves are related

to definite elements of the cross-section (frequently they are separate thin layers or packets of thin layers) and can produce stratigraphic correlation. In the background are waves which possess a considerably smaller amplitude and are related to media with weak velocity differentiation.

2. In most regions, the reflecting boundaries are located at all depths accessible to VSP observations, down to the crystalline basement. Therefore, problems of increasing penetration in MRLW are fully relevant.

3. In a thin-layered medium, the forms of reflected waves may differ greatly from the form of the incident wave and they strongly depend on the frequency content of the latter as well as on the structure of the reflecting packet. These concepts are also confirmed by theoretical calculations (Berzon et al, 1969). The duration of the reflected wave under these conditions is sharply increased. Reflected waves from various layers and packets in the cross-section may differ substantially from each other. Even a comparatively small variation of the frequency content of the incident pulse may lead to a considerable change in the shape of the reflected wave. Therefore, ghosts may differ a great deal from the shape of the primary reflected wave. in some discrete cases (even for a constant impulse of the incident wave and for the same structure of the heterogeneous packet), the form of the wavelet of the reflected wave may vary with distance (angle of incidence). In a detailed study it is not always permissible to approximate the heterogeneous packet by a homogeneous layer, and it is necessary in many cases to account for the interior structure of the packet.

4. The boundaries located in the upper portion of the cross-section, particularly in the ZLV, are the primary source of multiples. The existence of even one or

two such horizons may be quite sufficient to determine the wavefield emerging at the surface and in the interior at all depths accessible to observation. The most common unwanted waves are the partially multiple waves that have undergone intermediate reflection at boundaries of the upper portion of the cross-section (peg-leg multiples).[2]

5. In some regions, multiples may form at great depths. The reflecting boundary may also be the top of the basement embedded at a comparatively great depth (e.g., about 3500 m). Multiples may be observed at interior points of the medium even when surface seismograms are completely void of regular waves. In fact, lack of regular waves on surface seismograms does not indicate an absence of reflecting horizons in the cross-section. On the contrary, it indicates a large number of horizons.

6. The reflecting properties of the ZLV exert a very pronounced influence on the intensities of multiples. The bottom of the ZLV is the most contrasting boundary in the cross-section and a significant portion of energy arriving from depth is again returned by the latter to the depth of the medium. The dominant multiples undergo an intermediate reflection at the bottom of the ZLV. Under conditions of monotonic increase of velocity in the upper portion of the cross-section with a weakly contrasing ZLV, a comparatively low level of multiples is characteristic even in cases in which pronounced reference boundaries exist. Reflections from the surface are distinguished by comparatively low intensities and low-frequency compositions.

7. Observations at the surface and at accessible depths reveal that the greater portion of energy recorded on seismograms is from waves generated at boundaries in the upper portion of the cross-section. The influence of the upper

[2]Translator's interpretation.

portion of the cross-section may differ in each case; however, it usually complicates seismograms so that it becomes difficult to identify waves issuing from deep horizons. Even under conditions of weak velocity differentiation of the medium and no sharp boundaries, seismograms may indicate a large number of various unwanted waves of a different nature. These will probably be longitudinal and transverse refracted and multiple waves. The existence of multiples is explained by the presence in the medium of a vertical velocity gradient and by the excitation of transverse waves by the shot. The intensity of these waves occasionally is commensurate with, or in excess of, the longitudinal waves. Such a field of unwanted waves prohibits the enhancement of reflected waves from deep horizons.

8. Surface waves may possess high intensity and may dominate surface seismograms. However, these waves decay rapidly as they recede from the surface and are not recorded on VSP seismograms at a depth of approximately one wavelength. The transformation of a portion of the energy of spatial waves[3] into secondary surface waves, and surface waves into body waves (Tatel, 1954; Tatel and Tuve, 1954, 1958) as yet have not been studied sufficiently. Even for observations at great depths, the influence of such a transformation on the wavefield is probably significant. It is essential to pursue further specialized research on wavefields in the upper portion of the cross-section in order to study their effect on surface seismograms.

9. The study of parameters of reflected and multiple waves permits the objective appraisal of various procedures of multiple suppression and selection of optimal systems of observation in each situation.

To illustrate how reflected and multiple waves may be studied by VSP, we shall

[3]Translator's note: body waves.

discuss wavefields for two models of the media (see Figures 60 and 61). The cross-sections of the upper portion of the cross-section contain a sharp boundary. However, surface seismograms for the two cases differ substantially. For the first cross-section, a small number of primary horizons is characteristic and, for that reason, surface seismograms indicate the registration of a large number of regular multiples. For the second cross-section, a large number of primary horizons is characteristic. On surface seismograms, neither reflected nor multiple waves can be tracked. If on the first cross-section the entire field of multiples is basically related to the boundaries of the upper portion of the cross-section, then on the second, multiples are also generated down to the basement. In addition, we shall examine wavefields under conditions of nonexistence of sharp horizons in the cross-section but for a monotonic increase of velocity with depth.

LONGITUDINAL REFLECTED AND MULTIPLE WAVES ALONG A VERTICAL PROFILE

The process of generation of multiples shall be illustrated by means of the first model. After reaching the boundary, the direct wave is reflected and returns to the surface (see Figures 1 and 3). Further on, reflecting from the bottom of the ZLV, it again impinges on the interface (Figure 71a). The seismogram corresponding to the section of the profile that crosses the boundary indicates (Figures 71a and 71b) the emergence of an intense reflected wave t^3. All subsequent waves impinging on the boundary (regardless of their nature and trajectory) are reflected so that in a subsequent portion of the record, a large number of reflected waves is in evidence. On those sections of the seismogram (Figure 71b) where these waves do not interfere with each other, it is evident that for each incident wave there is a corresponding reflected

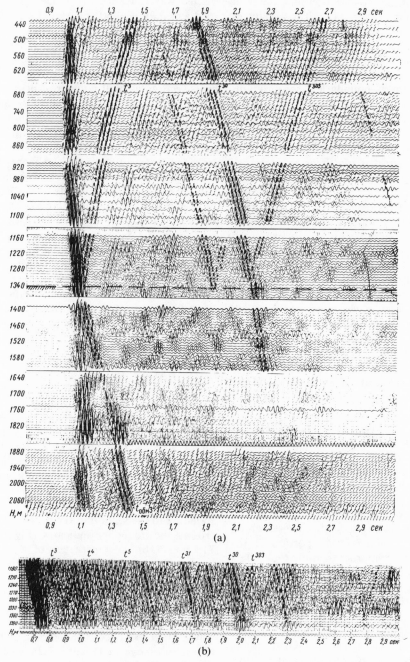

(a)

(b)

FIG. 71. (a, b) VSP seismograms.

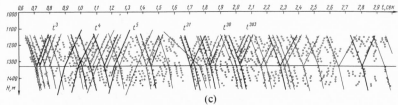

(c)

FIG. 71 (c) Vertical traveltime curves for a section of the borehole crossing boundary 3.

wave and a down-traveling refracted wave. A large number of waves is propagated toward the surface. These waves are again reflected at the bottom of the ZLV. These downward-reflected waves are commensurate in intensity to the incident waves; i.e., most of the energy impinging on the ZLV is returned into the depth of the medium. This process is multiply repeated and, as a result, the vertical profile registers a whole sequence of multiples that are reflected downward and upward. The latter are registered on surface seismograms. At the surface, waves of third, fourth, and higher orders of multiplicity may register.

Reflection coefficient. — The relative intensity and the form of reflected and multiple waves near the boundaries are determined by parameters of the incident wave, the values of the reflection coefficients K at the boundaries, and by their dependence on frequency $K(f)$. The latter function in turn depends on velocity ratios, densities, thickness of boundary layers, and angle of incidence of the wave on the boundary. When the reflecting boundary is an interface of thick homogeneous layers, the phase of the reflection coefficient for subcritical incidence angles is equal to zero or to π and is independent of frequency. The reflected wave duplicates the form of the incident wave. In a thin-layered medium, the reflection coefficient is a function of frequency, and the form of the reflected wave differs from the incident wave (Berzon et al, 1962; Gurvich, 1952). Knowledge of dependence $K(f)$ obtained

directly from field observation data permits appraisal of the intensity waves of various multiplicity.

Various procedures for the determination of K have been developed for surface observations (Berzon et al, 1962) as well as for observations at interior points of the medium (Mitrofanov and Vavilova, 1961; Pogonyailo, 1966; Jolly, 1953; Levin and Lynn, 1958). Surface observations cannot yield sufficiently accurate data on reflection coefficients. VSP permits the determination of $K(f)$ from observations of the direct wave at various points of the profile. Furthermore, K may be determined by comparing the form of direct and reflected waves at a particular point. K is obtained from records of the direct and reflected waves at points situated at such distances from boundaries at which the reflected wave has already emerged from the region of interference with the direct wave. Realizing that absorption evaluation involves large errors, the latter quantity should exert far less influence on K than in its determination from surface observations. In addition, for observations near the boundaries, the actual incident and reflected waves are used to determine K; this is not always possible from surface observations.

For example, the results of reflection coefficient determination associated with a packet of thin layers depends on frequency for two angles of incidence. For the determination of $K(f)$ records of waves from two shotpoints are used at 100 and 1200 m (Figure 72). The depths

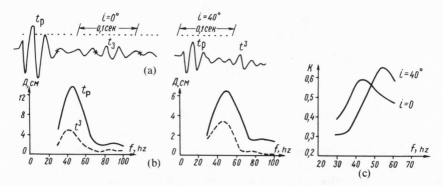

FIG. 72. Well no. 2, Staro-Minsk. (a) Records of direct and reflected waves for normal incidence (SP 100 m) and inclined incidence (SP 1200 m). (b) Corresponding wave spectra. (c) Spectra of relfection coefficient.

are 700 – 800, 900 – 920, and 1080 – 1100 m. The angles of incidence of these shotpoints at a depth of 1100 m are 0 and 40 degrees, respectively. The reflection coefficient K exhibits a sharply defined maximum that is shifted toward higher frequencies as the angle of incidence increases (from 43 hz for an angle of 0 degrees to 54 hz for an angle of 40 degrees). The peak values of the reflection coefficient are 0.58 and 0.65. The form of the reflection coefficient spectrum indicates the reflecting boundary is not a "thick" layer.

A procedure has been developed for the determination of K from records of direct and reflected waves not at a single point. The reflected wave is tracked over the entire interval and the direct wave is recorded at the region of the reflecting boundary (Pogonyailo, 1966). The determination of K and other parameters based on the dynamics of waves and registering on the subsequent portion of the record by VSP is very difficult because of interference phenomena and the impossibility of resolving reflected waves in their pure form.

REFLECTED AND MULTIPLE WAVES IN MEDIA WITH INDIVIDUAL THIN LAYERS OF INCREASED VELOCITY

An example of reflected and multiple waves in media with thin high-velocity layers is the Staro-Minsk platform which has a cross-section associated with several thin layers (see Figure 60). The first layer ($H_v = 270$ m) consists of sandstone with a boundary velocity $v_b = 2500$ m/sec and 11 m thick. It is located in a gradiented bed of sandy-clay deposits, the average velocity being $v_{av} = 1800$ m/sec (Figure 73). The second layer, a packet of thin limestone interstratifications alternating with terrigenous deposits of Paleocene age, is embedded in sandy-clay formations at a depth of 1334 – 1380 m (well no. 42). In well no. 52 (SWL cross-section shown in Figure 73), the depth of the top of the layer is approximately 1260 m. Basic information for the layers is listed in Table 2.

In addition to the above two layers, the cross-section also comprises a thin layer of chalk at a depth of 1850 m. If a certain variation in the depth of the embedded layers is discounted, it may be assumed that the cross-section extends over the area to a sufficiently reliable degree. The wavefields studied for the other boreholes (well nos. 2, 6, 20, and 42) are identical for practical purposes.

The presence of two thin layers in the upper portion of the cross-section, which persists over the area with large velocity contrasts, exerts a decisive influence on

Table 2*

No. of layers	H_v, M	d, M	v_{P2}, m/sec	v_{P1}	v_{P3}	$v_{P1\,av}$	$v_{P1\,av}/v_{S1\,av}$	$v_{P1\,av}/v_{P2\,av}$	d/λ_2	H_v/λ_1
1	270	6 – 11	2200 – 2600	1800	1800	1600	3.5 – 4.0	0.7 – 0.8	0.12 – 0.32	8
2	1330	25	4890	2500	3000	2000	2 – 7	0.49	0.20 – 0.24	2 – 6

*Index 2 designates the average parameters of packets of layers; indices 1 and 3 refer to the average parameters of layers (the thickness is about one wavelength) that overlie and underlie the packet, respectively.

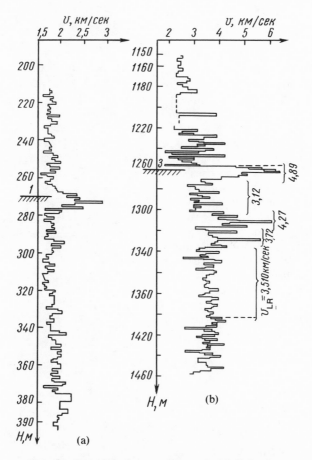

FIG. 73. Staro-Minsk, according to A. M. Epinat'yeva, 1967. (a) Velocity cross-section by means of SWL along the profile section crossing boundary 1 of well no. 42. (b) Same, for boundary 3 of well no. 52.

the wavefield observed on surface seismograms as well as in the medium. Observations at large depths outside the region of the registration of multiples indicate reflections from horizons located at great depths and represent information of geologic significance. These reflections are not evident on surface seismograms. Application of frequency selectivity increases the penetration of the investigation.

Wave pattern for surface observation

A large number of regular waves is characteristic of seismic surface records of the vertical component. These waves continuously follow one another for almost all record times, i.e., up to 4.0 sec (Figure 74a). The majority of the waves are well correlated along the profile for 2 – 3 km, forming continuous lineups. Numerous regions of interference are evident, for which the waves are not resolved, that form a prolonged train of quasi-sinusoidal oscillations. Horizontal traveltime curves of the waves consist of hyperbolic curves of regular form which fill the entire traveltime curve plane (Figure 75). Records obtained for various levels of amplification, without time-varying control (Figure 74b), indicate the amplitudes of the waves are markedly different. In subsequent arrivals, two waves can be discriminated according to amplitude: t^1 at 0.3 sec and t^3 at 1.3 sec. Wave t^1 is dominant on the initial portion of the seismogram and is reliably traced for 1.5 km where it enters the region of first arrivals and interferes with the first wave. Wave t^3 dominates the next portion of the record and can be tracked over the entire interval of registration, i.e., to 3.5 km.

The determination of the nature of the waves on surface seismograms and identification of singly reflected waves from great depths are implemented with the aid of VSP data.

Wave pattern along the vertical profile

Let us examine the singly reflected

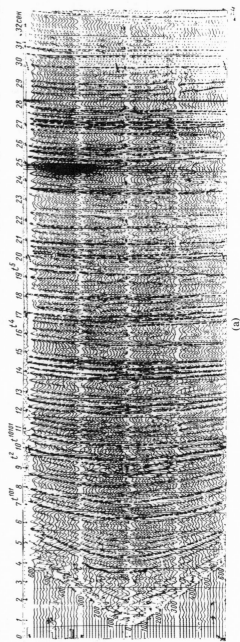

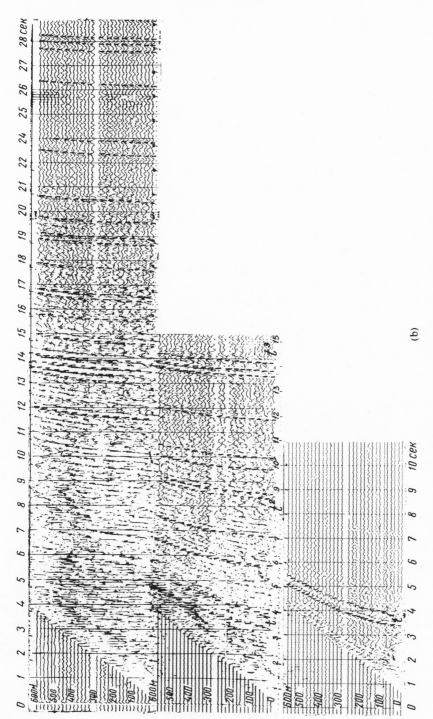

FIG. 74. (a) Surface seismograms obtained with ECA and ACA. (b) For different constant amplifications.

(b)

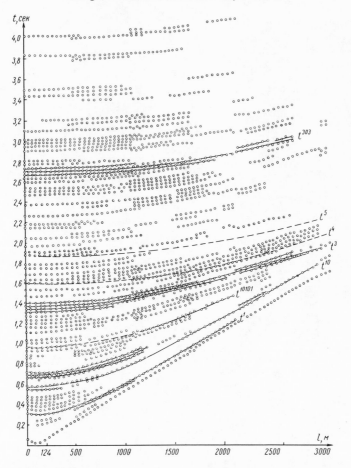

FIG. 75. Observed horizontal traveltime curves of longitudinal reflected and multiple waves, and computed traveltime curves for t^4 and t^5 waves.

waves associated with the two thin layers.

Singly reflected waves. — Wave t^1, reflected from the first thin layer ($H_v = 270$ m), exhibits high intensity. On the record of the vertical component, its intensity is no less than that of the direct wave. Wave t^1 is distinguished by its high-frequency composition. This is well illustrated by the record of its multiple t^{10} that after intermediate reflection at the bottom of the ZLV is reliably resolved even at depths of 1440 – 1900 m, for high pass filtering only (Figure 76); i.e., when

almost no other waves are registered.

Wave t^3 is associated with the top of the Paleocene ($H_v = 1334$ m) and is also a high-intensity reflected wave. It is reliably registered on seismograms from all shotpoints for a distance interval of 100 – 2500 m. On channels with minimum amplification (Figure 77) it is continuously trackable along the entire vertical profile and is reliably correlated with the wave along the horizontal profile appearing at $t = 1.3$ sec. For large separations (SP 2500 m), wave t^3 is recorded

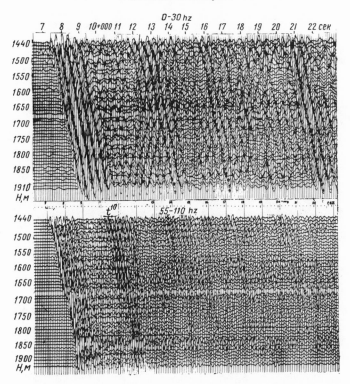

FIG. 76. Seismograms for two filter settings (0-30 and 55-110 hz) illustrating frequency composition of t^{10} wave.

as a transcritically reflected wave.

Waves reflected from other boundaries of the cross-section possess comparatively low intensities and may be tracked only at distinct sections of the vertical profile, i.e., in the vicinity of the boundaries. Moving away from these horizons, correlation becomes disrupted.

Multiply reflected waves. — Figure 77 shows records of multiples obtained for broadband filtering and for five levels of amplification. The neighboring amplifications differ by a factor of about three. Waves t^3 and its multiple t^{30}, reflected from the bottom of the ZLV, are marked on the seismogram: wave t^{30} is reliably trackable down to boundary 3 on channels with the second level of amplification. Also indicated is the fully developed

multiple wave t^{303} reflected from boundary 3 and reliably tracked on channels with the third level of amplification to the surface where it is again reflected from the bottom of the ZLV and returned to the depth of the medium. Wave t^{3030} is readable on channels with maximal amplification. Further increase of record duration (increase of instrument sensitivity or of weight of charge) would permit the registration of waves of higher multiplicity. In an analogous manner the process of formation of multiples associated with boundary 1 can be developed.

The graph of amplitudes of the direct, the reflected, and the multiple waves (Figure 78) yields the following conclusions:

1. The amplitudes of all waves propa-

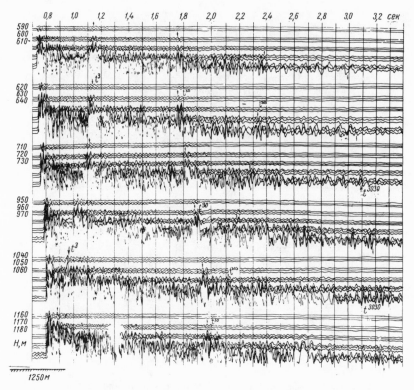

FIG. 77. Seismograms of discrete sections of the profile (for five levels of amplification) illustrating multiples (SP 1200 m, well no. 20, Staro-Minsk).

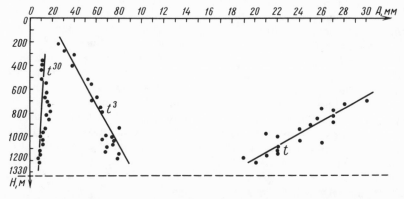

FIG. 78. Graphs showing the variation of amplitudes of recordings of the vertical component with depth for the direct t waves, the reflected t^3 waves, and the multiple t^{30} waves (SP 100 m).

gating between the boundaries of separation vary continuously. The amplitude of the direct wave decreases by about 30 percent over the depth interval of 800 – 1200 m. The decay of wave amplitudes between the boundaries permits the determination of effective absorption.

2. Upon reflection, wave amplitudes vary discontinuously. The graph indicates that amplitude jumps for reflection from the lower boundary are larger than for reflection from the ZLV. Comparison of amplitudes and spectra of the incident and reflected waves, permits the determination of the coefficient of reflection and thus the appraisal of the intensity and form of the reflected wave (see Figure 72).

3. The intensity of multiples decreases sharply as the order of multiplicity increases. However, each multiple dominates in the time interval in which it registers (see Figure 77). This means that the intensities of multiples exceed those of singly reflected waves so that an increase of record duration in this situation does not contribute to the enhancement of primaries reflected from deeper horizons.

Frequency features of multiples along a vertical profile are of special interest (Figure 79). In spite of large scattering of values, Figure 79a indicates that the frequency content of waves from the nearest shotpoint contains the highest frequencies. As the separation from the

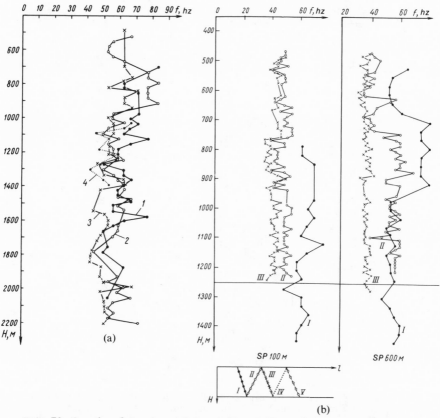

FIG. 79. Graphs of dominant frequencies (well no. 20 Staro-Minsk).

(Continued on p. 164.)

source and the depth of the point of observation increase, the frequency content of the record decreases.

Comparison of the dominant frequencies of waves of different multiplicity permits the following conclusions:

1. From all shotpoints, waves of different multiplicity have different dominant frequencies (Figure 79b). The wave with the highest frequency is 70 hz. As the order of multiplicity increases, the dominant frequency decreases. Thus, the average value of the dominant frequency for t^3 is about 64 hz; t^{30} is approximately 50 hz; wave t^{303}, 47 hz; and t^{3030} is approximately 40 hz. A discontinuous variation of dominant frequency occurs when waves are reflected from bound-

aries. In the process of propagation between boundaries, the visible frequency of waves varies smoothly for the observation interval of 750 m.

2. Waves reflected from different boundaries or those with different multiplicities from a given boundary show a frequency jump of varied magnitude.

3. The variation of frequencies of multiples as a function of l is not pronounced and the dominant reduction of frequencies is not significant as the separation from the source increases. Thus, in the interval of distances from 300 – 1200 m, the doubly reflected wave indicates a frequency reduction not exceeding 3 – 6 hz (Figure 79c). An analogous situation may be demonstrated for waves of a higher

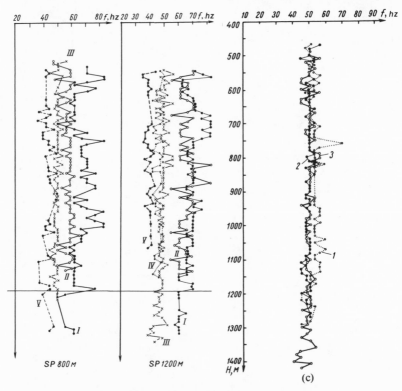

FIG. 79. Graphs of dominant frequencies (well no. 20, Staro-Minsk). (a) For the first wave from (1) SP 100 m; (2) from SP 600 m; (3) from SP 1200 m; (4) from SP 2500 m. (b) For the direct and reflected waves of various orders of multiplicity. (c) For the doubly reflected wave (1) from SP 300 m; (2) from SP 800 m; (3) from SP 1200 m.

order of multiplicity.

Multiples on records obtained with ACA in no way differ from other waves and are registered for all distances. Their traveltime curves are reliably identified from all shotpoints and also provide correlation with surface traveltime curves which permits identification of multiples on surface seismograms. Figure 74b shows multiples associated with only two basic horizons, 1 and 3. Nothing but reflected and multiple waves from the two thin layers can be shown successfully on the seismograms (excluding the reflected waves associated with the shallowest horizons, registered on the initial portion of the seismograms).

In addition to the basic dominant multiples that could be tracked and the nature of which could be determined, the seismograms contain numerous superimposed waves of various types formed as a result of interference. Waves of this type are not considered to be dominant waves.

Thus the existence of two thin high-velocity layers in the upper portion of the cross-section plays a decisive role in the formation of the wave pattern. It is not possible to identify a single wave from deep horizons on seismograms from the horizontal profile.

Waves reflected from deep boundaries

Observations made at great depths enable us to resolve waves reflected from deep boundaries. The most stable waves are associated with the two boundaries located at depths 1850 m (t^4) and 2310 m (t^5). For practical purposes, wave t^4 cannot be tracked along the in-line profile. Above the Paleocene layer ($H_v = 1334$ m), wave t^4 is contained in the region of interference with multiply reflected waves along the entire profile. Below the Paleocene layer, wave correlation is repeatedly disrupted by converted and multiple waves that propagate downward. The wave appears preeminently in the immediate vicinity of the boundary. As l

increases, relative intensity of the wave increases, it is dominant on recordings of the Z-component; and it can be tracked over a substantial section of the vertical profile, not just below the Paleocene layer (Figure 80). Vertical traveltime curves of reflected and converted transmitted waves for four shotpoints are compiled on a single diagram (Figure 81).

Wave t^5 is the most intense. It is as-

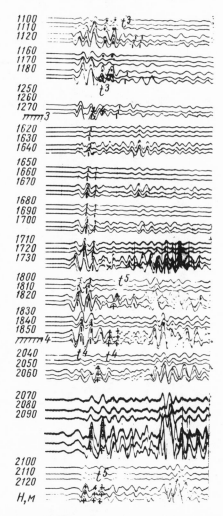

FIG. 80. Initial portion of record for two levels of amplification (SP 2500 m, well no. 42, Staro-Minsk).

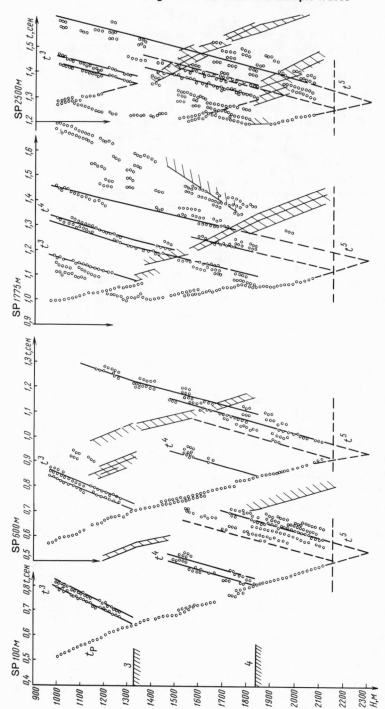

FIG. 81. Vertical traveltime curves of waves reflected from deep boundaries (well no. 42, Staro-Minsk). Crosshatching indicates regions of registration of converted transmitted waves that disrupt correlation of reflected waves.

sociated with Jurassic-Triassic deposits. In contrast to the t^4 wave, it is more stable and it registers at great depths from the nearest shotpoints (100 and 600 m). From SP 100 m, the intensity of the t^5 wave is equivalent to the intensity of the multiple and, as a result of interference, its correlation is disrupted (Figure 81). From SP 600 m, t^5 also appears near the boundary. Above that horizon, however, its correlation is disrupted. From SP 2500 m, t^5 appears only on a few sections of the profile for which converted downward transmitted waves do not register (see Figure 80). In the region where multiples are registered, it becomes impossible to track t^5 or t^4 along the vertical profile. Since t^5 is of considerable geologic interest, specialized experiments were conducted to appraise the possibilities of its enhancement and tracking along the vertical profile in the region of registration of multiples.

The study of spectra of reflected and multiple waves demonstrates the effectiveness of frequency selectivity in the suppression of multiples. Since the reflection coefficient associated with a thin layer (boundary 3) involving basic multiples possesses a peak frequency of 45 – 55 hz (see Figure 72), an attempt was made to enhance waves from the top of the Jurassic-Triassic bed in the region of much lower frequencies.

As shown in Figure 82, for a broad passband (lower trace), the reflected wave t^3 is well established at a time of approximately 0.8 sec; it possesses a clear first arrival and is dominant on the subsequent portion of the record. The visible frequency of the wave is about 60 hz. The center trace, corresponding to a passband characteristic of 15 – 30 hz does not indicate the reflected wave. Naturally, the upper trace (passband of 5 – 15 hz) shows no evidence of the reflected wave. Despite the difference in channel amplification, the recording of reflected waves is characterized by their lower intensity on channels emphasizing lower frequencies.

The composite low-frequency seismogram (Figure 83a) indicates that the wave t^5 reflected from the Jurassic-Triassic bed ($H_v = 2310$ m) can be tracked along the profile section that overlaps the registration of multiples. The visible frequency of that wave is about 12 – 14 hz. On the vertical traveltime curves (Figure 83b) the arrival times of waves recorded by low-frequency passband filtering are designated by bold symbols, in contrast to those obtained for broadband filtering. The seismograms and the traveltime curves indicate that low-frequency records are associated with considerably reduced multiples. Therefore, the low-frequency waves can be tracked more reliably along the investigated section. The registration of waves reflected from the top of the Jurassic-Triassic bed and recorded within the above frequency band

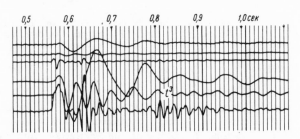

FIG. 82. Record of reflected wave t^3 for three filter settings and two levels of amplification ($H = 1000$ m, natural frequency of seismometer 4 hz.).

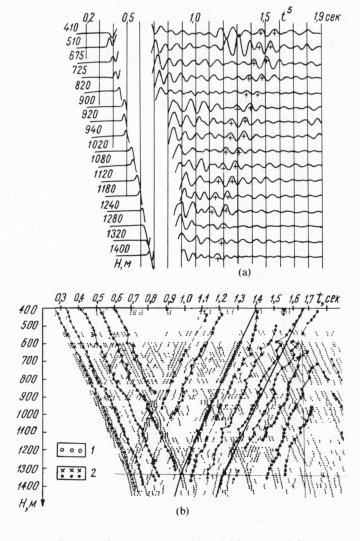

FIG. 83. (a) Seismograms and (b) traveltime curves for waves registered on low-frequency channels. For purposes of descriptiveness, waves registered for conventional (1) and low-frequency (2) passbands, are specially designated (SP 100 m, well no. 42, Staro-Minsk).

guarantees a more reliable correlation and improves the effectiveness of seismic observation. These results were confirmed by surface observations (Berzon, 1967).

The possibility of resolving the Jurassic-Triassic bed was initially questioned since there was no borehole that penetrated the bed and waves reflected from the bed could not be successfully observed in the region of multiples. Subsequent VSP efforts on a section crossing the formation indicated the section contains reflecting horizons that show weak waves

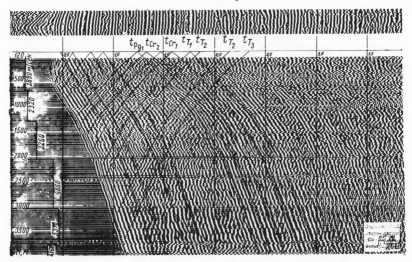

FIG. 84. Seismograms for horizontal and vertical profiles (well no. 52, Staro-Minsk).

reflected from these horizons (Figure 84). However, their continuous tracking to the surface is impossible. A large amount of experimental work is necessary to understand the parameters of these waves so that optimal systems for their enhancement may be selected. It is quite possible that the selection of a single frequency is insufficient.

REFLECTED AND MULTIPLE WAVES IN HIGH-VELOCITY CARBONATE CROSS-SECTIONS

Multiples in the carbonate cross-section may be evident even when surface seismograms are altogether void of regular waves. These waves may be associated with horizons both in the upper portion of the cross-section and at great depths.

Let us examine the pattern for the Russian platform. It is known that seismogeologic conditions for the right bank of the Volga near Saratov and Volgograd are extremely complex. In spite of a large amount of work, seismic exploration of terrigenous Devonian deposits remains largely ineffective. This is because reflected waves associated with deep boundaries cannot be identified with surface observations. Surface seismograms exhibit few regular waves, except for the stable and dominant wave reflected from the top of the Paleozoic where the terrigenous bed interfaces with carbonate deposits. The absence of regular waves on the seismograms, i.e., of waves associated with deep boundaries, was not explained in a sufficiently convincing manner. In many cases, this was explained by thin layering, nonconformity of the thickness of the thin layers in the cross-section of Devonian deposits, and by the irregularity of boundaries in the frequency range utilized in MRLW. Or it was explained by a frequency shift of dominant frequencies in the spectrum of reflected waves toward a region of very high frequencies so that the waves are dispersed and absorbed in the process of propagation toward the surface. The danger of such conclusions, making further exploration by MRLW unattractive, is obvious.

Considering the great economic value of the problem, it was important to study the reasons for the lack of reflected waves on the surface by using VSP. Observations conducted in 1966 for two areas on the right bank of the Volga at Volgograd, where there are sedimentary deposits with drastically different thickness, produced some new data on the wave pattern. It is first essential to establish the existence of boundaries at great depths (in particular in the terrigenous Devonian bed) that may produce sufficiently intense reflected waves. Furthermore, should such horizons be discovered, reasons for the lack of reflected waves on surface seismograms should be determined.

Reflected waves connected with deep boundaries

Observations by VSP near the top of the terrigenous Devonian bed (at depths to 2700 m) demonstrated that waves reflected from several horizons of the above formation can be identified in spite of the complexity of the wavefield. These waves are difficult to record on the vertical profile because of interference with numerous incident waves. Nevertheless, at discrete sections (Figure 85), reflected waves are sufficiently intense and their nature is unquestionable. Since surface seismograms do not allow tracking of reflected waves, the waves were tracked in horizontal directions at interior points of the medium (so-called "level-reduced" profiling). In this case, the wavefield is somewhat simpler than at the surface. The level-reduced traveltime curve permits one to identify the waves and to acquire supplementary data on their nature. Level-reduced traveltime curves, constructed for the cross-section having a high velocity carbonate formation (Figure 86), confirm the registration of re-

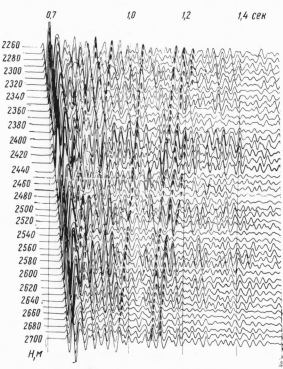

FIG. 85. Initial portion of VSP seismogram (SP 70 m, $h = 125$ m, well no. 90, Kudinov).

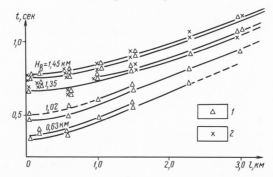

FIG. 86. Level-reduced traveltime curves (1) $H = 0.5$
km, and (2) $H = 1.0$ km. Time shift $\Delta t = 0.12$ sec
(well no. 1, Kletsko-Pochtov).

flected waves from the terrigenous Devonian bed.

The presence of reflecting horizons in
the terrigenous Devonian bed is of practical interest. In addition, numerous multiply reflected waves are formed at deep
boundaries. The seismogram (Figure 87)
was obtained without using any means
for improvement of wave correlation. Except for the incident wave and the wave
reflected from the bottom of the hole
($H = 2740$ m) and propagating along the
borehole fluid with low velocity, the entire seismogram is entirely "clogged" by
incident and multiply reflected waves. In

essence, all incident waves on the seismograms reflect from deep boundaries
and return to the surface. This abundance
of waves interfere with each other and it
is thus difficult to decipher the wave
pattern. All singly reflected waves involving the sedimentary formation are distinguished by high frequencies, a fact that
is well established by variable density
records. The first intense low-frequency
wave, sharply established against the
background of earlier reflected waves,
apparently represents the wave reflected
from the crystalline basement located at
a depth of 3400 m. The majority of the

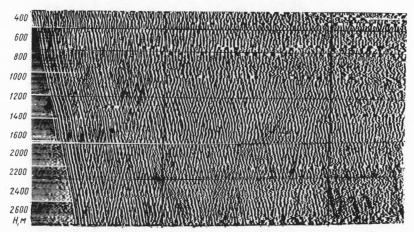

FIG. 87. VSP seismogram illustrating reflected and multiple waves associated with deep
boundaries in sedimentary bed (SP 70 m, filter 25-35 hz, well no. 90, Kudinov).

upward reflected multiples, registering behind the above wave, are distinguished by their comparatively low-frequency content. It is clear, however, that each of these waves can be reinforced by reflections from boundaries located above the basement. This is not significant here since it was important to demonstrate that intense multiples may be associated with boundaries located at great depths in the immediate neighborhood of the basement as well as at the top of the basement itself.

Directional reception permitted an increase in the number of resolvable waves on seismograms, and the majority of these waves may be traced along the entire profile (Figure 88). All these waves complicate the wave pattern for surface observations. However, because the upper portion of the cross-section causes a large number of multiple and converted

waves, it is still of decisive significance in the structure of the wavefield.

Wavefield associated with the upper portion of the cross-section

In other sectors of the southeastern portion of the Russian platform, the presence in the upper portion of the cross-section of boundaries with a pronounced velocity contrast is characteristic. Such a boundary is the top of the Paleozoic at which terrigenous deposits are replaced by carbonates. The boundary is stable over an enormous area, but its depth varies by several hundred meters over a large portion of the area.

VSP observations were conducted in a specially drilled borehole that hit the top of the Paleozoic at a depth of 374 m. The hole was cased and cemented to the top, allowing the acquisition of VSP records along the entire profile. The records were free of drilling noise. A combination sys-

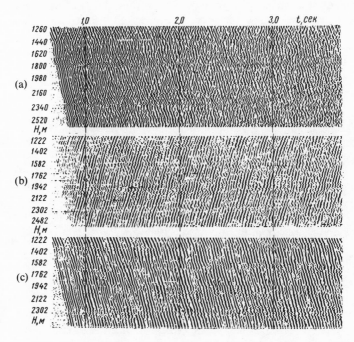

FIG. 88. (a) VSP seismograms; directional reception for (b) upward reflected waves, and (c) downward reflected waves. (SP 200 m, well no. 90, Kudinov.)

tem was produced that consisted of one horizontal and eight vertical profiles at an interval of 0 – 2000 m. Borehole observations were made with a three-point (Z-component) probe and a three-component symmetrical installation. The horizontal profile was made with a three-component XYZ installation. Both oscillographic and magnetic recordings over wide dynamic and frequency ranges were obtained, and source conditions were carefully monitored.

To produce the velocity model according to P- and S-waves, observations were made of directional horizontal explosions and impact sources. A detailed structure of the uppermost portion of the cross-section was obtained from data of velocity shooting, vertical profiling, and SWL.

These observations showed that the basic elements of the cross-section are the bottom of the ZLV ($H_v = 16$ m), at which a sharp velocity contrast from 560 – 1800 m/sec occurs, and the top of the Paleozoic ($H_v = 370$ m) with a velocity contrast from 1880 – 4000 m/sec. The sandy-clay bed contained between these boundaries is not well differentiated by longitudinal and transverse waves. The cross-section also exhibits two thin interstratifications of sandstone with comparatively small velocity discontinuities (see Figure 129).

Wave pattern. — Data obtained over the vertical profile are distinguished by their complex wavefield involving numerous waves of various types. The fundamental laws governing the wavefield are mainly associated with the presence in the cross-section of a pronounced horizon that constitutes the top of the Paleozoic.

Initial portion of record. — From the nearest shotpoints (40 and 200 m) the first wave to register on VSP seismograms is the direct incident wave, followed by a sequence of multiply reflected waves associated with the boundaries in the upper portion of the cross-section. The most intense multiple is the ghost (shown on

the record[4] from SP 200 m in Figure 89). The apparent frequency of that wave is somewhat lower than the first wave and its intensity is one half. A large group of incident waves are reflected from the top of the Paleozoic. On seismograms from SP 40 m, tracking of these waves is impeded by waves t_{FL} that occupy the entire seismogram. On records from SP 200 m, the reflected waves are already well established. These waves are reflected from the bottom of the ZLV and form complicated, intense, prolonged oscillations. On variable density records, wave correlation of a complicated interferential wave pattern is considerably improved. As l increases, the wave pattern for the initial portion of the record becomes more complex. From SP 400 m, first arrivals of the direct wave are replaced by the refracted wave associated with that boundary on the profile section that directly adjoins the top of the Paleozoic ($H = 360 - 380$ m). As the separation increases (SP 500 and 750 m), the region of registrations of the first arrivals of the refracted wave increases ($H = 230 - 380$ m). On the initial portion of the record, the refracted, the direct, and the transcritically reflected waves interfere with each other. The transcritically reflected waves are so intense that the direct wave is almost lost in their background.

From SP 1000 and 1500 m, the wave refracting in the Paleozoic registers as the first wave over the entire profile. It does not interfere with other waves and its form is stably preserved along the profile. There is no indication of the direct wave. The transcritically reflected wave exhibits high intensity and generates multiples. Further increasing the separation l (SP 2000 m), the initial portion of the seismogram shows that the interval occupied

[4]The initial portion of the seismograms obtained without time-varying amplitude control is shown in Figure 31.

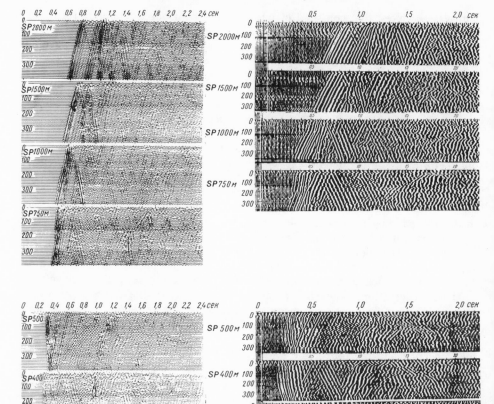

FIG. 89. VSP seismograms (well no. 90a, Kudinov).

by refracted waves is extended and that the region of registration of the trans-critically reflected wave, and the multiples associated with the latter, is transferred toward large time values. As the order of the multiples increases, the correlation of waves becomes impaired.

Subsequent portion of record. — The subsequent portion of the record indicates a complex wavefield that is caused by a superposition of numerous waves of different types. In addition to longitudinal waves, the seismograms (of the Z-component) also establish converted and transverse waves. As *l* increases, the number and intensity of multiply reflected waves increases.

For the analysis of the complex observed wavefield, vector seismograms were obtained of various apparent velocities (Figure 90) of basic recorded waves. Each wave impinging from above upon the top of the Paleozoic generates two reflected waves, i.e., the individual type[5] and the converted waves. Each wave impinging from below upon that same boundary also generates two transmitted waves — individual and converted. All these waves, regardless of their nature, in turn generate two waves when they are reflected from the bottom of the ZLV. In essence, the growth of the number of waves is avalanche-like.

[5]Translator's note: The author calls this a "monotypical" wave.

Converted waves are also very important in the formation of the wavefield. The identification and the tracking of converted waves on records of the three-component installations (Figure 91) may be accomplished more reliably than on records of the vertical component. From vertical traveltime curves of dominant converted waves registered from various shotpoints (Figure 92), it is evident that the waves primarily tracked from the nearest shotpoints are converted reflected waves. As *l* increases and refracted waves appear as first arrivals, converted transmitted waves are indicated on the initial portion of the record. From remote shotpoints (for example, from 1500 m), both transmitted and converted waves were established. Upon reaching the surface, converted waves again reflect back into the depth of the medium.

Thus, for short distances, the existence

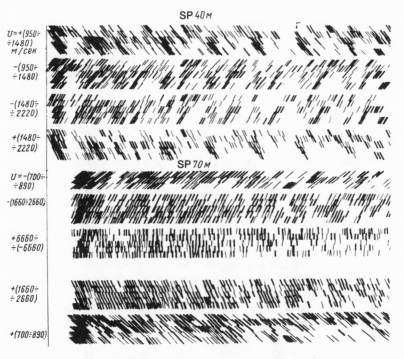

FIG. 90. CDR vector seismograms (well no. 90, Kudinov).

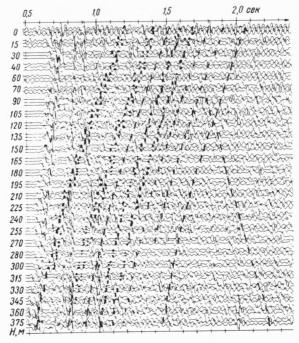

FIG. 91. Composite seismogram for three-component symmetrical installation. (SP 1500 m, well no. 90, Kudinov.)

of a sharp boundary in the upper portion
of the cross-section leads to the formation
of an aggregate of reflected and multiple
waves associated with the direct wave.
For large distances, intense secondary
waves on the initial portion of the record
involve primarily the wave refracting
along the top of the Paleozoic. However,
the direct wave propagating with low
velocity generates its own aggregate of
secondary and multiple waves on the subsequent portion of the record. All these
waves interfere with each other and thus
generate a complicated wave train of
incident waves which reflect multiply at
the boundary and seriously encumber the
identification of primary reflected waves
from great depths. VSP observations
demonstrate that lack of regular waves
on surface seismograms is explained by
the presence of many sharply reflecting
boundaries and a large number of re-

flected and multiple waves.

Where the top of the Paleozoic is located at comparatively large depth, it
exerts a substantial influence on surface
seismograms. But the wavefield is not as
complex as for shallow depths of burial.
The VSP seismogram (Figure 93) obtained for an area where the top of the
Paleozoic is located at a depth of approximately 1000 m, illustrates the tracking of primary reflected multiples, fully
reflected multiples, and partially reflected
multiples associated with basic and intermediate boundaries. These waves dominate the surface seismograms, almost
completely filling the entire record.

Thus, effective improvement of seismic
exploration over broad territories of the
Russian platform is significantly restricted by the noise wavefield associated
with the upper portion of the cross-
section.

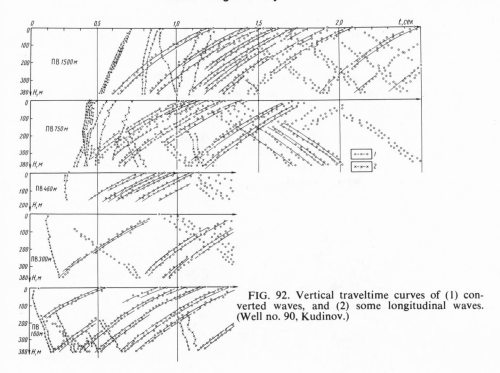

FIG. 92. Vertical traveltime curves of (1) converted waves, and (2) some longitudinal waves. (Well no. 90, Kudinov.)

WAVE FIELD FROM THE UPPER PORTION OF THE CROSS-SECTION WITH WEAK VELOCITY DIFFERENTIATION

The strong influence of the upper portion of the cross-section on the wavefield and on the capabilities of the MRLW exists even in the absence of sharp boundaries, i.e., under conditions of a gradiented medium or weak velocity differentiation. To illustrate this, data obtained in Central Asia shows that a monotonic increase of velocity with depth is characteristic and sharp boundaries are lacking for wide regions of depressions embedded by terrigenous sediments. In spite of this, seismograms register a complicated wavefield formed by refracted (longitudinal and transverse) waves and their multiples. The identification of reflected waves is not possible (Vol'vovskiy et al, 1960).

Surface investigations of the wavefield under these conditions were made under the direction of A. G. Rudakov by the Uzbek geophysical trust (Rudakov, 1962; Tsymbal et al, 1962; Tsymbal and Krauklis, 1966). Supplementary data of observed waves were studied by the IPE AS USSR by the VSP method on platforms located on the Naryn monocline (at the center and the southern flank) and also on the western edge of the Fergan Valley (Galperin et al, 1969). These regions belong structurally to the low foothills bordering the Fergan depression where a pronounced heterogeneity is typical. In most regions, the upper portion of the cross-section is composed on top of loessy argillaceous soil changing into conglomerates with individual lenses and thin interstratifications of clays, flintstones, sands and siltstones. The structure is highly variable along the profile. Observations were accomplished in specially drilled parametric boreholes. Detailed systems of observation in a vertical plane were developed (see Chapter 2), permitting contouring of the region of existence of each of the basic wave groups and construction of wavefields. VSP observations were conducted using a three-component symmetrical installation of seismometers with a natural frequency of 15 – 17 hz.

The velocity cross-section was studied by detailed observation and study of dis-

placement directions from velocity well-shooting data and from horizontal shooting. It was demonstrated that the structure of the uppermost portion of the cross-section (the ZLV and its underlying bed) varies for different regions (Gal'per-in, 1964c). The thickness of the zone changes, as do the velocities in the ZLV and in the formation underlying the latter. However, the basic velocity characteristic for all regions is the existence of a monotonic increase of velocity with depth (beginning at different depths, from

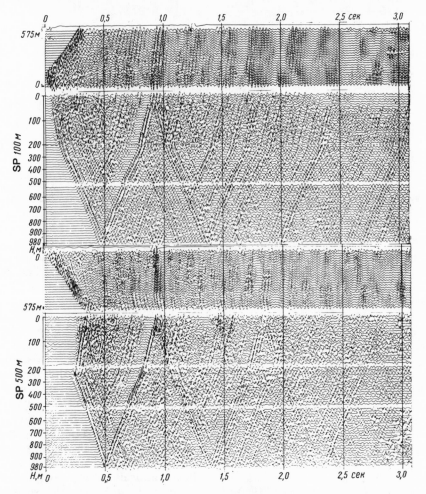

FIG. 93. Seismograms obtained in a section of deep embedding of the Paleozoic (according to data by V. M. Krivonosov).

10 to 40 m). The velocity values of longitudinal waves for various regions differ in the ZLV from 400 – 700 m/sec and in the underlying bed from 1200 – 2000 m/sec. The initial velocity of the gradiented portion of the cross-section is confined to values of 2100 – 3100 m/sec. The upper portion of the cross-section is not split up according to velocities of transverse waves; the wave velocities increase smoothly with depth (from 800 – 900 m/sec at 50 m to 1000 – 1100 m/sec at 200 m). The velocity ratio of longitudinal and and transverse waves for the gradiented bed varies from 2.2 – 2.5 in the upper portion, and is about 2.0 at a depth of 400 – 500 m. There is little change in this ratio as the depth increases. The value of the increment coefficient β for longitudinal waves of the gradiented medium and for a linear law of velocity increase is approximately 0.0010 m^{-1}. For transverse waves $\beta = 0.0015$ m^{-1}. The β values decrease with depth.

The wavefield for surface and VSP observations is a single type. The presence of a large number of distinct wave groups on surface seismograms is characteristic. They fill the entire seismogram or a significant portion of it (Figure 94a). These waves may be split into three groups according to their arrivals on seismograms. On surface records, all three wave groups comprise oscillations that diverge in a fan-like manner from the origin and are separated even in the immediate neighborhood of the shotpoint. At various points in the cross-section, the regions of existence of the waves strongly overlap but the relationship of the traveltime curves of various groups remains constant (Figure 94b).

Waves of groups I and II are the most stable and are only slightly affected by the structure of the uppermost portion of the cross-section. Waves of group III are the least stable and they are strongly affected by the structure of the upper portion of the cross-section. Their relative intensity varies sharply as the transition from one region to the other is made. For some regions they are dominant on seismograms (Figure 94a); for others their intensity is so low that these waves do not appear.

In addition to these wave groups, seismograms indicate less intense regular unwanted waves that are successfully revealed only after the "removal" of the dominant waves and the irregular noise background.

Waves of group I

Group I includes first arrivals on the initial portion of seismograms. The number of waves in a group is different for each region.

Surface seismograms indicate that the velocities of all waves are close to the velocities of first arrivals. The values of apparent velocity diminish as the transition is made from first to subsequent waves. Thus, in the Akbel region, at a distance $l = 400 - 500$ m the apparent velocity of the first phase (at $t = 0.3$ sec) is 2400 m/sec, and it decreases to 1600 m/sec for the last visible phases (at $t = 0.6$ sec). For $l = 2000$, the apparent velocity decreases from 3100 m/sec ($t = 0.9$ sec) to 2500 m/sec ($t = 1.5$ sec). The changeover of first arrival waves along the profile can be established only in the immediate vicinity of the shotpoint (50 – 100 m). The traveltime curve of first waves represents a smooth curve. As l increases, the apparent velocity values of first waves increase (see Table 3).

Wave group I is the least intense event on the seismograms and varies little with increase of l. Waves of this group are detected by both vertical and horizontal geophones. Wave frequencies in the vicinity of the shotpoint fluctuate for different regions within the limits of 50 – 80 hz and gradually diminish as the shotpoint becomes more remote (approximately down to 30 hz at a distance of

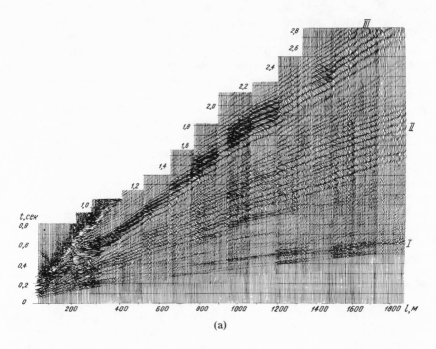

(a)

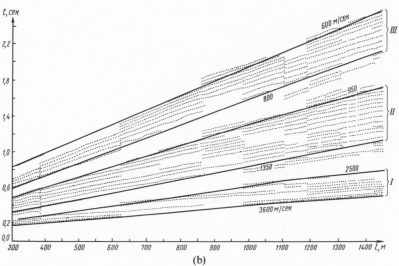

(b)

FIG. 94. (a) Seismogram of noise waves for horizontal profile. (b) Traveltime curves of three dominant groups (Kaptut, Uzbek SSR).

Table 3

Region	l, m	V_a, m/sec
Akbel	50 – 3000	2400 – 3600
Kaptut	50 – 2000	2200 – 4000
Dapchagai	50 – 2000	2800 – 3200
Dzheltmess	50 – 2000	2200 – 3100

3000 m). The visible frequency of waves is almost independent of the size of the charge. At interior points of the medium for an in-line vertical profile, the direct wave is registered in the form of identical in-phase oscillations (Figure 95). The form of the event is constant over the vertical profile. The visible frequencies of the direct wave for different regions cover

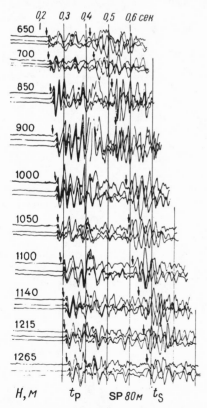

FIG. 95. Seismograms from three-component symmetrical installation (Airitan, Tadzhik SSR).

a range of 70 – 50 hz, diminishing as the depth increases from 70 hz ($H = 150$ m) to 50 hz ($H = 1265$ m) as seen in Figure 98c.

With increasing l the records of waves of group I become more complex. Additional phases appear (Figures 96 and 97) and visible frequencies are lowered to 30 hz. Linear polarization of first waves is usually maintained over the entire range of distances and depths. Starting with certain distances (500 – 1000 m), first arrival waves registering on vertical profiles may be considered to be pure refracted waves.

Waves of group II

These waves occupy the basic portion of seismograms. On surface seismograms, they form complicated oscillations, propagating at velocities similar to velocities of transverse waves. For increased l the values of apparent velocity along the horizontal profile increase smoothly. For example, in the Akbel region, they increase from 1000 – 1800 m/sec in the interval from 100 – 3000 m. As the shotpoint separation increases, the number of phases increases, the group broadens, and the waves become resolved. For transition to subsequent phases, the values of the apparent velocity gradually decrease to 1100 – 1200 m/sec.

Frequencies of waves in group II vary as the shotpoint becomes more remote. This is true for all regions. The frequencies change from 30 – 35 hz for $l = 100 – 300$ m and from 20 – 25 hz for $l = 2 – 3$ km. The first phases of the group are reliably established according to intensity for $l = 1500$ m and correlate along the profile. As l increases, their intensity weakens markedly and the correlation deteriorates compared with the correlation of the more intense later waves in the group (see Figure 94a).

In the vicinity of the shotpoints, the intensities of group II waves on seismograms of the Z-components exceed the intensities of waves of group I by about

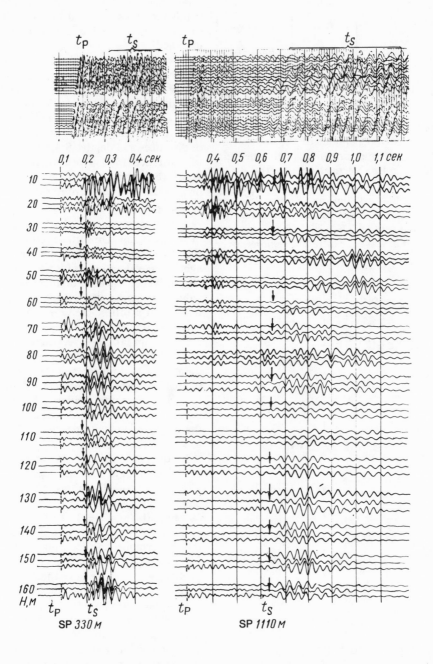

FIG. 96. Seismograms of Z-component along horizontal profile and three-component symmetrical installation for vertical profile (Kapchagai, Uzbek SSR).

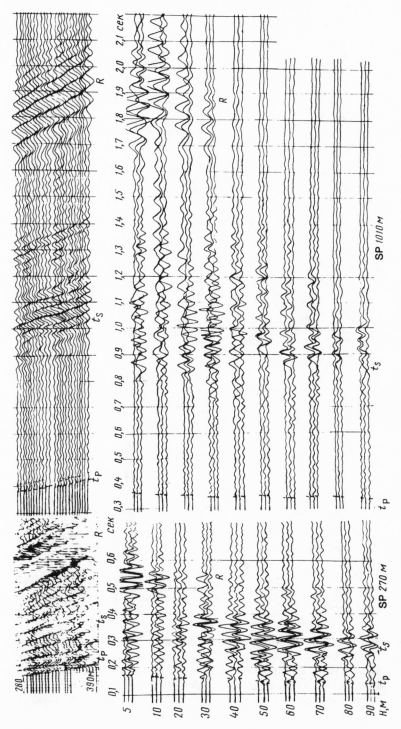

FIG. 97. Seismograms of Z-component for horizontal profile and three-component symmetrical installation for vertical profile (Kaptut).

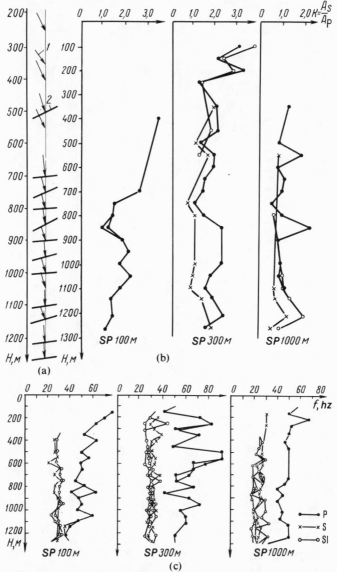

FIG. 98. (a) Graphs of directions of displacement, (b) for relative intensities, and (c) for frequencies (Airitan). Directions of displacement (1) in the first longitudinal wave, and (2) in the transverse wave.

one order of magnitude. As the separation from the shotpoint increases, the intensity decreases and, at distances of 2 – 3 km, intensities of waves of groups I and II are approximately the same. In contrast to waves of group I, group II waves indicate a dependence of recorded frequency on the size of charge. Thus, when the charge varies from 0.5 – 16 kg, the frequency for $l = 300 - 400$ m varies from 35 – 25 hz. Correspondingly, a variation of the ratio of intensities of group II waves to those of group I is observed: it amounts to a factor of 2 – 3 for a charge of 0.5 kg and to a factor of 10 – 12 for a charge of 16 kg. Group II waves register for both vertical and horizontal components and are polarized in the vertical plane.

For observations at interior points of the medium, waves of group II register everywhere and at all separations from the shotpoint, as well as for all accessible depths. For in-line vertical profiles, records of the first wave of group II are the same type at all sections and are illustrated by observations in a deep borehole in the region of Ayritan (see Figure 95). The wave is linearly polarized and directions of displacement are close to horizontal and are perpendicular to the directions of displacement in the first wave (Figure 98a). The ratio of velocities of waves of groups II and I is approximately 2.0. The frequency of waves in group II remains constant and amounts to 30 hz (for charges of 20 – 60 kg). As the distance from the source increases,

the visible frequencies of the record remain about 25 – 30 hz (Figure 98c). At shallow depths, the intensity of the wave of group II is approximately 3 – 4 times higher than that of the wave of group I (Figure 98b). This ratio diminishes as depth increases and, at 1200 m, the intensities of waves in both groups are almost the same. The form of events is constant along the vertical profile.

For increasing l, the number of waves in a group and the interval of their registration are both increased. But not all waves can be correlated along the profile (see Figures 96 and 97). However, the form of the first wave is conserved at all intervals of registration (Figure 99). At short distances, waves of group II are considerably more intense than group I waves. For increasing l, intensities of waves of groups I and II level out and barely change with depth (down to $H =$ 1265 m), as shown in Figure 98b. Vertical traveltime curves of first waves of group II are a single type for all regions and correspond to a gradiented medium.

Waves of group III

On surface seismograms wave group

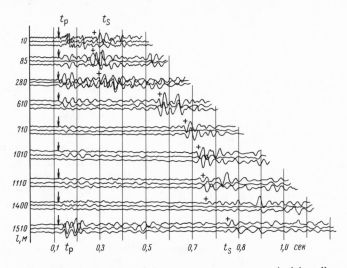

FIG. 99. Seismograms of three-component symmetrical installation along level-reduced profile, for $H = 200$ m (Akbel, Tadzhik SSR).

III is represented by fan-like, highly dispersed oscillations. In contrast to waves of either group I or II, their intensity is not very uniform, varying from region to region. On sections from Kaptut and Akbel they appear to be most intense; on sections from Kapchagai and Jeltmess they are recognized with difficulty or do not appear. The propagation velocities of waves of this group vary from 1000 – 2000 m/sec for the initial portion, to 200 – 300 m/sec for the end of the train. With increasing distance, the apparent velocities increase slightly. The dominant frequences of the initial portion of the records are 10 hz, and they are 40 hz at the end of recording. The waves are polarized in the vertical plane *(ZX)*.

At interior points of the medium, waves of group III show a characteristically sharp decrease of intensity with depth and this is observable for all distances from the shotpoint. Although they are most intense at the surface, waves of this group are barely present at 40 m. The decay of waves is well demonstrated on composite VSP seismograms (see Figure 97). The high-frequency components decay more rapidly. The spectral width is reduced as the depth increases and is shifted into the region of lower frequencies (Figure 100). The longer wavelengths penetrate into greater depths. The thickness of the layer in which waves of this group register amounts to about three-fourths of a wavelength. Thus, for a wavelength of 60 m, corresponding to the longest period on the initial portion of the record, the region of existence of waves is about 40 m. For a wavelength of 30 m, corresponding to the subsequent portion of the record, the penetration is 22 m.

Nature of noise waves

Comparison of the characteristics of three basic wave groups for different regions, on the surface and at interior points of the medium, establishes the

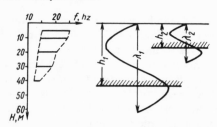

FIG. 100. Frequency composition and penetration of surface waves.

individual types of the waves in these regions. The nature of noise waves is discussed in many papers (Rudakov, 1962; Tsymbal et al, 1962; Tsymbal and Krauklis, 1966). The most detailed discussions concern waves of groups I and III. The nature of waves of group II remained vague, although various theories have been advanced.

Waves of group I are longitudinal waves propagating in the gradiented layered medium. In the vicinity of the shotpoint, reflected and multiple waves are superimposed on direct curved-path refracted waves; the reflected waves are associated with the bottom of the ZLV and the boundaries in the upper portion of the cross-section. As a result, a complicated interferential wave pattern is established. As the distance from the shotpoint increases, the influence of the upper boundaries diminishes and direct refracted waves and their multiples are the principal waves that are being recorded. The gradiented medium and the transcritically reflected multiples associated with the ZLV are important in the formation of the wavefield of group I. In addition to longitudinal waves, the first group also contains converted waves of type SP forming in the upper portion of the cross-section. These waves are distinguished by their intensity (in excess of that of the first wave), and by the lower frequency of recording as shown in Figure 98c).

Waves of group III are Rayleigh-type surface waves.

Waves of group II are characterized by the following features:

1) The recorded form of the first wave for all separations from the shotpoints coincides with the form of the direct transverse wave registered on in-line vertical profiles over the entire depth interval.

2) The wave velocities are equal to those of transverse waves.

3) Kinematics along horizontal and vertical profiles are compatible with results of kinematic computations on refracted transverse waves and their multiples. Theoretically, vertical traveltime curves computed for the case of a gradiented medium ($\beta = 0.0016$ m^{-1}) satisfactorily agrees with observations of traveltime curves of first waves (Figure 101).

4) Wave polarization is linear. Directions of displacement are perpendicular to those of longitudinal waves.

5) Recorded frequency is lower than dominant group I waves.

6) Visible dispersion is absent.

These features permit reliable identification of group II waves as direct refracted transverse waves and multiples. The formation of transverse waves at the source is corroborated by the following: (1) the much higher intensity of trans-verse waves compared to longitudinal waves for observations in the immediate vicinity of the source (10 — 30 m); (2) the decrease of intensity of transverse waves and the simultaneous increase of intensity of longitudinal waves as the charge is placed deeper; and (3) the lower frequency content of transverse waves.

The properties of basic groups of noise waves show that a substantial portion of the shot energy is converted into direct transverse waves. For comparatively small distances from the shotpoint, their vertical component is sufficiently intense to be registered on the surface by vertical seismometers because of the direction of their approach (close to the horizontal). The ratio of intensities of vertical and horizontal components of waves of group II on the surface diminishes as the distance increases. The increase of amplitudes of vertical components of the first waves of groups I and II is explained solely by the direction of approach of these waves for an increase of l. As the charge is further lowered, the relative intensity of transverse waves diminishes drastically. Thus, for $h = 0$, transverse waves are more intense than longitudinal waves by about one order of magnitude; for $h = 30$ m, transverse waves are already 3 — 4 times weaker than longitudinal waves; for $h = 60$ m and more, they are almost absent from seismograms.

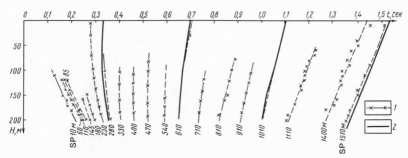

FIG. 101. Comparison of (1) observed and (2) computed vertical traveltime curves of first transverse waves (Akbel).

The presence of noise of groups I and II on seismograms is determined principally by two circumstances: (1) by the structural specifics of the uppermost portion of the cross-section, for shots in which intense transverse waves are generated; and (2) by the presence of a thick homogeneous bed, the velocity of which increases monotonously with depth. One should note that an analogous wave pattern is characteristic in many regions of the Antarctic (Kondrat'ev and Gamburtsev, 1963). The thick layer of ice is a good model of a homogeneous gradiented medium. The wave pattern obtained in this medium exhibits the same characteristic basic wave groups.

In spite of the absence of sharp boundaries in the upper portion of the cross-section, the latter is the source of a complicated wavefield that makes enhancement of reflected longitudinal waves difficult. The study of the properties of the wavefield (Rudakov, 1966; Tsymbal et al, 1962; Tsymbal and Krauklis, 1966) yielded information necessary for the computation of parameters of groups of seismometers and sources. As a result of application of multielement grouping, a substantial reduction of the noise level was made and an increase of useful recording sensitivity was achieved which, in turn, permitted the application of seismic exploration in certain regions previously inaccessible to seismic observations. However, there are many regions which cannot be studied by longitudinal reflected waves.

To improve the effectiveness of seismic exploration under such conditions, future work should be oriented in two directions. First, it is necessary to evaluate the conditions of excitation and develop procedures reducing the intensity of transverse waves. Second, because of the generation of intense transverse waves associated with the natural directivity of the source and the difficulty in assessing the medium by longitudinal waves, it is expedient to appraise the enhancement of reflected transverse waves on the surface. For an appraisal of the second proposition, special experiments were initiated to enhance SS waves on the surface. This was done in 1966 in two regions of the Fergan Valley in several sections where unwanted waves were being studied. In spite of the comparatively small scope of experimentation, surface observations by means of horizontal geophones registered reflected SS waves corresponding to the arrival of reflections from deep horizons (Figure 102).

The formation of transverse waves was studied in plains for which shots are produced in loess in the immediate vicinity of water, outside the regions of low foothills bordering the Fergan depression. Tests showed that under these conditions, intense transverse waves are not excited and seismograms involving the X-component register converted waves with

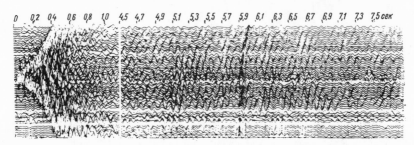

FIG. 102. Surface seismogram of X-component (Akbel).

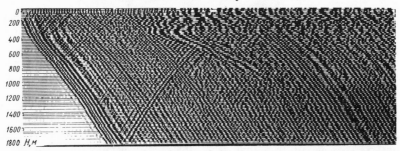

FIG. 103. VSP seismogram according to data by S. V. Kursin (SP 400 m, well no. 318, Ubin).

high apparent velocities, equaling velocities of longitudinal waves. In this case,
the conventional wave pattern characteristic for a layered medium is observed.
Experiments revealed transverse waves
are excited only by shots in structurally
heterogeneous zones (flintstones and conglomerates) that are characteristic for the
above mentioned foothill sections. In
those sections longitudinal reflected
waves are not brought out due to the high
noise background. Changing to recording
of reflected transverse waves, under these
conditions, should permit a substantial
simplification of observations and open
many sections that, in spite of multielement grouping still remain unavailable
to the study by longitudinal waves. Therefore, it is essential in VSP work to study
the conditions of propagation and the
reflection coefficients of transverse waves,
as well as the conditions for the enhancement and correlation of reflected SS
waves on the surface.

VSP AND EFFECTIVENESS OF THE METHOD OF REFLECTED WAVES

Experience with application of VSP
to study reflected waves makes possible
an improvement in effectiveness and penetration, one of the fundamental problems
of MRLW. It was necessary to determine
whether reflecting horizons exist at great
depths, if these boundaries give rise to
sufficiently intense waves, and how to
enhance and track these waves for observations at interior points of the medium

and on the surface. Observations at great
depths showed that at almost all accessible depths in the sedimentary bed, boundaries yielded fairly intense reflected
waves. In many cases in which the depth
of the borehole permitted observations
to be made in the neighborhood of the
crystalline basement, waves were brought
out that were reflected from either the
top of the basement or from boundaries
located in its immediate vicinity (Figure
103). The generation of reflected waves
at boundaries located at great depths is
the premise of further work on improvement of penetration by means of MRLW.

VSP indicated that the possibility of
enhancement of deep reflected waves on
surface seismograms is basically determined by the level of multiples and that
the bottom of the ZLV exerts a substantial influence on that level.

Reflecting properties of the surface and the ZLV and their influence on the structure of the seismogram

In recent years, a great deal of attention has been devoted to the influence
that the upper portion of the cross-section
exerts on the seismic record (Gal'perin,
1964; Gamburtsev et al, 1967). VSP not
only indicated the strong influence of the
ZLV on the level of intensity of multiples,
but it also opened new possibilities for
the study of reflecting properties of the
upper portion of the cross-section and the
ZLV. The most reliable data may be obtained by studying the ghosts of the direct

wave. For surface observations ghosts of the direct wave are not recorded, while ghosts of reflected waves are registered on the later portion of the record against the background of noise. For VSP, ghosts of the direct wave do register and are directly contiguous to the first wave, which substantially improves the accuracy of determination of the reflection coefficient. VSP data demonstrate that, as a rule, the influence of the upper portion of the cross-section on the seismic record is underestimated. If the absorption properties of the ZLV are inherent to the form of the record for each individual wave (in particular to the high-frequency composition of the event) and slightly influence the wave record, considering waves associated with great depths or registered at large separations from the shotpoint, then the reflecting properties of the upper portion of the cross-section and the ZLV may exert a decisive influence on the number of waves and on the structure of the entire seismogram. Therefore, in the study of the influence of the upper portion of the cross-section on the seismic record, special attention should be given to the reflecting properties of the surface and the bottom of the ZLV.

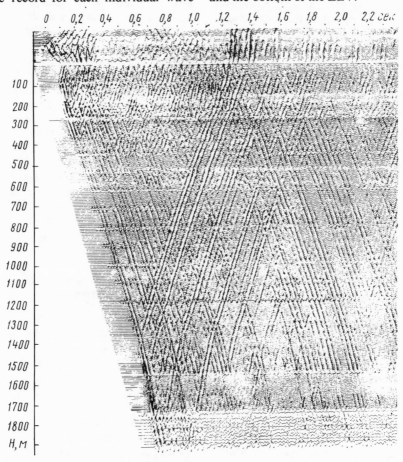

FIG. 104. Multiples in the case of a sharp pronounced velocity jump at the boundary of the ZLV (well no. 4, Balashov, according to data by A. N. Amirov).

The bottom of the ZLV is usually the most contrasting boundary in the cross-section (the velocity here may rise by a factor of 3 – 4), and it gives rise to the most intense reflected waves. It is not always possible to separate the reflections off the bottom of the ZLV from those off the surface. However, in rare cases when the thickness of the ZLV is sufficiently large, VSP seismograms do provide possible separate registration of reflected waves associated with the bottom of the zone and with the surface. Then it is demonstrated (see Figure 65b) that the wave reflected from the surface (because of the strong velocity gradient in the ZLV) is distinguished by its low-frequency content and by its comparatively low recorded intensity.

The reflecting properties of the ZLV manifest themselves primarily in the formation of ghosts which may complicate the recording the first incident wave (see Chapter 6). However, the basic influence of the reflecting properties of the ZLV and the surface manifests itself in the formation of full and partial multiples. The reflecting properties of these boundaries dictate that portion of the energy carried by waves approaching the upper portion of the cross-section that is again reflected into the depth of the medium. This, to a significant degree, determines the intensity of multiples. The influence of the ZLV on the multiple wavefield may be illustrated by data obtained in the Crimea (Figure 104). The presence of a sharp boundary at shallow depth (i.e., the bottom of the ZLV) plus reference boundaries of the cross-section at depths of about 1400 – 1500 m, cause numerous full and partial multiples that fill the interval to 5.0 sec. A similar situation was observed in the Staro-Minsk area (see Figure 74).

If the bottom of the ZLV represents a sharp boundary, multiples may be comparable in intensity to reflected waves, even if the cross-section is void of reference reflecting horizons. Also, when the ZLV is not sharply defined (or is altogether nonexistent), the relative intensity of multiples diminishes, even if reference reflecting horizons do exist in the cross-section, and singly reflected waves are dominant on records. The presence in the upper portion of the cross-section of a high-velocity layer may influence the intensity of multiples.

As an illustration in the wave field over a section of a profile adjoining the surface for one of the regions of the Volgograd district a thin layer of limestone is embedded in sandy-clay deposits at a depth of about 40 m (Figure 105a). VSP seismograms indicate that nearly all waves impinging on that layer are reflected and returned to the medium, and surface seismograms abound in multiples.

If the upper portion of the cross-section and the ZLV constitute a monotonic bed of thin sequential interstratifications of sands and clays, a sharp boundary of separation is missing. In spite of the presence of dominant deep boundaries in the cross-section and intense upward impinging waves, little energy is returned into the depth and multiples do not register on the seismograms (Figure 105b).

The intensity of multiples depends on the thickness of the ZLV. As the ZLV increases, the intensity of multiples decreases. This is due apparently to a reduction of velocity contrast at the bottom of the ZLV as its thickness increases. The values of the coefficient of reflection at the ZLV lie within ranges of 0.6 – 0.7 and 0.3 – 0.4.

The spectrum of the reflection coefficient at the bottom of the ZLV determines the composition of multiples, and substantially influences the effectiveness of frequency selectivity in suppression of multiples. A significant detailed study was made of the reflecting properties of the ZLV under various seismogeologic

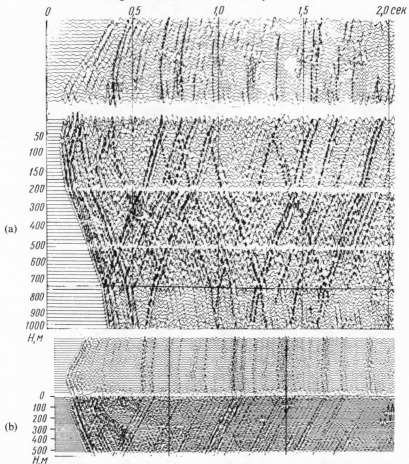

FIG. 105. (a) Multiples in cases of presence in the upper portion of the cross-section of a layer with increased velocity (SP 100 m, frequency 23-40 hz, well no. 1068, Umetov-Chukhonostov, according to data by V. M. Krivonosov. (b) Same, for absence of a sharp zone (well no. 4, Mitrofanov, according to data by I. M. Muzyka).

conditions and establishment of the relation of the structure of the ZLV on its reflecting properties (taking into account the surface). VSP not only reveals multiply reflected waves on seismograms but also affords a starting point for a serious study of the process of generation, and of characteristics of multiply reflected waves, in search of a procedure that would implement their suppression.

In cases where multiply reflected waves do not disrupt the correlatability of singly reflected waves, the appearance of multiply reflected waves in VSP data permits exclusion of the fictitious boundaries connected with the latter from the cross-section and improvement of the authenticity of interpretation. Figure 106 demónstrates cross-sections that were obtained over the same section of a profile in Eastern Turkman (Artamanova et al, 1969). On the seismic cross-section constructed without VSP data (Figure 106a), many boundaries are in evidence to a

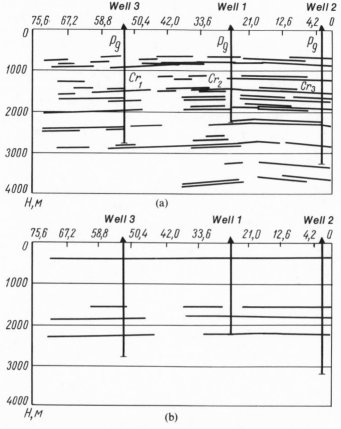

FIG. 106. Comparison of cross-sections (a) constructed without VSP data, and (b) based on VSP (Sakar, Turkmen SSR).

depth of 4000 m. On the cross-section constructed from interpretation of VSP data (Figure 106b), the number of boundaries is sharply diminished and, in addition, maximum penetration amounts to only 2300 m.

Multiply reflected waves

VSP cannot solve the complicated problem of suppression of multiples. However, information derived from VSP contributes substantially to its solution. VSP permits rigorous, objective appraisal of the effectiveness of various procedures for suppression of multiples and selection of the optimal system of observation, based on good understanding of param-

eters of singly and multiply reflected waves. The procedures for suppression of multiply reflected waves and enhancement of singly reflected waves are based on either frequency selectivity or selectivity according to apparent velocities by means of various interferential systems of observation: CDR, plane wavefront, directional plane wavefront, or CDP methods.

The effectiveness of the applicable interferential systems is largely determined by the reliability of concepts of the nature and characteristics of waves as well as the signal-to-noise ratio. In CDP, significant data are obtained from

VSP on the relative intensity of reflected and multiple waves, and raypath velocities. This information permits the selection of the optimal system of observation (observation base, number of stacks), and the acquisition of the necessary kinematic corrections used in summing. In this connection, the study of the relative intensity of multiples is of great interest. Difficulties here are caused by the complexity of wavefields for observations in the upper portion of the cross-section and on the surface. Waves are contained within the region of interference, and it is practically impossible to estimate their intensity. At present, various procedures are developed for appraisal of the relative intensity of multiples by means of VSP data. Of particular interest could be procedures based on utilization of incident waves observed at great depths (Muzyka et al, 1969), where the wavefield is considerably simpler and where individual waves are established more reliably than in the upper portion of the cross-section. However, these procedures are only approximations, are too unwieldy, and require further developmental research.

The comparatively scant available experience shows that the application of CDP based on VSP data, substantially improves the penetration capabilities for a more complete appraisal of these possibilities.

Chapter 8
WAVES OBSERVED ON THE INITIAL
PORTION OF SEISMOGRAMS FOR LARGE SEPARATIONS

At offset distances that are large compared to the depth of the boundaries, curved-ray refractions, transcritically reflected waves, and head waves usually register on the initial portion of seismograms. The study of the nature and relative intensity of these waves is of considerable theoretical and practical interest since they determine the capabilities of one of the fundamental methods of seismic exploration, i.e., the correlation method of refracted waves (CMRRW).

The above method was based on the observation of the first and subsequent arrivals of head waves (Gamburtsev et al, 1952). It was assumed that after the initial arrival of the intense head wave, the reflected wave was not tracked, as a rule. Exploration capabilities of CMRRW were based on the assumption that, even for a homogeneous medium (established from seismic well logging data), there exist many thin layers that give rise to intense head waves but no reflections; i.e., that reflecting and refracting boundaries did not coincide. The latter concept prompted combining MRLW with CMRRW.

Because of the development of the theory of propagation of seismic waves in actual media and the large volume of experimental data, we changed our concept of the role played by various waves forming the seismogram, particularly transcritically reflected waves. As a result of experiments with models (Bol'shikh et al, 1961; Gil'bershteyn and Gurvich, 1963; Shamina and Gurvich, 1960) and in actual media (Gorbatova, 1958; Epinat'yeva, 1960; Kosminskaya and Krakshina, 1961; Pomerantseva and Margot'yeva, 1959), and from theoretical calculations (Petrashen', 1957; Petrashen' et al, 1959; Smirnova and Yermilova, 1959),

the concept was abandoned that reflected waves can only be tracked prior to the head wave. These investigations show that transcritically reflected waves do register at significant distances with high intensity.

The important role played by refracted waves (Averbukh et al, 1963; Averbukh, 1961; Alekseyev, 1960, 1962; Gel'chinskiy, 1960; Kindrat'yev and Gamburtsev, 1963; Ozerov et al, 1962) was established by the study of waves registering on the initial portion of the seismogram. The wave pattern observed on the initial portion of the record often did not correspond to the expected wave pattern based on calculations. In discrete regions incompatability between geologic results obtained from CMRRW and those revealed by drilling was discovered. Doubts have arisen about the nature of waves registered in CMRRW and DSS work (Averbukh et al, 1963; Alekseyev, 1962; Pomerantseva, 1962; Pomerantseva and Margot'yeva, 1959). Original VSP efforts conducted by us in the Kubyshev district in 1960 (Gal'perin and Frolova, 1963) demonstrated that head waves associated with thin layers are so weak that it is almost impossible to bring them out on surface seismograms.

The ambiguity of the nature of waves led to a drastic reduction of CMRRW work and to a refusal to consider waves in subsequent arrivals obtained by this method.

Thus, the study of the nature of waves registered on the initial portion of the seismogram (at source distances that are large compared to the depth of the boundary), constitutes a major problem. The difficulty based on surface observations is that waves observed at large distances cannot be differentiated according to their kinematic properties. In spite of the large amount of surface observations accumulated over a period of many years, sufficiently clear concepts on the nature of waves observed on the initial portion of the seismogram have not been established up to now. VSP was used to clarify the situation. Observations at interior points of the medium at large distances from the shotpoint have the following advantages over surface observations (Gal'perin, 1966b, 1967b; Gal'perin and Frolova, 1963):

1. Study of the wavefield by observations in the medium that underlies the refracting boundary permits acquisition of the most reliable data on the mechanism of energy return and, therefore, on the nature of waves registering above that boundary and, in particular, at the surface.

2. Registration of waves as first arrivals in the immediate vicinity of the refracting boundary, and near the point of emergence of the wave, often permits their stratigraphic correlation.

3. Observations at interior points of the medium permit the utilization of such a sensitive parameter as the trajectory of particle motion of the medium to analyze the nature of waves.

4. The rapidly decaying noise background of seismic waves (with depth) permits greater useful sensitivity and wider dynamic range of registered waves (permitting the study of waves characterized by very low intensities).

5. Of great significance is the possibility of comparing intensities of waves at the boundaries, since the ratio of intensities may vary as one recedes from the boundaries.

A large volume of VSP work was done in structurally different media to study waves on the initial portion of records.

Waves connected with individual thin high-velocity layers were studied in the Kubyshev district, Krasnodar region, in a medium having thick layers in the Stavropol region, and in a cross-section of carbonates in the Volgograd district. The results are as follows:

1. It was confirmed that transcritically reflected waves are always more intense than head waves from the same boundary. Thin high-velocity layers are decisive in the formation of the wavefield at small distances from the shotpoint; and transcritically reflected waves may be more intense than head waves, exceeding them by two orders of magnitude. Therefore, head waves on surface seismograms cannot be brought out as subsequent or first arrivals (Gal'perin, 1966b; Gal'perin and Frolova, 1963). Under these conditions, the first visible arrivals on surface seismograms are due to transcritically reflected waves. As the distance from the shotpoint increases, the influence of the layer thickness diminishes and waves refracted in the underlying bed become dominant. The recording of the wave as a first arrival cannot serve as a reliable criterion for the nature of the wave. For increased layer thickness, the relative intensity of the head wave increases, but it is still much lower than the transcritically reflected wave.

2. By means of direct observations in the underlying layer at large distances from the shotpoint, we observed that an increase in velocity with depth is the rule and that the first wave observed on seismograms is the curved-path refraction, not the head wave. Refraction and transcritical reflection influence the intensity of waves and cause return of energy toward the surface.

3. The upper portion of the cross-section may exert a considerable influence on the wavefield for large distances on surface seismograms. Observations conducted at great depths below the source as well as at considerable distances from it (within the region of reception), permit one to resolve reflected-refracted waves and refracted-reflected waves, and to confirm the proposition that waves registering on the initial portion of the record with velocities equal to or near the velocity of first waves may be total reflected-refracted waves associated with the upper portion of the cross-section. The influence of the upper portion of the cross-section also is evident in the formation of low-velocity waves registering on the later portion of the record. The high intensity of these waves is caused by their interferential character.

4. In view of experimental and calculated data, it is imperative to review the physical fundamentals and the exploratory capabilities of CMRRW. The exploratory possibilities primarily involve thin-layered media with weak velocity differentiation. In the study of the top of the thick layer (e.g., the basement), consideration of refraction must be appraised in each situation. For the experimental study of waves recorded by CMRRW, decisive significance should be allocated to VSP.

WAVES ASSOCIATED WITH THIN HIGH-VELOCITY LAYERS

Questions related to thin high-velocity layers are of great interest since, on the one hand, the exploratory capabilities of CMRRW are based on them and, on the other hand, false concepts have persisted in regard to them for a long time. The literature describes registration of head waves from layers one-tenth and even one one-hundredth part of a wavelength thick (Berzon et al, 1962). Modeling results on solid-liquid media permit registration of intense head waves originating from layers less than 0.1 wavelength thick (Davydova, 1962). Subsequent efforts on solid models (Bol'shikh et al, 1961; Gil'bershteyn and Gurvich, 1963; Lavergne, 1961; Levin and Ingram, 1962) and theoretical research on these matters, demonstrated there can be no head waves issuing from thin layers. A study of waves in actual thin-layered media with increased velocity is essential since quantitative theoretical calculations are very difficult.

In the study of waves from thin layers, VSP was used in several regions. Let us examine the observed data on the Staro-Minsk platform.

Intensity of head and transcritically reflected waves from thin layers

Let us compare the intensities of head and transcritically reflected waves from two thin layers at depth $H_v = 270$ and 1334 m. Waves reflected from these layers (i.e., t^1 and t^3 in Figure 74) dominated the surface seismograms near the shot-point as well as for angles of incidence that exceed the critical angle and also at distances that substantially exceed the depth of the boundary. In essence, reflected and multiple waves from these two thin layers dominated the entire surface seismograms. But for surface seismograms, one was unsuccessful in bringing out head waves from thin layers (Gal'-perin, 1966b; Epinat'yeva and Karus, 1967) even though a large amount of specially conducted work was undertaken.

At interior points of the medium, the high useful instrument sensitivity, coupled with the possibility of observation in the immediate vicinity of the layers, permitted the registration of head waves associated with these layers, as well as comparison of the intensities of the head wave and the transcritically reflected wave for each individual layer.

First layer ($H_v = 270$ *m*). — On seismograms of the profile section that crosses the first layer (Figure 107), start-

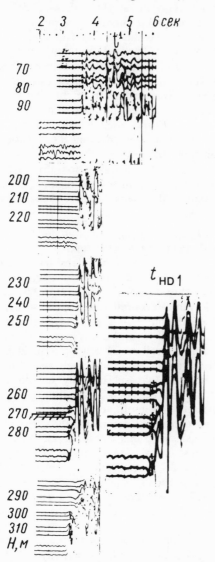

FIG. 107. Head waves and transcritically reflected waves. Registrations are at five levels of amplification. For $H = 260 - 280$ m, the seismogram is also shown magnified. (SP 600 m, well no. 42, Staro-Minsk.)

ing with a depth 220 m and down to the boundary ($H = 270$ m), channels with maximal sensitivity indicated the registration of a weak downward arrival of the head wave t_{HD1} with negative apparent velocity, preceding the sharp upward arrival of the direct wave. As the boundary is crossed, intensity and particle direction of the wave is sharply changed. Below the boundary the first recorded wave is the transmitted wave. The vertical traveltime curve of first waves (see Figure 22) indicates two characteristic points of sign inversions of apparent velocities. They correspond to the reversal from the positive apparent velocity of the direct wave to the negative velocity of the head wave ($H = 220$ m), and from the negative apparent velocity of the head wave to the positive velocity of the transmitted wave ($H = 270$ m). The head wave is successfully brought out only for sections where it registers as a first wave, while the intense direct wave registers in later arrivals as well.

The transcritically reflected wave t^1 cannot be enhanced in pure form on VSP seismograms at the immediate vicinity of the boundary because of its interference with the direct wave. Let us compare the intensities of t^1 and t_{HD1} waves at points where both record outside the zone of interference. Figure 107 shows for $H = 70 - 90$ m that wave t^1 dominates on channels with minimal amplification. If the levels of maximal and minimal amplification differ by a factor of about 150, then a qualitative comparison of recordings shows that the intensity of the transcritically reflected wave exceeds that of the head wave by a factor of more than 200. Comparison of intensities of t^1 and t_{HD1} waves is demonstrated on the seismogram (Figure 108) which corresponds to an instrumentation having a large dynamic range and is composed of recordings at different levels of amplification. It is almost impossible to enhance such a

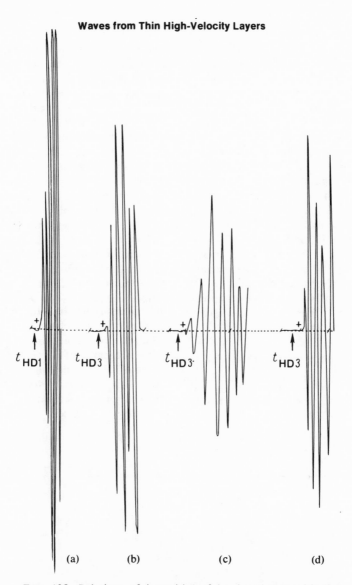

t_{HD1} t_{HD3} t_{HD3} t_{HD3}

(a)   (b)   (c)   (d)

FIG. 108. Relations of intensities of head and transcritically reflected waves (the first arrival times are denoted by arrows, head waves are indicated by " + " signs), Staro-Minsk. (a) $H = 260$ m (SP 600 m, well no. 42). (b) $H = 1260$ m (SP 1775 m, well no. 42), (c) $H = 1150$ m (SP 2500 m, well no. 42). (d) $H = 18$ m (SP 2500 m, well no. 20).

head wave on the surface and visible first arrivals on surface seismograms are formed by the transcritically reflected wave.

Second layer ($H_v = 1334$ *m*). — The head wave issuing from the second layer registers on seismograms corresponding to vertical profile sections continguous to the boundary. From SP 1550 m, this wave produces first arrivals within the depth interval of 1270 m from the boundary; from SP 1775 m, the corresponding depth is 1220 m; and from SP 2500 m it is 1090 m. Reversal of the direct and head waves is expressed in the composite traveltime curves (Figure 109) in which the locus is indicated by the dash-dot line.

The head wave t_{HD3} is trackable only as a first arrival and as a very weak oscillation on channels with maximal amplification (Figure 110). As separation from the shotpoint increases, the region of registration of that wave increases, while propagation velocity of the wave along the boundary diminished from $v_b = 4550$ m/sec (for SP 1550 m) to $v_b = 3990$ m/sec (for SP 2500 m). This may be explained by the lack of a first arrival or by the interferential character of the wave.[1] According to three-component registrations (Figure 110), the wave is linearly polarized.

The transcritically reflected wave t^3 in the neighborhood of the boundary lies

[1]In view of these results, we should treat the concept of boundary velocity very carefully which, strictly speaking, has lost its physical meaning.

within the zone of interference with the direct wave. On records where the transcritically reflected wave is outside the zone of interference (Figure 110a), it is of high intensity and registers on channels with minimal sensitivity. Comparison of intensities of waves t^3 and t_{HD3} indicates that the transcritically reflected wave is about $150 - 200$ times stronger than the head wave (see Figures 33 and 108). The head wave is brought out only on channels with maximal amplification where the entire subsequent portion of the record is washed out. An analogous comparison of intensities of the head and transcritically reflected waves is also obtained for the thin layer at 1850 m.

Influence of thin layer on wavefield observed at large separations from the shotpoint.

The influence of the thin layer varies when the shotpoint becomes more remote. Observations were conducted from a sequence of shotpoints located at distances from 900 to 400 m, along the vertical profile section that crosses the thin layer of interest at 1250 m. As the

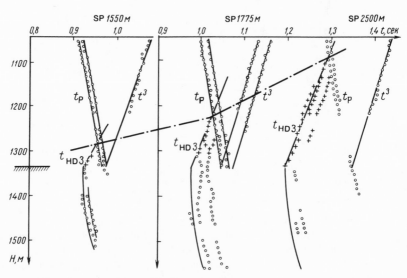

FIG. 109. Vertical traveltime curves of head waves and transcritically reflected waves for the section near boundary 3.

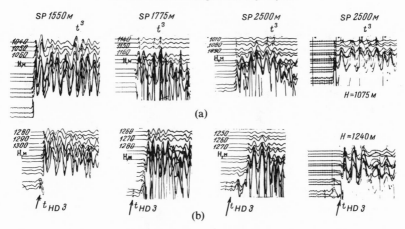

SP 1550 M   SP 1775 M   SP 2500 M   SP 2500 M

(a)

(b)

FIG. 110. VSP seismograms.

shotpoint separation increases, the observed interval in the bed underlying the thin layer is increased. The vertical component of motion was recorded and, at large separations, the full vector motion was also studied by three-component observations.

Let us discuss the seismograms and the traveltime curves of waves forming the initial portions of the records along vertical profiles (Figures 111 and 112). This concerns the direct waves, the head waves, and the transcritically reflected waves issuing from the thin layer, plus the wave refracted in the bed underlying the thin layer. Seismograms from SP 1775 m indicate that the direct wave is the most intense and is reliably trackable in its first and subsequent arrivals. On the profile section that is contiguous to the thin layer, weak arrivals of the head wave register (the wave having an apparent velocity $|v_a| = |-2500|$ m/sec) and it appears ahead of the direct wave. Head waves are brought out as first arrivals from SP 1000, SP 1775, and SP 2500 m. But from SP 1250 m, which is located near the starting point, the head wave registers only over an interval of 20 m (1240 – 1260 m). The region of observation of head waves widens as the source becomes more remote.

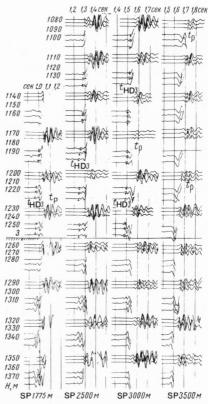

FIG. 111. Seismograms of head waves, transcritically reflected waves, and refracted waves (well no. 20, Staro-Minsk).

Computer correlation (Pogonyailo, 1968) improved the region of correlatability of head waves for each shotpoint through their enhancement on the background of the first phase of the direct wave, and permitted determination of their apparent velocity $v_a = $ -2300 m/sec and their dominant period of 0.025 sec. Moreover, it confirmed that in spite of the small amplitudes of the visible head waves, they are the first waves on seismograms.

From nearby shotpoints, intense reflected (longitudinal and converted) waves appear, associated with the thin layer. The intensity ratio of head and transcritically reflected longitudinal waves is approximately the same as described previously for observations in well no. 42.

As separation increases, waves approaching from below become increasinly significant on vertical profiling seismograms. The relative intensity of the Z-component of the direct wave diminishes, as the direction of approach approximates the horizontal. On seismograms from SP 3000, SP 3500, and SP 4000 m, wave t_P is dominant, and it propagates with velocity $v_a = $ -3700 m/sec. This two-phase wave is reliably tracked along the vertical profile. The relative intensity of t_P increases with distance.[2] The kinematic study of t_P (particularly level-reduced traveltime curves) confirms the law of increase of apparent velocities characteristic for refracted waves.

On graphs of observed amplitudes (Figure 113), the ratio of intensities of various wave types can be studied as the source becomes more remote. If for distances of 1250 m and 1775 m the intensity of the direct wave exceeds that of the head wave by almost two orders of magnitude then the intensity of the curved-

[2]A detailed analysis of waves at large distances was made by Pogonyailo (1968, 1970). Here we briefly cite some of her results.

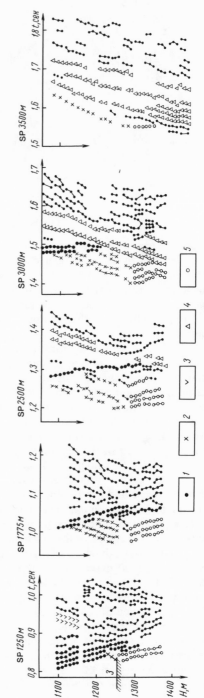

FIG. 112. Vertical traveltime curves (well no. 20, Staro-Minsk): (1) Direct waves, (2) head waves, (3) transcritically reflected waves, (4) refracted waves, and (5) transmitted waves.

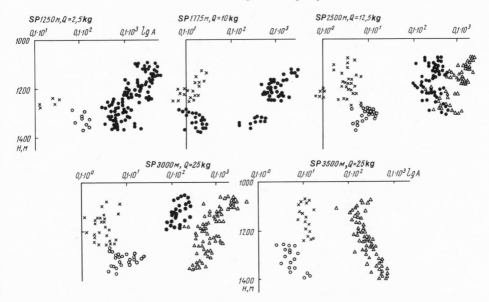

FIG. 113. Amplitude graphs of waves (well no. 20, Staro-Minsk). Same designations as for Figure 112.[3]

path refraction at distances of 2500 m and 3000 m exceeds that of the direct wave by a factor of 5 – 10, and that of the head wave by a factor of 150. Records from SP 3500 m indicate that the latter ratio is 10, and identification of the first wave as a head wave at this distance may not be correct. The amplitude graphs for 3500 m show the variation of amplitude of the refracted wave with depth — on a profile section of 300 m (from 1400 m to 1100 m) it decays by about one order of magnitude. Laws were studied governing the variations of amplitudes along horizontal lines at different levels. The amplitudes of the direct and refracted waves decay for $H = 1150$ and 1120 m in a legitimate manner. For $H = 1350$ m, the refracted wave does not indicate such a decay. Amplitudes of the head wave also decay, and this may be associated with measurement errors because of the low amplitudes of the head wave on seismograms.

As a result of computer correlation of waves along the vertical profile, it be-

came possible to separate interference of direct and refracted waves and to determine apparent velocities which are – 3400 to – 3700 m/sec for the refracted and + 4800 m/sec for the direct waves. Computer correlation also permitted the acquisition of average wave forms for various waves (Figure 114). The direct and

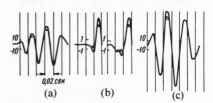

FIG. 114. Wavelet forms: (a) Direct wave, (b) head wave, and (c) refracted wave.

refracted waves contain several peaks and, allowing for phase inversion for the refracted wave, the forms of the two wavelets are identical.

[3]Editor's note: The measured amplitudes of the transmitted waves for SP 1775 m are erroneously plotted as solid circles instead of open circles.

For a more reliable identification of the wave type t_P (among the three possible variations; transcritically reflected wave, head wave associated with the deeper boundary, or continuously refracted wave), theoretical calculations were carried out on wavefields for given models[4] by computers programmed by T. B. Yanovskaya for the raypath method. Amplitudes of waves were computed along horizontal levels of the profiles. For data computed for distances $0 < l < 1500$ m, the most intense wave in the later portion of the record is the reflected wave. In the vicinity of the shotpoint it has one-third to one-tenth the strength of the direct wave (depending on the model), but it decays slowly and becomes dominant for remote shotpoints. Near the initial point, the amplitude of transcritically reflected waves exceeds the amplitude of the direct wave. As the distance increases (2500 m), the refracted wave dominates on theoretical seismograms. The levels of curves for the waves being considered is in fair agreement with theoretical levels.

The refracted t_P-wave on surface seismograms of the Staro-Minsk platform produces first arrivals in the distance interval 4000 – 6000 m, where it is replaced by the wave refracted in the basement.

Thus, if the cross-section contains a separate thin high-velocity layer, then this layer decisively influences the wavefield near the starting point. The intensity of the wave transcritically reflected from this layer may exceed the intensity of the head wave by two orders of magnitude and, on discrete profile sections, it may form visible first arrivals on surface seismograms. As the distance increases, the influence of the thin layer on the wavefield becomes less pronounced. The wave that dominates the record becomes the

wave refracted in the bed that underlies the thin layer, and this wave then produces first arrivals.

Relative intensity of head and transcritically reflected waves in the case of layers whose thicknesses are commensurate with the wavelength

When layer thickness increases, the relative intensity of the head wave increases. However, it still remains much weaker than the transcritically reflected wave. In actual media, homogeneous layers of great thickness are encountered less frequently than thin layers. In most cases, they are not homogeneous and, as revealed by detailed velocity measurements, consist of one or several packets of thin layers. For the cross-section of well no. 20 of the Staro-Minsk platform, such a boundary may be assumed to lie at 900 m. The velocity discontinuity is 0.9 ($v_{LR1} = 2040$ m/sec; $v_{LR2} = 2310$ m/sec) and the ratio of wavelength to layer thickness is $\lambda/d = 5.5$.

Records for maximal amplification (Figure 115) indicate first arrivals and reversal of wave polarities. In the depth interval from 580 – 670 m, seismograms indicate "upward" arriving waves that correspond to the direct wave. Beginning with $H = 680$ m, and deeper, sharp arrivals of the "downward" head wave register as a weak low-frequency oscillation, complicated by an event of higher frequency; the apparent velocity is negative. On seismograms taken with minimum amplification, a more intense interferential event of direct and reflected waves is perceived behind the head wave. As the distance from the boundary increases, the reflected wave separates from the direct wave and, starting at 520 m deep, it begins to register outside the region of interference. Comparison of intensities of head and transcritically reflected waves shows that the head wave is weaker by about one order of magnitude. Along the vertical profile, it is impossible to resolve the head wave in its

---

[4]In selecting the model of the medium, all the data from VSP, velocity well-logging, and SWL for P- and S-waves was employed.

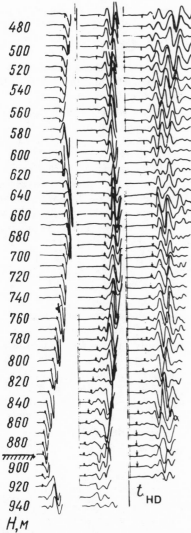

480
500
520
540
560
580
600
620
640
660
680
700
720
740
760
780
800
820
840
860
880
900
920
940

t_{HD}

H,м

FIG. 115. Seismograms of head waves associated with the boundary at depth 900 m (SP 2500 m, well no. 20, Staro-Minsk).

subsequent arrivals against the background of the transcritically reflected wave.

An analogous situation exists for well no. 42. In both boreholes the relative intensity of the head wave (associated with the boundary at 900 m) is substantially higher than the intensities of head waves associated with the thin layers in the cross-section because of the increase of the thickness of the layer. However, it is possible that the intensity is influenced by refraction.

The situations examined at interior points of the medium demonstrate that head waves associated with thin layers possess very low intensity and are almost unobservable on surface seismograms. Therefore, the study of head waves from thin high-velocity layers is possible only by use of VSP in the immediate vicinity of the boundaries, and large dynamic-range instrumentation. VSP data on the insignificant intensity of head waves associated with thin layers in actual media concur with theoretical work (Molotkov and Krauklis, 1963). In principle, the theory proves that head waves cannot possibly exist off thin layers associated with hard contacts. VSP data are also compatible with theoretical work (Smirnova and Yermilova, 1959) that demonstrates that head waves, even under the most favorable conditions, are weaker than transcritically reflected waves and that their intensity rapidly decays as the thickness of the layer decreases.

VSP results were confirmed recently by new research. In spite of specially organized field surface observations (Epinat'yeva and Karus, 1967), we were still unable to record head waves from a thin layer. Although head waves from such a layer were registered by VSP, tracking of these waves was successful only adjacent to the boundaries. In model research (Faizulin and Epinat'yeva, 1967) carried out on solids with "welded" contacts between layers, the relative intensity of head and reflected waves as a function of layer thickness was studied. It was shown that the amplitude ratio of reflected and head waves does vary drastically with layer thickness by reduction of head wave intensities. As distance increases, the amplitude ratio increases; and as thickness of the layer increases, the amplitude ratio diminishes. An erroneous appraisal of head-wave intensity associated with thin layers is explained, in large measure, by the transfer of modeling results on solid-fluid specimen to actual media, a common practice until recently (Davydova, 1962).

WAVES IN CARBONATE CROSS-SECTIONS OF PLATFORM REGIONS

A large number of sharp boundaries is characteristic in carbonate cross-sections where there is a sequence of carbonate and terrigenous deposits. Study of the wavefield of such cross-sections, according to CMRRW records, is important since such cross-sections are prevalent over wide areas of the Russian platform. For the Kletsko-Pochtov platform (see Figure 61), the formation of the initial portion of the surface seismogram is controlled by high-velocity layers; these are principally limestone layers. There are many such layers in the cross-section. For practical purposes, however, two layers of comparatively great thickness are significant. The first layer with interstratifications of terrigenous deposits occurs at depths of 125 – 270 m; the second, thicker layer is located in the depth interval of 640 – 850 m. These layers are associated with high-velocity waves that form the initial portion of seismograms taken at distances up to 5000 – 6000 m. For large separations in the initial portion of the record, the leading role in formation of the wavefield is gradually transferred to waves refracted in the basement. A combined system of observations (see Figure 10) was designed to study the wavefield in the distance interval 0 – 32 km. Detail is largely lost as the distance from the source increases.

The nature of first arrivals at the surface was determined from results of joint treatment of data from surface and borehole observations. From combined traveltime curves (Figure 116), waves registering on the surface and on the initial portion of the record for an interval of 0 – 11,000 m may be subdivided into three groups.

The first group, t_{P1}, is associated with the middle carboniferous layer (125 – 270 m), with a higher velocity. It is formed by the wave refracted at the top of the Paleozoic (up to a distance of 1.5 km), confirmed by vertical traveltime curves from SP 600, SP 1000, and SP 1500 m. In the later portion of the record, singly refracted and multiple waves issuing from the Paleozoic bed are observed, as are waves reflected from sharp boundaries represented by thin layers of limestone at depths of 390 – 520 m. The wave group t_{P1} is tracked as first arrivals for distances 3500 – 4000 m with a velocity $v_a = 4500 – 4700$ m/sec.

The second group t_{P2}, representing curved-ray refractions and their multiples in the second limestone layer (the lower carboniferous layer 640 – 850 m), plus waves reflected from boundaries down to the top of the terrigenous Devonian, appear along the horizontal profile in the interval of 1000 – 8500 m and as first arrivals for the section of 4000 – 9000 m. The characteristic of this wave is a certain increase of apparent velocity from 4600 m/sec at a distance of 3 km to 5000 m/sec at 10,000 m.

The third group of oscillations t_{P3} is composed of waves refracted in the basement. Possessing high apparent velocity ($v_a = 5700$ m/sec) they are an added complexity on records of $l = 6000$ m. Starting at $l = 8000$ m the t_{P3} waves can be tracked as an independent event, and it registers as a first event on seismograms for $l = 9000$ m. At the starting point, that group of oscillations registers as a wavelet with a duration of up to 0.3 sec. This is a complicated interferential group composed of refracted and multiply refracted waves. The reversal of waves of various groups occurs as a result of a gradual

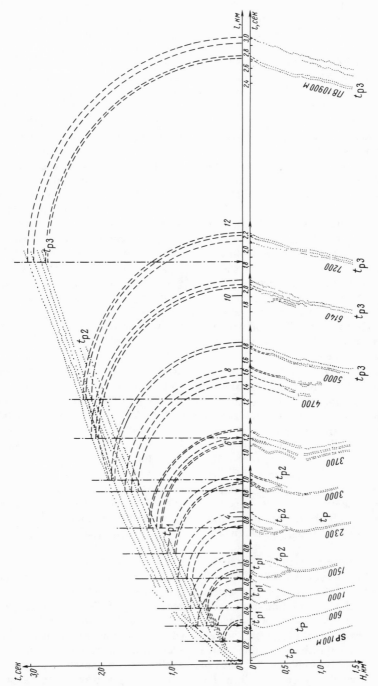

FIG. 116. Combination traveltime curves of first waves (well no. 1, Kletsko-Pochtov).

decay of first-arrival waves.

Three groups of refracted waves register on both vertical and horizontal profiles. The first wave with a negative velocity registers from SP 6000, SP 1000, and SP 1500 m. The refracted wave connected with the second layer begins to be trackable along the vertical profile from SP 1500. Its appearance as a first arrival widens gradually as distance increases, and it arrives on the surface from SP 4700 m. Multiply refracted waves connected with the second layer are also recorded on the vertical profile from SP 1500 m. The first refracted wave dominates up to a distance of 3000 m, while the multiply refracted waves become more intense as distance increases further. The wave associated with the crystalline basement appears on the vertical profile when shot from SP 5000 m. All waves approaching the surface are reflected from the bottom of the ZLV and from the top of the Paleozoic, producing a complex total wave field.

It is most convenient to examine the nature of waves producing first arrivals on surface seismograms by considering waves associated with the second layer. It is difficult to analyze waves of group t_{P1} because of the shallow depth of the first layer and the complexity of the field dictated by the upper portion of the cross-section. Waves of group t_{P3} associated with the basement are not important since they are sufficiently well understood (Averbukh et al, 1963; Pomerantseva, 1962).

In overlapping vertical traveltime curves of first waves from SP 1020, SP 1500, and SP 2300 m at a profile section that crosses the second limestone layer (Figure 117a), the locus of points of conversion from direct to refracted waves is indicated by the dash-dot line above the layer. This also indicates the locus of horizontal particle motion within the layer, corresponding to the reversal in

sign of apparent velocity of the refracted wave. The region of negative apparent velocity is contained between the two lines, i.e., the upward directions of approach of the refracted wave (cross-hatched).

Seismograms of the Z-component (Figure 117b) demonstrate the conversion from the direct to the refracted wave. From SP 1020 m this conversion occurs in the immediate vicinity of the boundary. From SP 1500 m, the refracted wave appears as a first wave on the profile section comprising 50 m. From SP 2300 m, the seismogram is obtained for low amplification, and the curved-ray refration is recorded and tracked over the entire record. The intensity of the latter wave increases somewhat as it propagates from the refracting layer to the overlying one. This is due to a decrease of velocity as well as to the fact that the wave direction approaches the vertical. Below the refracting boundary, the form of the event is preserved, but a gradual decay of amplitudes, phase inversion, and a gradual increase of amplitudes takes place. All these features lead to the concept that curved-ray refraction does occur and that the wave below the boundary of 640 m is, in fact, a wave refracted in the middle carboniferous limestone bed.

Thus, not a single head wave was recorded on the surface or for VSP, as first arrivals or as subsequent arrivals.

WAVES ASSOCIATED WITH THICK LAYERS

As a rule, actual media are highly heterogeneous and it is extremely difficult to find a sufficiently thick homogeneous layer. The most favorable medium could be the crystalline basement which is considered a half-space. However, rarely are boreholes drilled to great depths into the basement. Usually, boreholes barely approach the basement and seldom penetrate its top. Pure salt is considered to be the most homogeneous bed among sedimentary deposits. A thick salt layer can also serve as an excellent model for the study of head waves because a characteristic of salt is the constancy of velocity, or the insignificant velocity increment with depth. However, in real media, such homogeneous layers seldom occur.

Deposits of the Jurassic-Triassic complex at Stavropol appear to be suitable for the study of waves associated with a thick layer. According to electric well-logging data, the cross-section appears to be homogeneous in the depth interval of 1880 – 2700 m. Judged by its properties within the seismic range of wavelengths, this bed seems to be the most homogeneous layer that was encountered by us. The great thickness of the section, a significant portion of which (more than 900 m) is revealed by well no. 162 of the North-Stavropol platform, results from the location of the borehole in the zone forming a graben. Lithologically, the deposits represent a variegated monotonic bed of siltstones.

The thin layer of high-velocity chalk deposits ($v_{LR} = 5000$ m/sec) located above the top of the bed ($H_v = 1790$ m) substantially complicated the wave pattern and provided difficulties in the study of the refracted wave near its emergence from the basement.

Refracted waves were recorded for off-line profiles for shotpoint separations from the top of the borehole in the interval from 1200 – 14,100 m (Figure 118). From SP 1580 m and SP 2020 m, only the vertical profile section of interest was shot with the purpose of detailing the observations near the point of emergence of the refracted wave. From all shotpoints, except for the farthest one, Z-components of motion were recorded and observations were conducted by three-point probes. The vertical profile from SP 14,100 m is produced by means of a three-component installation. The high values of layer velocities (3250, 5000 m/sec) encumber interpretation of results for off-line vertical profiles, as values of the apparent velocities of first arrivals on the initial portion of the record are nearly infinite.

Refracted waves associated with the Jurassic-Triassic complex appear on the vertical profile between SP 1200 m and SP 1580 m, (Figure 118). From 1580 m, both refracted waves along the thin layer and the top of the thick bed are observed separately. In essence, they appear within the region of mutual interference with the direct wave. On seismograms, these waves are characterized by a reversal of polarity of particle motion of the medium near the boundaries. Let us first discuss the polarities of the motion.

First arrivals are shown on the composite seismogram obtained from SP 1580 m for high amplification (Figure 119). They indicate that within the depth interval of 1750 – 1760 m the upward direction of arrival corresponding to the direct wave changes into an equally sharp downward arrival that corresponds to the refracted wave. At the boundary of the thin layer ($H_v = 1790$ m), again a reversal of arrival polarity occurs that is caused by the conversion from refracted waves to transmitted waves. An analogous situation is observed at the top of the basement ($H_v = 1880$ m) where, within the depth interval of 1860 – 1870 m, the first arrivals are directed downward, corresponding to the refracted wave. As it crosses the boundary, the refracted wave changes again into first arrivals of the transmitted wave which registers first and remains such to the end of the profile; i.e., the directions of arrival are upward. In this manner, two waves are reliably brought out from SP 1580 m, and they are associated with the thin layer in deposits of chalk and the basement, respec-

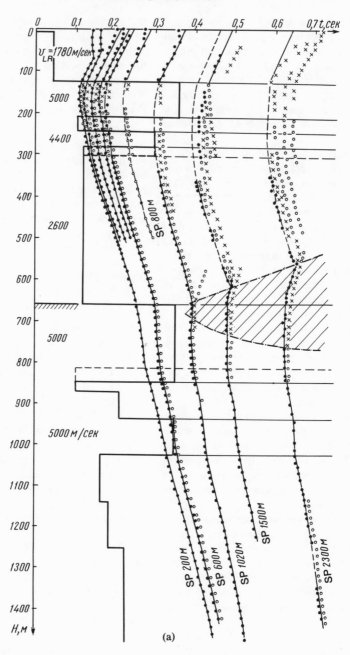

FIG. 117. (a) Vertical traveltime curves of first waves. (b) Seismograms of first waves. Well no. 1, Kletsko-Pochtov. The velocity cross-section is schematically indicated on the traveltime curves.

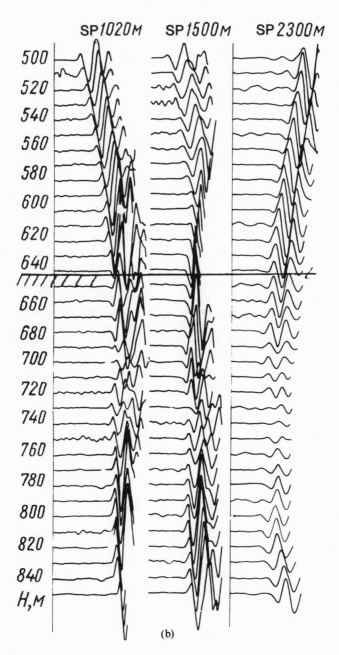

(b)

tively. For observations from remaining shotpoints, these waves are not resolved and a single, apparently total, wave appears as a first arrival. One may suppose that the intensity of the wave associated with the thin layer decays rapidly with distance and does not influence the intensity of the first wave for large distances.

From SP 2400 m, the conversion from the refracted wave to the direct wave is detected by reversal of the polarity of arrivals, which occurs at a depth of about 1570 — 1580 m. At SP 14,000 m, the refracted wave is trackable as a first wave over the entire section of the vertical profile above the boundary.

For the determination of the nature of the wave that registers first, the study of polarities of motion in the basement itself is of fundamental interest. Here, the following law is observed: as the distance increases, the depth at which the polarity changes ; increases. From SP 2020 m, reversal occurs at a depth of 1890 m, from SP 2400 m, at 1920 m, and from SP 5100 m at depth 2230 m (Figure 118).

From SP 14,100 m, observations were conducted by a symmetrical setup but because of low amplitudes, it is difficult to determine accurately the reversal of polarities. The apparent velocities of the refracted wave above the top of the basement from all shotpoints is negative and equal to 4000 m/sec. The apparent velocities of the transmitted waves at profile sections from the top of the basement to the point of polarity reversal are nearly infinite. The form of the recorded refracted wave from SP 1580 m and SP 2020 m, above the boundary, is complicated since there the refracted wave interferes with the direct one.

Below the boundary, the relative intensity of the refracted wave decays while the wave form simplifies. Receding from the boundary, the recorded amplitude of the Z-component increases. A sharp increase of the recorded intensity of the refracted wave occurs in the seismogram obtained from SP 5100 m (Figure 119). The wave form recorded above the boundary, although interferential, is sim-

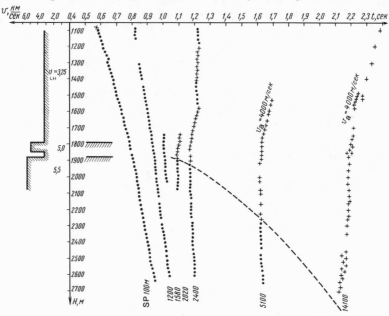

FIG. 118. Vertical traveltime curves for a profile section that crosses the Jurassic-Triassic age.

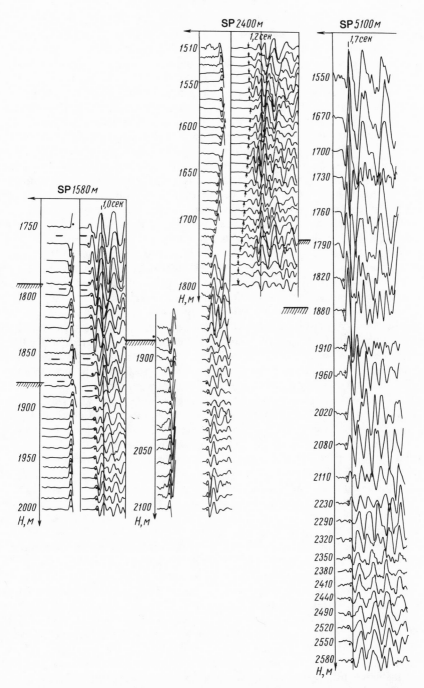

FIG. 119. Seismograms recorded for the profile section that crosses the top of the Jurassic-Triassic bed.

pler and more stable than the wave from the nearer shotpoints. As the wave crosses the boundary, wave intensity gradually diminishes to depths of 2230 – 2290 m, where polarity reversals of the particle motion of the medium and of the apparent velocities occur, after which the intensity again rises slowly. With further increase of depth, the intensity of the record increases. If we discount the differences in intensities at the upper and lower extremities of the vertical profile, we can see that the character of the record is almost constant. A sharp dependence of the recorded form (basically the number of phases) on depth of charge is evident for all shotpoints.

These details permit certain conclusions to be drawn as to the nature of the first wave registered along the vertical profile. Let us first of all examine the features of the wave above the refracting boundary. According to the kinematic features, the wave may be interpreted both as a head wave and as a refracted wave. Values of boundary velocities determined from vertical traveltime curves of first waves vary within the interval of 5100 – 5400 m/sec. These variations are not governed by a particular law and constitute a scatter connected with the accuracy of velocity determination. Thus, values of the boundary velocities are not a criterion for the determination of the nature of the wave.

The computed theoretical traveltime curves of the head waves and curved-ray refractions indicated that, kinematically, they are practically identical and, therefore, the two traveltime curves satisfactorily average the observed data. It was impossible to utilize the dynamic particulars of the wave for increasing separations because of the difference in charge weight (from 2 to 50 kg). Thus, available data on the wave that registers first above the top of the basement do not permit a unique determination of the nature of the wave.

For this reason, it appears to be of interest to consider the particulars of the wave that registers below the refracting boundary within the basement. A wave having a negative velocity, ie., approaching from below, is registered below the boundary. Receding from the boundary, the record of the vertical component is associated with reduced amplitudes and reversal of polarity of motion and apparent velocity from negative to positive. This conversion occurs at points of minima of traveltime curves of first waves and the corresponding depth increases as the shotpoint becomes more remote. The locus of points of reversal is indicated by the dashed line in Figure 118. All these features are characteristic for a medium described by a monotonic increase of velocity.

Study of the line of reversal of polarities of arrivals permitted determination of the coefficient of increment $\beta = 0.00005$ m^{-1} under assumption of linear velocity increase. According to computed data, the minimum point of the traveltime curve of the refracted wave from SP 14,100 m is located at depth 4000 m, and therefore it could not have been confirmed by observations.

Comparison of recorded wave forms at different points of the profile may have a significant bearing on determination of the nature of the wave. Let us examine such a comparison for the two SP 2400 m and SP 5100 m where the first waves emerged from the region of interference with subsequent waves. From SP 2400 m, the comparison was between waves obtained above the refracting boundary ($H = 1750$ m), immediately below the boundary ($H = 1930$ m), and at a comparatively remote depth with reference to the boundary, i.e., at a profile section for which the wave possesses a positive velocity ($H = 2070$ m and 2190 m), as shown in Figure 118. At the first two points, the waves are directed from be-

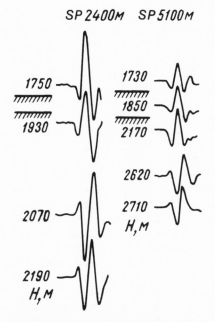

SP 2400M   SP 5100M

1750

1930

2070

2190
H,M

1730

1850

2170

2620

2710
H,M

FIG. 120. Comparison of wavelet forms for the first wave on profile sections above and below the refracting boundary.

low, the events are in-phase, and their wave forms are identical. At the two deeper locations, the record wave forms are identical to records obtained for points above the boundary, except for their phase inversion (Figure 120).

From SP 5100 m, another comparative study was made of records obtained above the upper refracting boundary ($H = 1730$ m), between the boundaries ($H = 1850$ m), immediately below the top of the basement ($H = 2170$ m), and at sections for which a wave of positive velocity is observed ($H = 2620$ m and 2710 m). The wave form of the first wave is the same at all points, except for phase inversion at the two deep locations.

The identity of the wave forms for the first wave above the refracting boundary, below it, and for a region where direct transmitted waves register, shows that the wave registering above the boundary is a curved-ray refraction. Such a procedure to establish refraction by ob-

servation at interior points of the refracting layer, considered to be a novel approach, confirmed that for large separations and thick layers, the first wave to register is the curved-ray refraction. Analogous results were obtained earlier in the study of the nature of waves connected with the crystalline basement (Averbukh et al, 1963; Pomerantseva, 1962). Thus, in the case of a thick homogeneous layer in the medium, an increase of velocity with depth takes place, and the curved-ray refraction is the first to register.

To appraise the influence of curved-path refraction in the underlying layer on the intensity of refracted waves at sections close to the point of origin (for which the formulas of the raypath method are not valid), computations employing the formulas of Chekin (1965) were used. This was done for seven values of β ranging from 0.00010 to 0.00026 m^{-1} and for the following parameters of the medium: $H_v = 1880$ m; $v_{av} = 2600$ m/sec; $v_{|LR|} = 5500$ m/sec; and $t = 30$ hz. The influence of curved-ray refraction on intensity was calculated for $l = 2500 – 6500$ m. Figure 121 demonstrates the strong influence of the velocity gradient on intensity of the first wave. If for $\beta = 0.00010$ m^{-1} and $l = 5500$ m, the intensity of the curved-path refraction exceeds that of the head wave by a factor of 11, then for $\beta = 0.00020$ m^{-1} this ratio becomes 67. For $l = 3500$ m, the curved-path refraction is more intense than the head wave by a factor of 7; for $l = 5000$ m, this ratio is about 70; and for $l = 5500$ m, it is more than 100.

Thus, for a thick layer, experimental data permits identification of a velocity gradient, while computations demonstrate the strong influence of the gradient on the intensity of the first wave (usually taken as a head wave). The intensity of the curved-path refraction can exceed that of the head wave significantly (by a factor of more than 100).

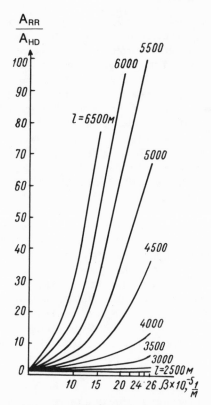

FIG. 121. The influence of refraction on intensity of refracted waves.

Media with weak velocity differentiation are characteristic particularly for areas of inflections filled out by thick beds of terrigenous deposits or by extremely thin-layered marine deposits. For these media it was supposed that head waves possess significant intensities (Epinat'yeva, 1960). VSP work demonstrates that head waves in media with weak velocity differentiation are not observed. This is illustrated in well no. 3 of the AFIP platform of the Krasnodar region, situated in the area of an inflection. To bring out the head waves, a vertical profile from eight shotpoints located over a distance interval of 0 – 1500 m was shot. From all shotpoints (see Figure 15), the first wave to appear along vertical profiles is the curved-path refraction, and in later arrivals a large number of reflected waves are observed. Analogous results were obtained for regions with weak velocity differentiation, expecially some foothill and intramountainous depressions (Ilyi, Fergan, and Naryn monoclines) filled-in by a thick layer of coarsely fragmented terrigenous deposits.

Computational data — Experimentally, the lower intensity of head waves as compared to transcritically reflected waves is in good agreement with theory. Calculations of the intensity of head waves from thin layers are very difficult. But even for the case of a layer over a half-space, for which the computational procedure is available, calculations confirm the lower intensity of head waves.

As an illustration, let us cite computed data for the intensity of head and transcritically reflected waves corresponding to a layer over a half-space. The velocity discontinuity at the boundary is equal to the discontinuity of the layer velocities in the overlying bed and in the layer (well no. 42). The source function $f(t)$ was assumed in the form of two arches of period T, approximately equal to the given duration of the interaction. Calculations[5] were made on the assumption that waves are generated by a normal force on the surface, while points of observation are distributed along the surface beyond the point of emergence of the head wave: $r_o/(2d) < r/(2d)$, where r_o = distance to the initial point of the head wave, d = thickness of layer, r = distance from the shot to the point of observations. The following parameters were assumed:

$$\gamma = \frac{v_{S1}}{v_{P1}} = 0.394; \qquad \delta = \frac{v_{S1}}{v_{S2}} = 0.558;$$

$$\frac{d}{v_{P1}} = 16,5, \qquad \sigma_0 = \frac{\rho_1}{\rho_2} = 1;$$

$$\Delta_0 = \frac{v_{S2}}{v_{P2}} = 0.5;$$

where ρ = density.

[5]Calculations by Smirnova (1959) of the AS USSR

The results are shown in Figure 122a. For the distance $r/(2d) = 1.8029$, the head wave emerged from the zone of interference with the reflected wave, and for increasing distances the time difference between the waves increases. The intensity of the head wave is $1/5 - 1/7$ that of the intensity of the transcritically reflected wave. As thickness of the layer diminishes, intensity of the head wave should decay rapidly. It remains less than the intensity of the transcritically reflected wave for any given ratio of velocities of longitudinal waves in the first and the second layers.

Let us examine the theoretical seismograms (Figure 122b) computed for various velocity ratios v_{P1}/v_{P2}. At a distance $r/(2d) = 1.58$, for which the head wave has been completely separated from the transcritically reflected wave, its intensity is below that of the reflected wave by almost one order of magnitude. As the velocity discontinuity becomes less pronounced, i.e., for transition to layers having a weak velocity differentiation ($v_{P1}/v_{P2} = 0.90$ and 0.99), this ratio varies but little; the head wave remains weaker than the reflected wave. In certain cases of structure of the medium, these interrelations may vary due to absorption.

Thus, detailed study of the nature of waves in the underlying thick layer demonstrates that a velocity increase with distance takes place and that therefore a curved-path refraction, and not a head wave, registers above the boundary at interior points of the medium and at the surface. Computations indicate that intensity of the curved-path refraction can exceed that of the head wave by two orders of magnitude when the velocity in the underlying layer is constant. Even in the most favorable case of weak velocity differentiations and a thick layer, head waves still remain weaker than transcritically reflected waves.

It is essential to review critically the

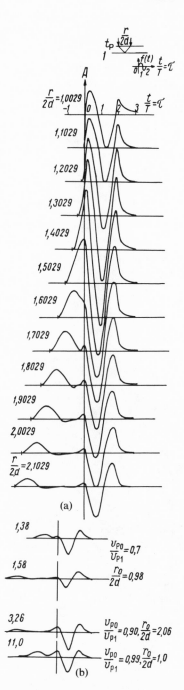

(a)

(b)

FIG. 122. Computed seismograms of head waves and transcritically reflected waves.

data on wave patterns in media with weak velocity differentiation where, apparently, curved-ray refractions and reflected waves were in many instances tracked as head waves. Experiments should be made to evaluate the influence of curved-path refraction on the intensity of waves previously assumed to be head waves.

INFLUENCE OF THE UPPER PORTION OF THE CROSS-SECTION ON OBSERVATIONS AT LARGE DISTANCES (CMRRW)

A large amount of data has been accumulated in regard to the influence of the upper portion of the cross-section on observations at large distances. The importance of the upper portion of the cross-section is already being accounted for, to a larger or smaller degree, in the process of MRLW interpretation. But the influence of the upper portion of the cross-

section at large distances, particularly characteristic for CMRRW, has been studied but little and is practically ignored in the interpretation of data. At the same time, available VSP experience indicates that the upper portion of the cross-section may substantially influence surface seismograms obtained at large separations from the source. This influence manifests itself in two ways. First, seismograms are complicated by various types of noise waves, and second, natural seismic noise background connected with the upper portion of the cross-section restricts the useful sensitivity of instrumentation that is essential for observations at large distances.

For seismograms obtained by observation at large distances, two groups of waves are characteristic (Figure 123). The first group forms the initial portion of the seismogram and consists of a num-

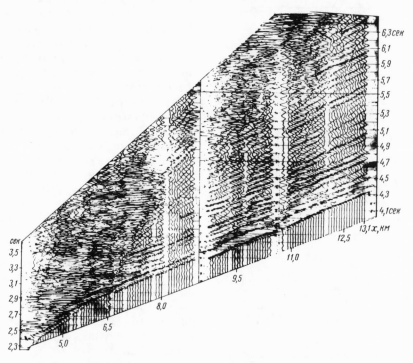

FIG. 123. Surface seismograms for CMRRW (Staro-Minsk).

ber of waves associated with velocities near the velocity of the first wave. The duration and intensity of the group is different for various regions and substantially depend on geologic structure of the upper portion of the cross-section. In some regions the intensity of these waves may exceed that of the first wave.

The second wave group, appearing much later, is composed of intense low-velocity waves which may persist for very large distances (15 – 20 km). The low-velocity values and straight-line travel-time curves, starting near the point of explosion, prove that these waves do not penetrate very deeply and are connected with the upper portion of the cross-section.

Let us examine the influence of the upper portion of the cross-section according to data obtained on the Staro-Minsk and the Kletsko-Pochtov platforms.

Observations on the Staro-Minsk platform

A system of combined horizontal and vertical traveltime curves in the distance interval of 0 – 12.1 km was obtained to study the influence of the upper portion of the cross-section and to determine the nature of the waves recorded at the surface.

Waves on the initial portion of the record. — The influence of the upper portion of the cross-section on CMRRW seismograms is based on observation of the wave pattern at great depths near the source as well as in the reception area. The study of the wavefield at great depths demonstrates that conditions near the shot often create a large number of multiple waves of various types, associated with boundaries preeminently located in the upper portion of the cross-section. Therefore, the initial portion of seismograms obtained for vertical profiles at great depths is composed of numerous incident waves equal in intensity to the first wave. In some cases, these waves occupy the record interval from 1.0 – 1.5

sec. After reflection at deep horizons, a portion of the wave energy is returned to the surface in the form of multiply reflected waves. The remaining energy portion (refracted waves) penetrates into the depth of the medium after the first wave along the same kind of trajectory. At interior points of the medium, at great depths and for sufficiently large separations from the source, we are able to record these reflected-refracted waves and to study their parameters up to the region of registration of refracted-reflected waves associated with the upper portion of the cross-section.

At a distance of about 6.0 km, seismograms (Figure 123) obtained over a section of the horizontal profile that includes well no. 42 indicate the first arrivals of the dominant wave with an apparent velocity $v_a = 5.0 - 5.1$ km/sec. This is the most intense wave on the initial portion of the record and remains the first wave to the end of the profile (13.1 km). For the later portion of the record, (starting with a distance of about 7 – 8 km), less intense waves with the same apparent velocities are recorded following the first wave. Their traveltime curves are practically parallel to that of the first wave; these waves occupy the time interval of 0.8 – 0.9 sec on the seismograms.

Observations along the vertical profile at distances from 0 – 2.5 km, permit determination of waves and time intervals involved in the penetration from the source to the depth of the medium, and also the appraisal of their intensity.

The trajectories of these waves are demonstrated schematically in Figure 124, indicating that numerous longitudinal and converted waves penetrate into the depth of the medium (see Chapter 7). The most intense longitudinal waves on the later portion of the record are the multiples connected with the principal horizons, t^{10} and t^{30}, while the most intense of the converted waves is the wave

t_{CV3}. All these waves reaching the top of the basement (boundary 5), are refracted waves that emerge for large distances in the same sequence as the reflected-refracted waves.

Figure 124 identifies the various waves, i.e., waves registering on the initial portion of the record associated with large distances and great depths, and waves registering for small distances generated in the upper portion of the cross-section. Comparison of wave patterns at great depths in the region of the shot and at the point of reception indicates the majority of waves registering on the initial portion of the record are total reflected-refracted waves and refracted-reflected waves.

Low-velocity waves. — Seismograms of Figure 123 show that the most intense of the low-velocity waves is the one having $v_a = 1750$ m/sec, and the observation area shifts rapidly to the end of the record. Preceding this wave there appear waves with velocities $v_a = 2400 - 2200$ m/sec. The apparent velocities of waves along the vertical profile lie in the range $3900 - 4600$ m/sec. Horizontal and vertical traveltime curves of these waves are straight lines. The low-velocity waves are tracked along the vertical profile at shallow depths and they are of lower frequency (22 hz) than the first waves (about 35 hz). VSP showed that such waves might be connected with horizons located

at shallow depths in the presence of a velocity gradient in the underlying layer. In such cases, interference waves are formed at the boundary, and the kinematic aspect of these waves, for practical purposes, coincides with that of the head waves; however, the intensity of the interferential waves is considerably higher than that of the head waves and the waves decay very slowly with distance.

Such waves may be recorded for very large distances, and their intensity persists on the seismograms. Occasionally these waves are identified as head waves. Sometimes the intensity of low-velocity waves is not very high and they decay rapidly, because of the absence of a gradient of velocity in the upper portion of the cross-section or its low value.

Observations on the Kletsko-Pochtov Platform

Observations in the Volgograd district illustrate the influence of the upper portion of the cross-section even more descriptively. The example refers to the study of waves forming the initial portion of the record shot for large distances. VSP seismograms obtained from SP 60, SP 200, and SP 600 m (Figure 125),[6] indicate the initial portion of the record consists of a large number of multiple incident waves with parallel lineups associated with the upper portion of the

[6]Translator's remark: The seismogram from SP 2300 m (Figure 125) has been used as the jacket design of the original book.

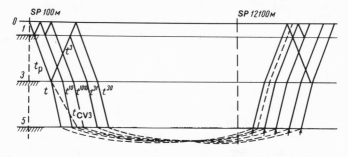

FIG. 124. Schematic trajectories of propagation of multiple waves.

cross-section. The waves are sufficiently intense and are reliably correlated along the entire profile. The most stable waves appear on the initial portion of the seismogram.

As distance increases (from 1020 – 2300 m), the wave refracted in the bed of carbonate deposits appears as the first arrival on different sections of the vertical profile; this wave is returning to the surface. In the later portion of the record, details of the first wave are duplicated. Some multiply refracted waves appear, exhibiting the same time intervals between waves that were observed from the closest shotpoints. At large distances the initial portion of the seismogram is also formed by incident waves which, after reaching the crystalline basement, are refracted and returned to the surface. These waves are illustrated on seismograms out of SP 7200, SP 10,900, and SP 31,700 m (see Figure 141). Multiples connected with the upper portion of the cross-section "duplicate" the wavefield of the first wave, resulting in a complex wavefield with nearly parallel line-ups observable on the initial portion of surface seismograms.

Thus, for comparatively small distances where waves refracted in carbonate deposits are recorded, and for large distances where waves refracted in the crystalline basement are recorded, the initial portion of the record is composed of waves connected with the upper portion of the cross-section.

The above cases show that for large distances intense waves (forming the initial portion of the seismogram and following the first wave with the same apparent velocities) may be associated with the upper portion of the cross-section and do not penetrate deeper than the first wave. For this reason, a careful interpretation of waves on the initial portion of the seismogram is required.

Seismograms of waves of this type

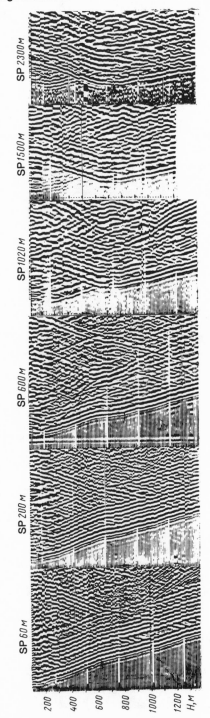

FIG. 125. Initial portions of seismograms (well no. 1, Kletsko-Pochtov).

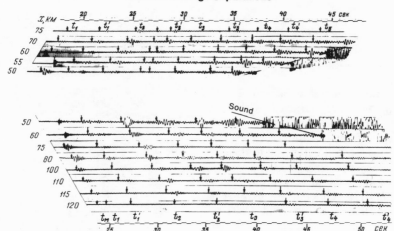

FIG. 126. Total reflected-refracted waves and refracted-reflected waves recorded in the Sea of Okhot (Gal'perin, 1964).

were demonstrated in DSS observations in the Pacific Ocean (Gal'perin, 1964a). Because of the presence of several sharp boundaries (the air-water interface, the ocean bottom, and the sedimentary bottom) separated by the thick (5 – 7 km) body of water with a low velocity of wave propagation, good results have been obtained. Under these conditions, intense total reflected-refracted and refracted-reflected waves were recorded on the later portion of the record, with a multiplicity of the fifth to sixth order (Figure 126).

As multiplicity increases, intensity of waves decays very slowly and as a rule, the intensity exceeds that of the first wave. If the water depth decreases for transition into shallow waters, the initial portion becomes complex, i.e., the wave pattern complicates gradually, the reflected-refracted waves are "crowded" into the initial portion of the record and, for transition to shore, the usual wave pattern observed for land seismograms is established.

In this manner, the vertical velocity gradient exerts the decisive influence on the wavefield for large distances. In addition, wave kinematics on horizontal profiles differ slightly for gradiented and layered homogeneous media, and may not be reliable criterion for the determination of the nature of waves. Also, in a layered medium, the formation of the initial portion of the record can be strongly influenced by transcritically reflected waves which, for large distances, closely approach the initial portion of the record and interfere with the first curved-path refractions. Occasionally, even the first wave may appear complex on seismograms. Possibly this explains the intensity of waves recorded behind the first wave in some cases of CMRRW investigations. The relationship of reflected and curved-path refractions for the initial portion of the record should be considered for special research. In the formation of the wavefield on the initial portion of the seismogram, the upper portion of the cross-section may be responsible for numerous intense superimposed multiples.

For future development of exploratory capabilities of the method of refracted waves, the kinematic and dynamic characteristics of waves forming the initial portion of seismograms should be studied.

Chapter 9
TRANSVERSE AND CONVERTED WAVES

The advantages of procedures based on the study of transverse, converted reflected and converted refracted waves are well known (Andreyev, 1967; Berzon et al, 1966; Vasil'ev, 1961; Volin and Rudakov, 1956; Gal'perina, 1968; Gamburtsev, 1939; Kirnos et al, 1934; Ogurtsov and Ozerov, 1959; Puzyrev and Khudobina, 1962; and Scherbakova, 1966). The more significant advantages are improvement of detailing and accuracy of construction[1] required for the solution of such problems as mapping of dipping structures and study of wedged layers. In principle, we can also use converted transmitted waves to improve the accuracy of construction in regional work. However, between theoretical advantages and their realization in a concrete geologic situation, contradictions may arise that strongly encumber the utilization of these procedures.

In spite of the fact that initial efforts in the development of procedures utilizing transverse and converted waves were undertaken more than thirty years ago (Gamburtsev, 1939), and that during the last 15 years a large amount of research has taken place, these procedures still have not found wide practical application. This is largely because of certain specific difficulties in the basic concepts. Up to the present, the difficulties of the method of transverse waves have been caused by the source, since it restricts penetration. We have been able to overcome most of these difficulties by using explosive directional sources. In the methods of converted, reflected, and transmitted waves, the difficulties concern the identification of longitudinal and converted waves that correspond to a single boundary, and the stratigraphic

correlation of waves. The lack of information on velocities of propagation of transverse waves impeded the development of the procedures.

The study of source conditions and propagation of transverse and converted waves in actual media by VSP has furthered the development of the physical basis of these methods and increased their exploratory capabilities; primarily, it has increased the penetration.

The VSP method was used to study transverse and converted (reflected and transmitted) waves in regions having the most diverse seismogeologic conditions. These investigations disclosed the following:

1. In spite of the limited scope of work, we have learned through the study of sources of transverse waves that VSP enables us to appraise objectively the effectiveness and purity of the source. Wavefields generated by directional percussion or explosion sources are distinguished by their simplicity. Direct transverse waves possess high intensity and deep penetration. In many cases, intense transverse waves are generated for conventional shots and influence the wavefield significantly. In some situations, they dominate the records and may be used for the solution of geologic problems.

2. Converted waves are extremely prevalent in actual media. Converted reflected waves were brought out at great depths ($H = 2500$ m) and from almost all boundaries at which longitudinal reflected waves are formed, including the top of the crystalline basement. This appears to be the principle of the premise to increase penetration by means of the method of converted reflected waves. Concerning this approach, one must yet refine the procedure for enhancement and tracking

[1]Translator's remark: Probably refers to the final plot of the cross-section.

of converted waves for surface observations as well as for VSP. For converted reflected waves associated with thin high-velocity layers high intensity, and a comparatively low-frequency composition are characteristic. These features originate in the conversion process and vary but little as the waves propagate.

3. Converted downward transmitted waves, for observation at interior points of the medium and at comparatively small distances from the source, are distinguished by their high intensity and stability. As a rule, they are formed at all boundaries and they dominate the seismograms. These waves may provide information on velocities of transverse waves, particularly at great depths that are not always accessible to well logging.

4. VSP observations for large separations (up to 32 km) permitted the study of generation of converted upward transmitted waves. In the appraisal of exploratory capabilities of the method of converted transmitted waves within the platform portion of the Volgograd district, the structural identity of the horizontal and vertical components of the record was demonstrated. Any abrupt boundaries in the upper portion of the cross-section may exert a decisive influence on the wavefield. In addition, a complex, extensive train of incident longitudinal waves is formed in the neighborhood of the shot, while in the region of reception secondary and multiple converted waves are formed, producing a complex interferential wavefield. Under these conditions, surface seismograms are virtually devoid of simple waves. For this situation there are no reliable criteria, based on physical aspects for the identification of longitudinal and converted waves associated with deep boundaries of conversion.

The method of converted transmitted

waves may be effective (from the point-of-view of identification of P- and PS-waves) for the study of the upper reference boundary (e.g., the top of the carbonate or salt deposits or the top of the basement for an overlying terrigenous bed) with which the dominant waves are associated.

5. Although these results do not directly refer to converted transmitted waves caused by earthquakes, nevertheless analogous difficulties may be encountered in the mechanism of generation of the X-component of the wavefield caused by earthquakes. In earthquakes, a simple form of the first longitudinal wave is to be expected for deep-seated foci. However, the decrease of velocity differentiation of the medium with depth lessens the probability that intense converted transmitted waves will be formed at deep boundaries in the earth's crust. This question goes beyond the scope of the present work and demands special consideration.

6. Transverse and converted waves associated with the upper portion of the cross-section may be significant in forming a complex wavefield and thus complicate the correlation of useful waves on seismograms, even for the structurally simplest media. In the presence of even a single sharp boundary in the upper portion of the cross-section, a complex field of converted (reflected, transmitted, and multiple) waves between that boundary and the bottom of the ZLV is formed. These waves, together with multiple longitudinal waves, might be the reason for the lack of regular waves on surface seismograms.

The method of converted transmitted waves has been actively used in seismic exploration during the last few years. Converted reflected and downward transmitted waves, recorded along the vertical profile from the same shotpoints, are examined jointly.

TRANSVERSE WAVES

The initial efforts in the study of transverse waves in boreholes involved well logging by means of transverse waves developed simultaneously with the method of transverse waves. Although an important role was allocated to well logging by means of transverse and longitudinal waves, it was, however, of secondary importance in the overall study of velocities of transverse waves for the interpretation of surface observations. Procedures were developed for three-component observations in boreholes, and a large amount of research was completed on the dynamics of direct longitudinal and transverse waves. Significant results in this area were achieved by Berdennikova et al (1959), Vinogradov (1967), and others. Also, this research concerned with the propagation of transverse waves should definitely facilitate and stimulate the development of the method of transverse waves.

Excitation of S-waves

The necessary creation of an asymmetric strain field may be achieved by various means: directional impacts, directional explosions, and grouping of asymmetric sources. Thus VSP capabilities applied to the method of transverse waves are important for objective appraisal of the effectiveness of the source, i.e., its purity, intensity, and stability.

As in the method of longitudinal waves, direct transverse waves were excited by directional impacts and shots. Experiments were conducted with explosions at flanks of gullies and in artificial ditches, but such sources appeared to be of low effectiveness and were technically complicated. Let us examine records obtained in one borehole by means of directional impacts and explosions and by means of conventional sources.

Impact excitation. — An apparatus employing an automatic crane was used for impact excitation (Brodov, 1967; Puzyrev, 1967). A 1300 kg weight, suspended from a height of 4 m as a horizontal pendulum, struck a vertical wall. The horizontal percussion possesses good directivity, closely approximating an idealized horizontal force. Such percussions usually permit excitation and registration of direct transverse waves to a depth of 1200 – 1400 m, depending on the cross-section.

Duplication of records is excellent for impact excitation. From typical seismograms (Figures 127 and 128) it is seen that for a horizontal impact, both an intense transverse wave of *SH* type and a fairly intense longitudinal *P*-wave are excited, and the recorded form of the latter is preserved along the vertical profile. The *Z*-component of the longitudinal wave decays rapidly in the upper portion

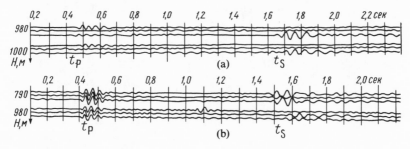

FIG. 127. Seismograms of direct waves t_P and $t_{|s}$, excited by an impact directional source and registered on an in-line vertical profile. (a) By an *XYZ* installation and (b) a symmetrical installation (well no. 42, Staro-Minsk).

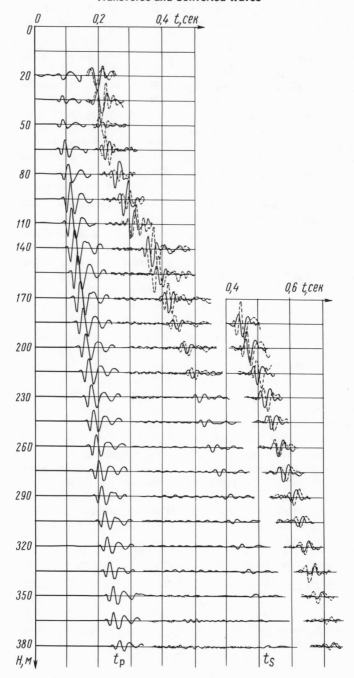

FIG. 128. Seismograms of the direct longitudinal t_P wave (Z-component) and the transverse t_S wave (two horizontal components starting with depth of 185 m and for two levels of amplification). Registered for impact excitation ($l = 40$ m, well no. 90, Kudinov).

of the profile, consistent with the direction of approach of the wave. Longitudinal waves on records of XYZ installations are recorded only by the vertical seismic receivers, while transverse waves are recorded only by the horizontal seismic receivers. In this case, $l = 0$, and the three-component XYZ installation possesses an advantage over the symmetrical installation, the records of which contain longitudinal and transverse waves from all detectors of the group (see Chapter 5).

On the composite seismogram of P- and S-waves, excited by horizontal impacts (Figure 128), records are obtained without controlled orientation of the geophones, yet the correlation of waves proceeds reliably. From vertical traveltime curves of S-waves (Figure 129), the cross-section is split into several layers with small velocity discontinuities and boundaries established according to P- and S-waves do not always coincide.

The low power of impact sources led to the development of a directional explosive source for S-waves.

Explosive source. — An explosive source is most widely used at present and is used in the neighborhood of artificially created inhomogeneities representing a disrupted zone, or in a cavity formed by auxiliary shots (Malushin, 1967; Puzyrev et al, 1967). VSP work on the Kudinov platform confirmed that dense and dry clayey deposits provide favorable conditions for the excitation of transverse waves by means of directional explosions.

For directional explosions, the transverse wave is observed on a comparatively weak and basically irregular background. Seismograms involving an off-line profile ($l = 110$ m) indicate that the intensity of the vertical component of the transverse wave exceeds that of the longitudinal wave (Figure 130) at depths down to 200 m. As depth increases, the amplitude ratio changes. The longitudinal wave

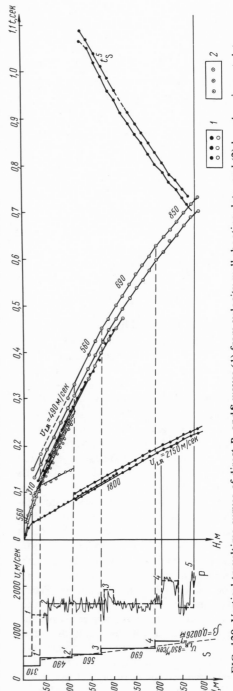

FIG. 129. Vertical traveltime curves of direct P- and S-waves (1) from velocity well-shooting data, and (2) based on impact data.

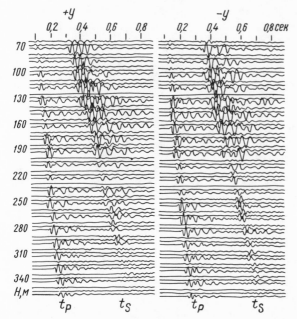

FIG.130. Seismograms of t_P and t_S-waves by three-component XYZ installation for directional ($\pm Y$) explosive excitation. (SP 200 m, $Q = 600$ gm, well no. 90a, Kudinov.)

is basically recorded by the Z-component.

Comparison of the effectiveness of impact with explosive sources indicates that the explosive method permits excitation of more intense transverse waves than impacts. However, the impulse of the transverse wave excited by a shot appears to be of longer duration and is more complex. For borehole observations, considerably less noise is usually generated by impacts compared to explosions. This permits observation of first arrivals in purer form and, in many cases, qualitative records in the upper portion of the cross-section are obtained which are not always produced by explosive excitation.

It is interesting to compare records obtained from directional and conventional shots. A conventional explosion (Figure 131) due to its natural directivity, likewise excites transverse waves. However, between P- and S-waves numerous regular incident and reflected longitudinal waves are recorded, so that the intermediate noise background is considerably higher than for a directional explosion. For good conditions of excitation, the complete phase inversion of the transverse wave permits application of wave selectivity according to the character of its polarization at the source, based on

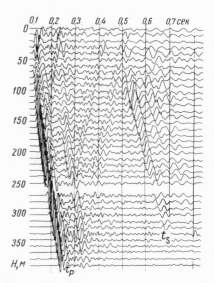

FIG. 131. Seismogram for nondirectional explosion (SP 100 m, $Q = 600$ gm, well no. 90a, Kudinov.

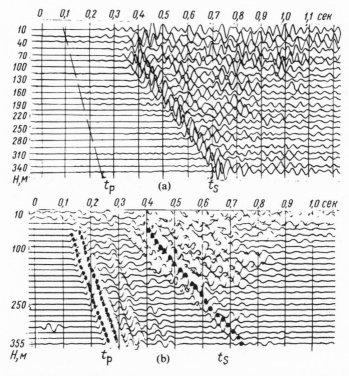

FIG. 132. (a) Seismogram of Y-component and (b) seismogram of Z-component (SP 110 m, $Q = 400$ gm, $h = 3$ m, well no. 90, Kudinov).

the utilization of oppositely directed shot interactions, and thus, for practical purposes, the complete suppression of the wave that is not inverted in-phase. The effectiveness of such selectivity shall be illustrated by a seismogram (Figure 132a) for which all waves prior to the arrival of the S-wave are almost completely suppressed (arrival times of first longitudinal waves are indicated by the dotted line in the figure). As a comparison, Figure 132b shows the seismogram of the Z-component: the direct P- and S-waves are seen clearly. In addition, between these waves, some other incident waves are observed. The record of the Y-component is more regular than that of the Z-component.

On the Kletsko-Pochtov platform, where the upper portion of the cross-section is characterized by sandy clay deposits of high saturation, conditions for

exciting transverse waves are extremely unfavorable. Though the form of the longitudinal wave varies only slightly along the profile, the form of the transverse wave is quite variable. Amplitude ratio of P- and S-waves at the source is extremely unfavorable for the S-wave and does not remain the same along the profile. Under these conditions, the phase inversion feature of SH-waves is not maintained, so that wave selectivity according to the character of polarization is not effective.

Frequency composition of P- and S-waves

Direct transverse waves excited by a directional impact source possess a frequency spectrum of lower frequency composition than that associated with longitudinal waves from the same source. The predominant frequencies of S-waves are approximately $1.5 - 2$ times lower than *P*-wave frequencies (Figure 133). The spectrum of *P*-waves is broader than that of *S*-waves. The differentiation of frequency composition of *P*- and *S*-waves is pronounced in the immediate vicinity of the source, where transverse waves just begin to emerge from the region of interference. The frequency composition of waves, as a rule, varies insignificantly with depth. The difference in the frequency composition of *P*- and *S*-waves is controlled by the source, i.e., by its mass, area of contact, and properties of the soil at point of impact (Berdennikova and Limbakh, 1966). With constant source conditions, excellent duplication of records for observations in a single borehole is achieved. A substantial variation of wave spectra may occur even for comparatively small displacement of the impact. Frequency composition of *S*-waves for explosive and impact excitations are almost identical for this example. But frequencies of longitudinal waves are

higher for explosive excitation than for impacts (Figure 133). The frequency variation of transverse waves at shallow depths may be due to the fact that the shots were produced at a distance of 110 m while the impacts were made at a distance of 40 m from the borehole.

Thus, frequency composition of the impulse is formed at the source and the decisive influence exerted on the impulse in the process of propagation are phenomena at the boundaries of separation (reflection, refraction, and conversion).

Polarization of transverse waves

Until recently, wave polarization has found little practical application to analysis of the wave pattern. In the study of transverse waves in boreholes, the splitting of the transverse wave, for inclined rays, into two waves, *SV* and *SH*, was investigated in detail. These waves propagate with different velocities and are characterized by different directions of displacement (Berdennikova, 1959). The *SH*-wave propagates with a higher velocity than the *SV*-wave. The velocity difference between these waves was observed for impact and explosive interactions. The *SH*-wave is polarized horizontally, i.e., perpendicular to the direction of propagation, and is recorded on the *Y*-component. The *SV*-wave is polarized in the vertical plane and recorded on the *Z*- and *X*-components. The recorded forms are also different for these waves. The spectrum of the *SV*-wave usually contains more high frequencies than that of the *SH*-wave.

For some regions, a disruption of linear polarization of vibrations in the horizontal plane was observed, and is shown on seismograms by phase shifts (see Figure 128). Trajectories of particle motion are nearly elliptical and are closely repeated for duplicate observations. For a reversal of polarity at the source, a reversal of ellipse orientation takes place. Some correlation between the direction

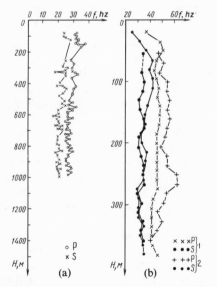

FIG. 133. Graphs of frequencies of t_P- and t_S-waves. (a) Impact excitation (well no. 42, Staro-Minsk). (b) Impact excitation (1) and explosive excitation (2) (well no. 90a, Kudinov).

of particle motion along the ellipse and lithology is observed.

The above phenomena (splitting of the transverse wave into two waves, nonlinear polarization) observed for the propagation of transverse waves in anisotropic media are comparable to double refraction of rays occurring in optics when light passes through optically anisotropic bodies (Berdennikova, 1959). It is not always possible to detect the splitting of transverse waves along in-line vertical profiles since, for observations in horizontally layered media, the vertical borehole may coincide with the direction of the axis of symmetry of the elastic properties of the medium. In that case, velocities of SH- and SV-waves are equal to each other, and cannot be separated on the seismogram. The velocity ratio of SV- and SH-waves is strongly dependent on the relation of elastic constants in the anisotropic medium.

In sedimentary formations as a rule the wave velocities are functions of their directions of propagation and, in the majority of cases, this is more pronounced in the horizontal direction than in the vertical. This may be associated with anisotropy of media that are homogeneous within an element of space (strict anisotropy), as well as with thin layering (transverse anisotropy), and macro-layering (quasi-anisotropy) of the medium. The study of polarization of transverse waves at interior points of the medium permitted us to obtain certain data on anisotropy of the medium. In particular, for some regions, anisotropy of the medium for S-waves was discovered while it was absent for P-waves. Experimental data obtained for several regions are in good agreement with results of theoretical computations on transversely anisotropic media: (a) the vertical velocity of SH-waves must be equal to the horizontal velocity of SV-waves; (b) the velocity of SV-waves along the horizontal and verti-

cal directions are identical; and (c) the degree of anisotropy for P- and S-waves may not be equal. Thus far, observations are insufficient to establish any more general conclusions. The above results should indicate the potentials involved in using directions of particle displacement for detailed study of actual media and details of propagation of seismic waves in the earth. Related to this, CDR-I and other procedures of wave selectivity by means of polarization characteristics open up new possibilities in principle. Data on velocity ratios of P- and S-waves for VSP are in good agreement with data obtained by other investigators (Kulichikhina et al, 1964; Molotva, 1963). In particular, VSP confirmed the fact that this ratio is strongly dependent on lithology and may vary widely. In most regions, it fluctuates from 2.0 for coarsely fragmented terrigenous deposits, to 3.5 − 4.0 for sandy-clayey formations.

For some platforms, a considerably broader range of variations in the ratio v_p/v_s is observed. Thus, for the Kudinov platform, v_p/v_s varies from 5 − 6 in the uppermost portion of the cross-section, to 2.0 in the Paleozoic formation ($H = 380$ m), and large values of the ratio v_p/v_s may also be observed at great depths. For example, on the Staro-Minsk platform of the Krasnodar region, the ratio of average velocities v_p/v_s down to depth of 1300 m is 3.3.

In the study of reflected transverse waves by VSP, no specialized efforts were undertaken, although transverse reflected waves were frequently observed. For example, the seismogram of the Z-component indicates a transverse reflected wave at boundary 3 (Figure 134). VSP results demonstrate that observation at interior points of the medium reveals the propagation process of transverse waves in actual media. In addition to appraisal of effectiveness of various means of excitation of transverse waves, it is possible

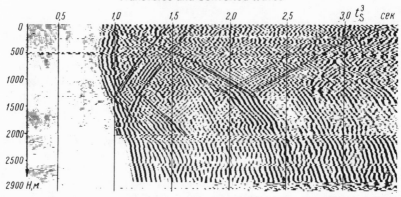

FIG. 134. Longitudinal and transverse waves reflected off boundary 3 (SP 1500 m, $f = 0 - 35$ hz, well no. 52, Staro-Minsk).

to determine reflection coefficients off boundaries distributed at various depths, stratigraphically correlate transverse waves, and study the conditions for which they may be brought out in the upper portion of the cross-section and on the surface. Consequently, VSP may be as significant for the method of transverse waves as it is for longitudinal waves in developing physical fundamentals improving its effectiveness. VSP should advance the development of the method of transverse waves.

CONVERTED REFLECTED AND DOWNWARD TRANSMITTED WAVES

Among the various types of converted waves, converted reflected waves have been studied most completely for surface observations (Berzon et al, 1966; Gamburtsev, 1939). Their considerable exploratory possibilities are based on the fact that the region of registration of converted waves is shifted toward later times where the noise background connected with multiples is considerably lower than for the region of registration of longitudinal waves.

For converted reflected waves, possibilities for direct determination of the nature of waves and their stratigraphic correlation by VSP are such that fundamental difficulties inherent in the pro-

cedure are resolved. Observations of converted waves were carried out by means of off-line vertical profiles and by symmetrical installation of seismic receivers (Gal'perin and Frolova, 1961, 1963, 1966). Problems in correlation of converted waves in VSP (see Chapter 4) substantially complicated the study. Let us examine converted reflected waves associated with two thin layers in a gradiented medium on the Staro-Minsk platform.

The combined system of observations, consisting of a horizontal and a vertical profile (the latter was produced from a sequence of shotpoints distributed within an interval of distances from 0 to 2500 m from the vertical profile) permitted the study of converted reflected waves and downward transmitted waves from the nearest shotpoints and involved boundaries at shallow depths. As distances increased, converted downward transmitted waves associated with deeper boundaries were observed. At the same time, converted upward transmitted waves involving finely divided horizons were brought out in the upper portion of the cross-section.

Thus, for observations from SP 2500 m, converted downward transmitted waves associated with the last boundary crossed by the borehole ($H_v = 1850$ m) were recorded, while in the upper portion of the cross-section, at that separation, converted upward transmitted waves appear from the thin layer ($H_v = 270$ m). In this manner, the selected system permitted the study of basic types of converted waves along the vertical profile traversing the cross-section.

Converted waves are generated for incidence of first and various secondary waves upon the boundary for the initial as well as for the subsequent portion of the seismogram. However, a description of the wave pattern will be restricted to the first converted waves produced for incidence of the first longitudinal wave upon the boundary.

Wave pattern. — The most intense waves registered on seismograms are associated with two layers at $H_v = 270$ m and 1334 m. The general feature of the wave pattern is the emergence of converted downward transmitted waves off increasingly deeper boundaries as re-

corded by the Z-component. From vertical traveltime curves of first longitudinal and converted transmitted waves (Figure 135) we see that only one converted wave t_{cv1} from boundary 1 is registered from SP 600 m. From SP 1550 m, wave t_{cv2} is registered, and from SPs 1775 and 2500 m, waves t_{cv3} and t_{cv4} are recorded.

To judge the quantity of various types of converted waves observable for the cross-section, the vertical traveltime curves of dominant converted waves are shown in Figure 136. In the upper portion of the cross-section (down to 600 – 700 m), converted reflected and transmitted waves dominate, are associated with the first boundary ($H_v = 270$ m), and are the most intense waves on surface seismograms. At large depths, the wave pattern is dominated by the second layer linked to the most intense converted waves that propagate upward and downward. On the surface the reflected converted wave from that boundary appeared

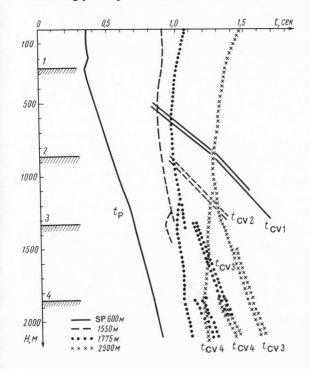

FIG.135. Vertical traveltime curves of first longitudinal waves and converted downward transmitted waves registered from different shotpoints.

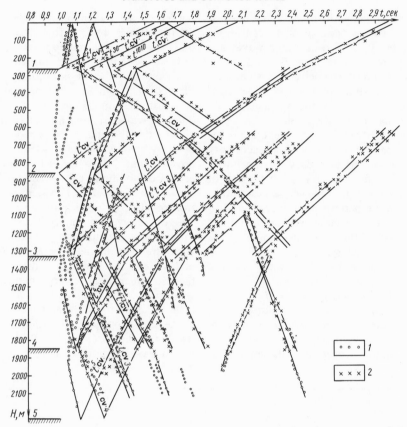

FIG. 136. Vertical traveltime curves of converted waves: (1) Constructed according to records of the Z-component, and (2) constructed by means of records of a three-component installation (SP 1775 m, well no. 42, Staro-Minsk).

only after its discovery and reliable tracking by vertical profiling.

Dominant converted waves in the upper portion of the vertical profile are demonstrated in Figure 137. The seismogram establishes converted reflected waves t_{cv}^1, t_{cv}^3, and the downward transmitted wave t_{cv1}. Waves t_{cv}^1 and t_{cv1} are characterized by high intensity, simple form, stable linear polarization, and comparatively low frequencies. The predominant wave frequency is $30 - 35$ hz, which is lower than the first longitudinal waves by a factor of 1.5. In addition to these intense converted waves, the upper portion of the cross-section indicates weaker

multiply reflected converted waves formed between the bottom of the ZLV and boundary 1 (Figure 136).

At depths $700 - 1000$ m, converted reflected waves off boundary 3 are dominant.

The converted reflected wave t_{cv}^3 is distinguished by its stability and the wide extent of the region over which it is recorded. Its correlation is disrupted only for the upper portion of the cross-section. The form of the event is well duplicated at different depths and for different separations from the shotpoint. This event is a two- or three-cycle oscillation linearly polarized and usually associated with

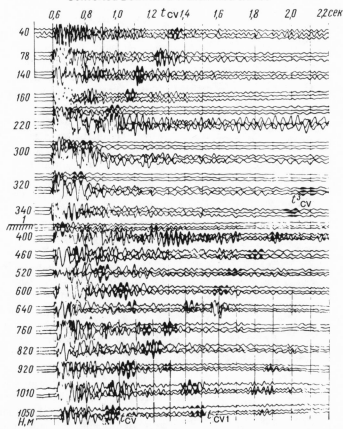

FIG. 137. Seismograms from three-component symmetrical installation (SP 1200 m, well no. 2, Staro-Minsk).

phase inversion on seismograms of the three-component clusters. Wave t_{cv}^3 is reliably correlated for a large interval of the profile. Its correlation significantly deteriorates in the upper portion of the cross-section because of interference with converted downward transmitted waves. The visible recorded frequency is lower by a factor of $1.5 - 2.0$ than frequencies of first longitudinal waves.

The converted transmitted wave t_{cv3} appears to be the most intense and most stable of all converted waves and is easily tracked from all shotpoints over the entire extent of the record (Figure 138). This wave is equally stable and intense on seismograms of the three-component

installation as well as on those of the vertical component. This may be explained by the large angle of approach of the transverse wave shown in Figure 41. Wave t_{cv3} dominates the later portion of the record while, at large depths, it even exceeds in intensity the first longitudinal waves. The recorded form is extremely stable and remains almost constant with depth, except for zones of interference. That wave produces a definitive reflection from boundary 4 ($H_v = 1850$ m). Traveltime curves of waves t_{cv3} (see Figure 136), constructed from records of vertical and inclined seismometers, conform well with each other and produce the most reliable source of infor-

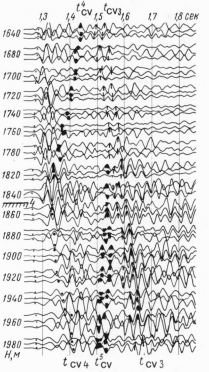

FIG. 138. Seismograms of converted waves, reflected off deep boundaries, obtained by three-component symmetrical installation (SP 2500 m, well no. 42, Staro-Minsk).

mation on velocities of transverse waves below boundary 3 ($H_v = 1320$ m).

Of particular interest are waves t_{cv}^4 and t_{cv}^5 which are reflected from deep boundaries ($H_v = 1850$ m and 2310 m). On seismograms corresponding to the symmetrical installation (Figure 138), both waves appear on the initial portion of the record in the region of registration of intense longitudinal waves and converted downward transmitted waves t_{cv4} and t_{cv5}, indicating that their apparent form is not particularly stable. Waves t_{cv}^4 and t_{cv}^5 correlate reliably up to the zone of their interference with intense converted downward transmitted waves off the overlying boundaries. These waves are not trackable to the surface, and do not appear on surface seismograms.

The generation of converted reflected waves at deep boundaries requires specialized work to improve penetration of the procedure, to study their parameters, and appraise their application to the top of the basement. Hopefully, a more sophisticated technique would permit an improvement of correlation of converted waves along the vertical and horizontal profiles, and make possible reliable enhancement and continuous tracking of those waves.

Frequency characteristics of converted waves. — From surface seismic observations we know that converted reflected waves are characterized by their frequency content which is shifted toward lower frequencies than is the case for longitudinal waves (Berzon et al, 1966). Observation at interior points of the medium indicated (Figure 139) that, even in the immediate neighborhood of boundaries, converted waves are distinguished by their considerably lower frequencies as compared to longitudinal waves. The change in frequency composition of longitudinal and converted waves during propagation between boundaries is not very significant, as a rule. Thus, the loss of high-frequency components for converted waves is associated with the phenomenon of conversion by a thin-layered medium.

VSP has demonstrated that converted reflected waves are generated at most boundaries which produce longitudinal reflected waves, and is particularly important at all depths accessible to investigation (see Chapter 7). Observations also showed that thin high-velocity layers give rise to the most intense converted waves. This agrees with the study of converted reflected waves for surface observations and with theoretical calculations (Berzon et al, 1966). According to VSP data, converted waves in thick-layered media are also abundant and their frequency composition differs only slightly from longitudinal waves.

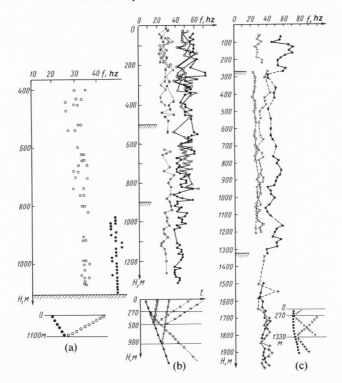

FIG. 139. Graphs of predominant frequencies of converted waves of various types: (a) SP 1250 m (well no. 20, Staro-Minsk); (b) SP 1250 m (well no. 15, Chelbass, Krasnodar region); and (c) SP 1775 m, (well no. 42, Staro-Minsk).

CONVERTED UPWARD TRANSMITTED WAVES

The difficulties in the interpretation of data according to CMRRW and DSS are based on the study of waves propagating over a considerable portion of their path along a direction close to the horizontal. This caused a sharp increase in the volume of regional work using the method of converted transmitted waves in seismic exploration utilizing shots (Vasil'ev, 1961; Naidis, 1967; Scherbakova, 1966), as well as in seismogeologic investigations where the source is an earthquake (Bulin, 1960; Kuz'mina, 1959). In the refinement of the latter, decisive significance was attributed to the commercially available instrumentation developed in the Soviet Union (A. N. Mozzhenko, I. V. Pomerantseva).

In the interpretation of data obtained by the method of converted transmitted waves, problems frequently arise in the identification of *P*- and *PS*-waves on records produced by horizontal and vertical oscillations that correspond to the same boundary. Therefore, it was necessary to appraise the exploratory capabilities of the method including: (1) the conditions of generation of converted transmitted waves at boundaries located at great depths, and (2) conditions and possibilities of their appearance as well as their enhancement and identification on the surface. The latter is primarily dictated by the interrelation between regions of registration and intensity ratios of useful and noise waves.

VSP capabilities for the study of converted transmitted waves consist of the following. For surface observations by means of explosions, the source and the receiver are on one side of the boundary of conversion. In this geometry, it is hard to produce, at sufficiently large depths, longitudinal waves that impinge from below on the boundary of conversion at different angles of incidence. In order to study a large range of incidence angles,

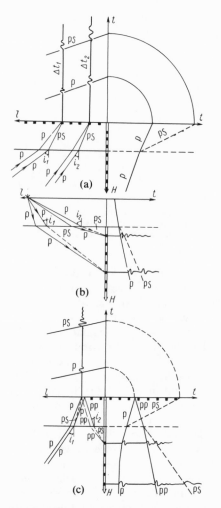

(a)

(b)

(c)

FIG. 140. Raypath schematics and combined traveltime curves for converted transmitted waves.

therefore, it is necessary to record for a large range of separations from the source, which is complicated and sometimes impossible in practice (Figure 140a). For such observations, the usual difficulties persist related to the determination of the wave type and the identification of waves. The possibilities are considerably enhanced where the source and points of observation are on opposite sides of the boundary of conversion. Such a system for surface observations is possible for "torpedoing", when explosions are produced in boreholes, or for earthquakes. However, such investigations are limited basically by the difficulties in obtaining deep boreholes suitable for shooting.

An analogous scheme may be easily accomplished, both technically and economically, by using VSP for observations conducted at interior points of the medium and explosions are produced at the surface. In this case, as in torpedoing, the source and receiver are disposed at either side of the boundary of conversion, and converted transmitted waves are continuously tracked along the vertical profile. This permits construction of a vertical traveltime curve of waves, determination of their nature and, simultaneously, the establishment of the boundaries of conversion. Also, the realization of stratigraphic correlation of waves and the production of the velocity cross-section are achieved (Figure 140b). In addition, observations from several shotpoints at different separations from the top of the borehole permit the study of generation of converted transmitted waves over a broad range of angles of incidence. Occasionally, it is possible to observe converted downward and upward transmitted waves by VSP (Figure 140c).

In this manner, the wavefield of incident waves may be observed in the region of reception at large depths near the explosion. At the same time the wavefield of the approaching longitudinal waves, conditions of generation, and characteristics of converted transmitted waves generated at deep boundaries of conversion are accessible for study. Tracking of waves along the vertical profile shows the conditions of their appearance in the upper portion of the cross-section and the possibilities of their enhancement at the surface. From a sequence of shotpoints distributed over an interval of $0 - 32$ km (see Figure 10), a combined system of observations in the vertical plane revealed that longitudinal waves impinging upon the top of the basement at incidence angles ($65 - 75$ degrees) are optimal for the generation of converted transmitted waves. The shallow depth of the crystalline basement ($H_v = 1880$ m) permitted the study of deep converted transmitted waves for minimal influence of multiples which register at large times. We will not describe the experiments in detail, but let us cite the basic conclusions and illustrate the situation with separate examples.

The seismogram of the horizontal component of motion is largely governed by the seismogram structure of the vertical component. Observations at large depths near the source indicate that inhomogeneities in the upper portion of the cross-section dictate the complicated train of incident longitudinal waves occupying the entire initial portion of the record (Figure 141). For observations at large separations within the region of reception, all these waves approach the top of the basement from below. Propagating toward the surface, they cross all boundaries of sedimentary beds and form numerous converted waves sequentially arriving from boundaries disposed at various depths. These waves dictate the structure of the seismogram of the horizontal component. Even a single sharp boundary in the upper portion of the cross-section may be sufficient to explain fully the entire seismogram of the horizontal component.

Comparing surface seismograms of the Z- and X-components (Figure 142) shows that the record of the X-component almost duplicates that of the Z-component and is time-displaced by $t = 0.25 - 0.30$ sec. This lag is caused by the conversion at the top of the Paleozoic ($H_v = 125$ m). Pure waves off a single boundary of conversion are observed on the surface seismogram at comparatively small separations from the source. On the surface seismogram of the X-component as distance increases, waves appear that are caused by deeper boundaries of conversion.

Generation of converted waves at the next deeper sharp boundary ($H_v = 640$ m) was observed along a vertical profile produced from a shotpoint located at a distance of 31,700 m from the profile. On the composite seismogram of the Z-component (Figure 143a), many upward propagating longitudinal waves are recorded, their intensities being commensurate with those of the first longitudinal wave. The seismogram in Figure 143c, composed of the vertical (2) and the complete horizontal (1) components, indicates that to each longitudinal wave impinging on the boundary a converted transmitted wave corresponds above the boundary that is reliably correlated along the vertical profile[2]. As they cross the boundary at 125 m, all these waves (longitudinal and converted), initiate a new sequence of secondary waves subsequently recorded on surface seismograms.

Intense converted transmitted waves are formed at the most distinct boundaries usually located in the upper portion of the cross-section. Difficulties arise in the identification of converted waves along the vertical profile at large depths, since the intensity of the horizontal component of longitudinal waves often may exceed that of the horizontal component

[2]The seismograms are normalized in such a manner that the arrival times of the first longitudinal waves coincide.

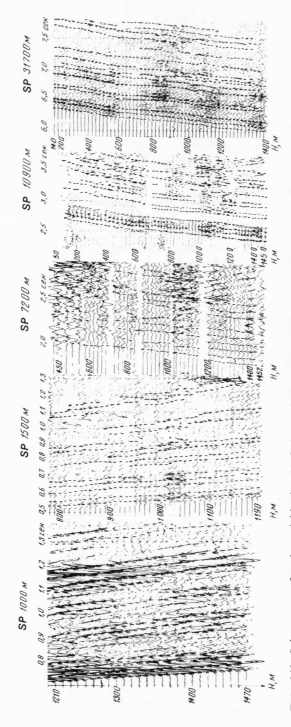

FIG. 141. Seismograms for the neighborhood of the explosion (SP 1000 and SP 1500 m) and for regions of reception (SP 7200, SP 10,900, and SP 31,700 m).

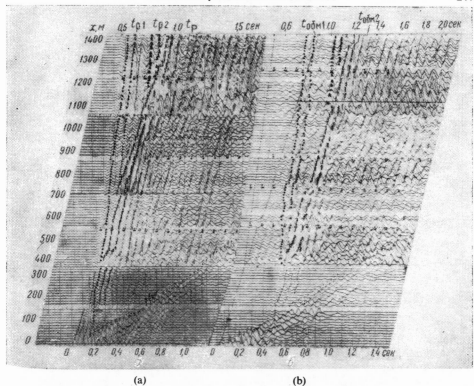

(a) (b)

FIG. 142. (a) Surface seismograms of the Z-component of oscillation and (b) for the X-component. The dashed line designates arrival times of the first refracted wave t_{P1} and the direct longitudianal wave t_P. Seismograms for $x = 0 - 325$ m are obtained for coarsely adjusted amplification.

of converted waves. This refers to observations in layers with high velocities and largely explains why converted waves are poorly trackable along the vertical profile at great depths (Figure 143b). By applying CDR-I in a computer, the existence of converted waves was established and identified through their nonlinear polarization (see Figure 37). An analysis of summation tapes of CDR-I determined that components were optimal for the enhancement of converted transmitted waves. Composite seismograms of the optimal component produced further computer correlation of seismic waves according to apparent velocities and dynamic characteristics. Application of CDR-I permitted us to establish converted transmitted waves and to check

their existence at separate regions of the vertical profile. The wave diagram (Figure 144) computed by means of programmed correlation (Krauklis et al, 1966), indicates converted waves at great depths. At certain intervals, the converted transmitted wave originating at the basement can be tracked.

Thus, the influence of sharp boundaries in the upper portion of the cross-section led to formation of a complex field of incident longitudinal waves near the source and led to the formation of a large number of repetitive converted waves near the receiver. In addition, in the upper portion of the cross-section near the receiver, a large number of multiples is formed that may possess high intensity and may substantially affect the structure of the X-component of the seismograms.

Under conditions of a complicated interferential wavefield, the current criteria for identification of P- and PS-waves (according to registered form, delay time, polarization) prevent reliable determination of the nature of the waves at large depths. And even for a comparatively uncomplicated cross-section (two or three sharp boundaries in the upper portion of the cross-section) the interpretation of converted waves may not be unique in practice. By virtue of a thin-layered medium and comparatively low frequency of registered waves (5 – 10 hz), converted transmitted waves usually appear to be interferential and are characterized by a complex wave form. Figure 145 represents seismograms that illustrate the complexity and conventional interpretation of the wavefield. The seismograms, for practical purposes, do not differ from those obtained by the method of converted transmitted waves in that same region. The seismogram of the Z-component is comparatively simple: the initial portion of the record produces a sequence of wave groups of similar intensity. For the X-component of the seismogram, the crosshatched areas are converted transmitted waves associated with sharp boundaries at depths 125 and 640 m. All converted transmitted waves of importance, i.e., those connected with the top of the basement and with the sequence of deep boundaries in the sedimentary bed, are wholly in the region of complex interference. Under these conditions, no criteria exist for the identification of waves, i.e., criteria based on sound principles of physics.

All of the above does not apply to converted waves recorded as first arrivals on seismograms of the X-component, whose interpretation presents no difficulties. However, in most cases, the first wave is associated with upper boundaries and is of no particular geologic interest. In certain regions, the first sharp bound-

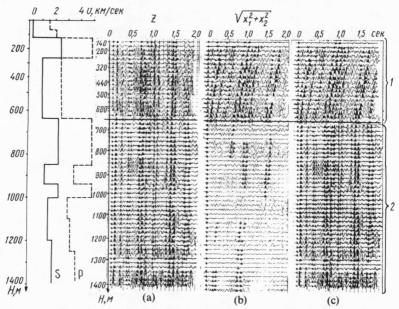

FIG. 143. Seismograms of the Z- and X-components (SP 31,700 m, well no. 1, Kletsko-Pochtov). (a) Z-component, (b) full X-component, (c) X-component (1), and Z-component (2).

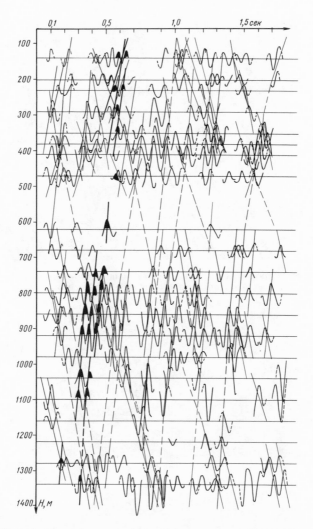

FIG. 144. Wave diagram calculated by computer (SP 31,700 m).

ary may be located at depths of 4 – 6 km (e.g., inflections where the basement is covered by a thick bed of weakly differentiated terrigenous deposits). The converted wave associated with that boundary may be of interest to exploration, and utilization of converted transmitted waves for the study of the first boundary appears to be very effective. Figure 146 represents surface seismograms obtained for the Illyi depression that is filled in by a 4-km thick bed of terrigenous deposits, and for the platform portion of the Krasnodar region (Kuschev area) for a comparatively thin (1500 m) section of deposits. The lack of sharp boundaries in the upper portion of the cross-section for either region produced the very simple structure of the Z-component seismogram and the easily interpretable wave pattern of the X-component record.

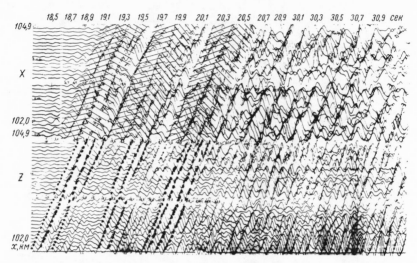

FIG. 145. Surface seismograms of X- and Z-components for the distance interval of $102 - 104.9$ km from the shotpoint (Kletsko-Pochtov).

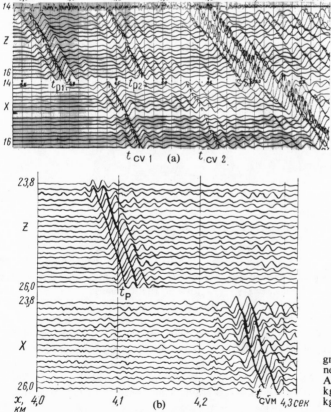

FIG. 146. Surface seismograms of Z- and X-components: (a) Ilyi depression of Alma-Ata district ($Q = 900$ kg); (b) Kuschev ($Q = 200$ kg).

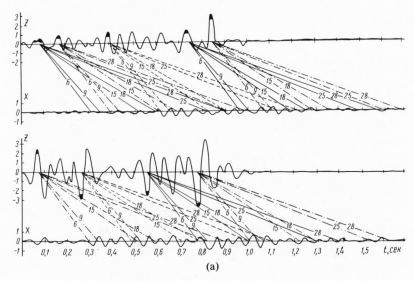

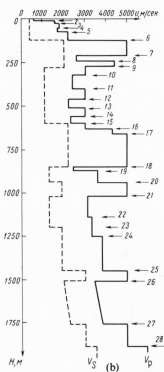

FIG. 147. (a) Computed seismograms of Z- and X-components of converted and multiples waves for two different forms of wave trains impinging on the top of the basement under an angle of incidence of 70 degrees. (b) Velocity model of the medium. The numbering corresponds to the boundaries with which the converted waves are associated.

Results of experimental study of converted transmitted waves in the seismic exploration frequency range agree well with computational data. Figure 147a illustrates synthetic seismograms of the Z- and X-components computed for a model of a medium represented in Figure 147b, and for two initial impulses of the longitudinal wave taken from experimental seismograms at depths 1450 m (SP 10,900 m) and 1400 m (SP 31,700 m). A complicated interferential oscillation is observed on seismograms of the X-component, a result of superposition of converted transmitted waves off various boundaries. Under these conditions, a unique identification of phases of longitudinal and converted waves is almost impossible.

This information casts doubt on the exploratory capabilities of the method of converted transmitted waves, as far as application to horizons located at great depths is concerned (when there are sharp boundaries in the upper portion of the cross-section). Further research is needed on conditions of generation and the physics of propagation of deep converted transmitted waves.

The study of boundaries located in the earth's crust at great depths by means of converted transmitted waves, requires an extremely remote source; therefore, earthquakes are employed. VSP results obtained in the study of converted waves from shots permit the following comments:

1. The records of the X- and Z-components possess a simple form for earthquakes having foci located at great depths.

2. For the most pronounced boundary in the lower portion of the crust (the Mohorovčić surface), the ratio v_{s1}/v_{s2} — which basically controls the intensity of converted waves — is not less than 0.75. For all intermediate horizons in the crust, this discontinuity is considerably lower. VSP data, obtained for media with weak velocity contrasts, indicate that at such boundaries intense converted waves are not generated within the seismic exploration frequency range. Specialized research is essential for the study of formation of intense converted waves within the seismogeologic frequency range.

Chapter 10
EXPLORATORY CAPABILITIES AND FUTURE DEVELOPMENT
OF THE VSP METHOD

The VSP method is still in its initial phase of development. However, the preceding discussion enables us to appraise the significance of VSP in improving the effectiveness of seismic exploration and to search for ways to further refine the method.

The exploratory capabilities of the major seismic exploration methods are dictated by the formation of the wavefield. As we have seen, VSP permits the splitting of a complex wavefield as it is observed on the surface, identification of various wave types, and determination of elements of the cross-section with which the wave types are associated.

The information discussed in the preceding chapters involving the study of basic wave types, the theoretical computations and the large amount of data, permit the enumeration of the principal capabilities of the major methods:

1. Basic exploratory capabilities are connected with waves that propagate almost vertically.

2. Reflected waves permit one to resolve the cross-section in the most detailed and accurate manner. Transverse reflected waves, in principle, possess advantages over longitudinal waves, a greater resolving power and accuracy of construction. This is of considerable significance in the solution of such problems as mapping of sloping structures and zones of wedging, and detailing of tectonic faults of small dimension. Exploratory possibilities for transverse reflected waves are also dictated by the simpler wave pattern conditioned by lack of converted waves and reduced influence of multiples.

3. Except for the first wave, there is no complete interpretation of the nature of waves observed at large distances. Exploratory capabilities of CMRRW are highly limited. In principle, converted transmitted waves that also propagate in a nearly vertical direction may have good potential.

Hence, the effectiveness of seismic exploration depends largely on its utilization. Unfortunately, many difficulties exist that restrict the effectiveness of seismic investigations. Let us examine the basic capabilities of VSP in the light of improvement of the effectiveness of seismic exploration.

EXPLORATORY CAPABILITIES OF VSP
Source conditions

The seismic effect of the source of vibration, as applied to seismic exploration, is tentatively understood to be the total influence of the source on the wavefield. Experience with VSP indicates that the influence of the source (the weight of the charge, its shape, its explosive ingredients, etc.) must be examined in conjunction with the heterogeneities of the medium near the explosion. These heterogeneities may transform a simple impulse in the source into a complex train of incident waves. Source and medium represent a single complex focus. Conditions of excitation may affect the form of each separate wave in a substantial manner. Thus the structure of the entire seismogram and, consequently, the effectiveness of seismic exploration are influenced. However, present procedures for the selection and appraisal of source conditions based on surface observations primarily are not always successful.

Experience with VSP demonstrates that the most rigorous and objective appraisal of source conditions may be accomplished through the direct wave and the train of incident waves immediately adjacent to the direct wave as observed at different depths at interior points of the medium. The direct wave indicates the effectiveness of the explosion and dictates the recorded form of all waves on the seismogram. The train of incident waves controls the overall quantity of waves on the seismogram and its structure. The influence of source conditions on the effectiveness of seismic investigations is still underrated. More research is needed on the relation between source conditions and structure of seismograms and, consequently, to the overall effectiveness of seismic exploration.

VSP permits the study of the influence of various elements making up the concept of source conditions upon the form of direct and incident waves. This includes the upper portion of the cross-section and quantitative appraisal of parameters (frequency spectrum, intensity, directivity, etc.) of various types of sources, both explosive and nonexplosive. The appraisal of the directivity of each shot and of the effectiveness of grouping shots in time and space are very important. The effectiveness of single excitations for various procedures of stacking also may be significant. In the method of transverse waves, the directivity and purity of the source are fundamental. Developmental research concerned with the study of source conditions will definitely lead to an improvement in effectiveness of seismic exploration.

Nature of recorded waves

The determination of the nature of recorded waves is the fundamental phase of interpretation which determines the authenticity of results and the effectiveness of seismic research. Experience shows that reliable determinations of the nature of registered waves in surface observations may be accomplished only for the simplest structures. In most cases, however, proven criteria for determination of the nature of recorded waves are lacking for surface observations.

The development of the dynamic theory of propagation and interpretation of seismic waves has led to improvements during the last few years. In principle, this theory permits us to determine dynamic properties of the record in cases where kinematic characteristics alone are insufficient. The significance of dynamics in the interpretation of seismic data increases each year. Just the same, kinematic wave characteristics thus far remain fundamental in most surface observations as well as those at interior points of the medium.

Kinematic properties of various wave types express themselves more clearly in VSP than in surface observations, and may be considerably more essential in the interpretation of seismic data. The kinematic features of waves discussed in this monograph relate to vertical profiles and demonstrate that the nature of waves in VSP often may be determined directly from the observed data even without a preliminary study of velocities and structure of the cross-section. The basic difficulties here are presently associated with the complexity of the wavefields observed at interior points of the medium. As a result, VSP seismograms create unfavorable conditions for tracking of useful waves. To overcome these problems, it is essential to improve the correlatability of waves along the vertical profile. One should mention that, for VSP, as the separation from the shotpoint increases, difficulties in the determination of the nature of observed waves increase progressively.

Stratigraphic correlation of seismic horizons

Reliable stratigraphic correlation of seismic horizons by means of surface observations is not always successful, even if the nature of the waves has been determined correctly. This is because information is insufficient on the law of velocity variation with depth. Phase shifts created by instrumentation may also be of considerable significance. Therefore, in the majority of cases, correlation is of tentative character, and one only speaks of a boundary (either reflecting or refracting) within the limits of this or that bed. But in those situations where the nature of the waves cannot be accurately determined, it seems altogether meaningless to talk about stratigraphic correlation.

Stratigraphic correlation for VSP may be accomplished more reliably since the nature of the waves may be determined more safely, but the question of accurate correlation has not been resolved. In this connection, the particulars of vertical traveltime curves of waves are significant.

For reflected waves in particular, this feature is represented by the point at which traveltime curves of direct and reflected waves intersect. For strong dominant waves reliably tracked along the entire profile, these stratigraphic identifications are accomplished easily and accurately. The accuracy of stratigraphic correlation for such waves is restricted by mutual interference of incident and reflected waves on profile sections adjoining reflecting horizons, and where one is unsuccessful in tracking the reflected wave near the boundary. Various procedures (directional reception, augmentation of traveltime curves, etc.) permit extension of the traveltime curve of the reflected wave to the intersection with the traveltime curve of the incident wave, improving the accuracy of correlation. In addition, identification of phases of the incident and reflected waves substantially decreases errors of correlation caused by phase shifts in the recording channel. A considerable improvement in the accuracy of stratigraphic correlation may be accomplished by comparing VSP data with conventional geophysical research.

Conventional research portrays details of the cross-section associated with reflected waves.

Presently available information (primarily SWL data) on the nature of boundaries reveals that, as a rule, one should reject the conventional concepts of horizons as boundaries between thick layers. Most reflecting boundaries are represented by either-thin layers or packets of thin layers. Under these conditions, reflected waves appear to be interferential, and their stratigraphic correlation assumes specific meaning and required specialized research.

In the case of a single thin layer, the best approach is correlation with the top of the layer. Still greater difficulties are connected with stratigraphic correlation of waves in media where velocities are weakly differentiated. Reflected waves in such media possess low intensities and, as a rule, are not continuously trackable along the vertical profile. In addition, the reflected wave may not even be associated with any single horizon, rather a total wave related to a definite interval of the cross-section. In such cases, combining of VSP with computations of synthetic seismograms based on SWL may be important as far as stratigraphic correlation of seismic waves is concerned.

Stratigraphic correlation of refracted waves (weakly refracted waves and head waves) may be accomplished by making use of the form of traveltime curves of first waves, and by observable disruption of linear polarization of waves as they cross the boundary (basically, head waves). The accuracy of stratigraphic correlation for refracted waves is considerably lower than for reflected waves.

In spite of current difficulties in stratigraphic correlation of waves, VSP substantially enhances accurate stratigraphic correlation. This is especially so for data of conventional geophysical and acoustical investigations. In the majority of cases, it should guarantee the accuracy required for exploration problems.

Increase of depth of penetration of seismic investigations

Experience in the application of VSP yields the following possibilities of improving the penetration in seismic investigations. In each concrete situation it is essential to study directly the parameters of seismic waves generated at deep boundaries. Such observations are extremely important and may only be accomplished at interior points of the medium.

The next phase should be the study of factors that interfere with the identification of waves on surface seismograms. In MRLW, as VSP experience demonstrates, multiples are fundamental for the reduction of penetration of investigations. VSP does not provide the means to suppress multiples, but data on the nature and parameters of useful waves and noise should permit more objective appraisal of the capabilities of various interferential systems and selection of the optimal system for enhancement of wanted waves.

For the application of the most effective current procedure for suppression of noise (the CDP method) it is essential to have data on raypath velocities that may be acquired by VSP. Experience confirms that the application of VSP data provides a substantial improvement in depth penetration of investigations.

Seismic exploration capabilities and selection of optimal procedure of investigation

To appraise the seismic exploration capabilities of VSP and to select the optimum procedure of investigation for a spectific geologic situation, a large amount of surface investigation is necessary. It is essential to comprehend the complex wavefield observed on the surface and to bring out waves involved .in the deposits of interest. In most cases these waves possess relatively low intensity, it is very difficult to enhance them

in the absence of reliable criteria and, occasionally, impossible. Therefore, it is not always possible to appraise particular seismic procedures to solve concrete geologic problems. The solution of these problems often implies the expenditure of a great amount of field work.

Observations at interior points of the medium indicate a new approach to the appraisal of exploratory capabilities of seismic procedures. Instead of cumbersome surface work, it is expedient to conduct observations at interior points of the medium near deposits of geologic interest in order to study all waves associated with the structure and select the most effective conditions of excitation. Furthermore, vertical profiling facilitates the tracking of these waves up to the surface, the estimation of their relative intensity, and most important, the study of the conditions of their registration.

In examining exploratory possibilities, both the intensity of waves and the region of their tracking along the surface are of substantial value. For example, in some cases it is expedient to utilize less intense waves that register at large times, instead of more intense waves recorded on the initial portion of the record that are obscured by unwanted converted or transverse waves.

In our opinion, such an approach in many cases is more effective and more advantageous commercially. Seismic observation in boreholes can be regarded as reconnaissance work and should precede surface observations. Data acquired in such observations constitute the basis for overall planning of surface work and selection of the optional procedure of observation.

The importance of acquisition of results in reconnaissance work is such that in some regions where a great volume of seismic work is planned and boreholes are not available, it may be advantageous economically to drill special boreholes for VSP.

In addition, because of the complexity of surface seismograms and the presence of numerous waves, an objective checking of the effectiveness of various new procedures is not always possible. As a result, much time and effort are wasted. VSP usually allows appraisal of results and effectiveness of various procedures in a more reliable and objective manner.

Velocity cross-section

According to the vertical traveltime curve obtained as a result of conventional seismic well shooting, we can construct a curve of average velocities. This is essential for the interpretation of MRLW and CMRRW data. We know that the determination of layer velocities from seismic well shooting data is less reliable, particularly in the identification of layers whose velocities differ only slightly. The identification of thin layers with increased or decreased velocities in the cross-section is almost impossible.

In VSP, in contrast to conventional well shooting, not only the first wave, but all waves generated in the medium by its heterogeneity (and registering on the initial and subsequent portions of the record), may be utilized for construction of the velocity cross-section. Velocities of longitudinal and transverse waves can be identified directly from vertical traveltime curves of these waves. In addition, velocity values may be obtained not only for vertical but also any inclined direction. This is important for observations at large separations and, especially in strongly anisotropic media. Also, converted downward transmitted waves permit subdivision of the cross-section according to velocities of transverse waves.

The procedure for construction of the velocity cross-section in VSP is as follows: The curve of layer velocities is constructed according to data of first waves of an in-line vertical profile (as in seismic well shooting). In so doing, only the coarsest heterogeneities in the cross-section can be identified, e.g., refracting boundaries corresponding to thick layers associated with considerable velocity discontinuities. According to traveltime curves of first waves registered for off-line profiles, the cross-section is supplemented by refracting boundaries, and velocity gradients are established in thick layers. Also, the coefficients of velocity increment with depth are determined.

The study of waves on later portion of the record (reflected, longitudinal, and converted) for in-line and off-line profiles, permits identification of reflecting boundaries in the cross-section. These horizons often represent thin layers with sufficiently intense waves (reflected and converted). These features of the cross-section may be lost when constructing the cross-section according to first waves within the seismic frequency range. Naturally, the thickness of such individual layers, or its structure, cannot be determined from VSP data. To do that, observations involving higher frequencies are necessary; otherwise, data of conventional geophysical observations may be very significant for the determination of the thicknesses of individual thin layers.

The velocity cross-section thus constructed although not as detailed as cross-sections obtained by means of high-frequency observations (e.g., SWL), nevertheless shall be more detailed than cross-sections constructed from observations within the seismic frequency range. This is because this construction includes all basic waves generated in the cross-section. Therefore, in its first approximation, such a cross-section may be regarded as a velocity model of the cross-section that corresponds to the observed wave pattern.

This model, constructed for nearly vertical angles of wave incidence usually does not conform with observations for large separations. Theoretical off-line traveltime curves of waves computed for comparatively small *l* may lag behind observed traveltime curves. However, as distance increases the influence of discrete thin high-velocity layers and differentiation of the cross-section itself diminishes; and theoretical traveltime curves may "lead" the observed ones. In the study of kinematics of waves at large distances, it is essential to conduct VSP observations from remote shotpoints. Significantly, values of raypath velocities may be determined that are essential for processing of data involving systems of interferential reception, in particular those of CDP.

Structural features of boundaries in the section contiguous to the borehole

The strong influence of the upper portion of the cross-section upon the wavefield, which substantially restricts the exploratory capabilities of surface seismic investigations, dictated further development of observations in boreholes to study the structural features of horizons at a section contiguous to the borehole. Some of these problems were solved until very recently by means of borehole seismic exploration In particular, it involved the study of steeply dipping boundaries (most importantly, the slopes of salt domes) using first transmitted waves.

VSP results enable us to solve a broad range of problems by direct observations in boreholes. Such investigations include use of the method of converted traveltime curves (Teplitskyi, 1969). At sections with complicated noise fields associated with the upper portion of the cross-section where tracking of reflected waves on surface seismograms is unsuccessful, registration of waves below the upper reference boundaries often permits tracking of reflected waves and construction of sections of deep reflecting horizons (Gal'

perin, 1964c; Teplitskyi, 1969). This is because the noise background is reduced as the surface becomes more remote. For borehole observations, application of a whole group of detectors disposed along the vertical permits selection of waves according to their direction of approach, thus improving conditions of correlation of reflected waves. Shotpoints usually are disposed along the surface according to profile lines. Therefore, the quality of the method of the converted traveltimes curves records is substantially influenced by duplicating source conditions which basically is dictated by the constancy of the structure of the ZLV in the uppermost portion of the cross-section. Kinematically, such investigations are equivalent to surface observations for explosions at great depths (at the point of observation). Most frequently, such observations permit us to obtain the cross-section near the borehole being investigated. However, with enough boreholes, the method of the converted traveltime curves could guarantee continuous profiling as well. It appears most effective to combine the method of the converted traveltime curves with drilling for structure.

When tracking of reflected waves is unsuccessful for the method of the converted traveltime curves, it is often desirable to determine by observations along the vertical profile the stratigraphic detail of the boundary at a section contiguous to the borehole. This would serve as a guide for drilling. To solve this problem it is necessary to develop procedures of spatial observations by means of VSP. Up to now, we have been restricted to two-dimensional problems in VSP work. The development of spatial systems, coupled with a wide class of waves, should substantially broaden exploratory capabilities of borehole seismics.

VSP CAPABILITIES IN PROCEDURAL INVESTIGATIONS

VSP may acquire special significance

with improved results yielded by various procedures of investigation. We shall examine VSP possibilities for the solution of only those problems which in our opinion are presently most essential.

Actual media and associated wavefields

This problem encompasses basic questions determining the development of procedures of seismic exploration. Its solution should contain the most significant results. The propagation of seismic waves is, in essence, the process of transporting or transferring seismic energy, and the medium may be considered a conductor of energy. VSP permits the realization of this general approach to the study of an actual medium. It also enables us to study the medium according to its reaction upon a seismic impulse, similar to the concept of studying parameters of electric networks according to their reactions to an electrical impulse.

Each surface seismogram may be considered to be the result of the reaction of the medium to the seismic pulse introduced at the source. But this is the composite reaction and is one of the difficulties of the study. From observations at interior points of the medium, as demonstrated, we can split the total reaction into separate components, and bring out in the cross-section those elements that decisively influence the wavefield.

It is primarily necessary to examine waves which are basic to the major procedures of seismic observations; in particular, reflected waves since they are most significant in seismic observations. It is also necessary to review the physical fundamentals of CMRRW where registration occurs principally by refracted and transcritically reflected waves. VSP permits the study of the nature of waves forming the initial portion of the seismogram for observations at large distances, and appraisal of the intensity of these waves.

Construction of simplified models of the medium

The basis of any method of interpretation of seismic observation is some particular model of the medium to be used. The effectiveness of the entire process of interpretation depends substantially on the model selected.

Only 10 to 15 years ago, interpretation of observed data was conducted on the basis of extremely unsophisticated models (two and three layers). Since then, the development of high-frequency observations demonstrated that the concept of actual media being represented by homogeneous or layered homogeneous models should represent a first approximation only. Actual media are complex and, in most cases they are thin layered. The more detailed the methods for the study of the medium, the more complex and heterogeneous the medium appears.

In a conventional seismic sense, a homogeneous layer is composed of separate thin layers, or else of packets of thin layers. Transition into a region of still higher frequencies would probably permit the splitting of these thin layers as well. In this respect the problem is inexhaustible. In addition, in the last few years procedures for computation (synthetization) of seismograms involving thin-layered media have been developed. Thus, exceedingly sophisticated models consisting of hundreds and more layers are now available.

VSP has demonstrated that usually intense waves are formed by a comparatively small number of elements of the cross-section and in almost every case they involve concrete, geologically expressable elements of the cross-section. Total waves associated with weakly differentiated (in regard to velocities) regions of the cross-section are not especially significant. However, the general level of intensities of reflected waves is lowered so that total waves may become basic under conditions of a thick bed composed of deposits that are weakly differentiated as far as velocities are concerned, and when strong boundaries are nonexistent.

VSP experience demonstrates that propagation of seismic waves may be described by a few effective parameters using comparatively simple models. The main problem is the construction of such a simplified model. Construction of a model corresponding to the observed wavefield requires rigorous principles of averaging parameters of actual media. Only then can we predict the seismic effect for any given set of interactions. Also, the wavefield itself "averages" the cross-section and "composes" its own model. The model substantially depends on the working range of wavelengths.

As the same elements of the cross-section express themselves unequally in the wavefield at large and small distances from the source for different wave types, seismic models of the same medium may differ from each other for different distances and different wave types. To compose the model of the medium, experimental study of wavefields is of great importance. VSP permits the study of the principles of averaging the cross-section and serves as the fundamental source of information for the construction of a simplified model of the medium. Such information contains velocity parameters of the medium (average velocity, average interval velocity, and raypath velocities, plus velocity gradients), as well as dynamic characteristics of waves formed in actual media (polarization, amplitude and form, effective coefficients of reflection, and absorption).

During the last few years, a simplified effective seismic model has been developed under the leadership of B. Ya. Gel'-chinsky. The basic elements of the cross-section of the model (i.e., those exerting a determining influence on the wavefield)

are given in considerable detail, whereas the intermediate regions of the cross-section are highly averaged. The wavefield computed for the model should correspond to the plane-average of the observed wavefield of principal waves. A seismic model has been constructed for use in certain regions of Uzbekistan.

The effective seismic model constitutes a novel approach to interpretation of seismic data, based on the subsequent utilization of more detailed data on wavefields in the course of the interpretation.

Absorptive and dispersive properties of actual media

The dependence of the coefficient of absorption on frequency (in actual media) is of particular significance in construction of the absorptive model of the medium. Unfortunately, this question has hardly been studied experimentally. A considerable portion of published data obtained mostly from surface observations is not very reliable and cannot always solve the problem.

For observations at interior points of the medium, it is possible to track the variation of the form of the impulse as the wave propagates continuously in the medium. This indicates the decay of waves associated with nonideal elasticity and with macro and micro inhomogeneities of the medium. Moreover, this may be done with greater confidence.

One should note, however, that observations at interior points are difficult to achieve because of the thin layering characteristic for the cross-section. But to find a sufficiently homogeneous bed in actual media is a fairly difficult task. In most published experimental data, it seems that at best the discussion refers not to pure absorption but to some kind of total effect involving the decay of amplitudes. Perfection of procedures for obtaining and processing of VSP data should provide the required data on absorptive and dispersive properties of actual media, especially the opacity of the medium (i.e., the parameter that characterizes dispersion).

Physical substantiation and evaluation of procedures for direct search for petroleum and gas

Presently, two basic criteria for the direct detection of petroliferous deposits by seismic means are being developed (Mirchink et al, 1961). The first criterion concerns the sharp variation of dynamic properties of waves above the deposit because of increased absorption in the upper layers. The second criterion implies the detection and tracking of reflected waves off oil-water contacts and off gas-fluid contacts. Both these criteria are thus far not sufficiently understood as far as the physics of the situation are concerned, and are in need of rigorous quantitative substantiation. Here, too, observations at interior points of the medium should prove helpful.

According to the first criterion, it is essential to determine quantitatively the coefficients of absorption in reservoirs saturated with petroleum and gas and to compare them with the coefficients of unsaturated reservoir rocks. Such determinations cannot be accomplished by observations at the surface.

The possibility of observing reflections from oil-water and gas-liquid contacts may be reliably accomplished by observations in the immediate vicinity of the contact itself. It is at such contacts that parameters of waves associated with them can be studied and continuous tracking of these waves up to the surface can be attempted. A careful evaluation of the observed waves might not be correlated with geologic boundaries. The most reliable criterion here might be the variation of apparent velocities of waves reflected from contacts of interest and reflections off geologic boundaries of invading formations. The detailed study of the velocity cross-section in the vicinity

of the stratum also appears to be essential. It seems highly effective to study the cross-section at acoustic frequencies (2 – 5 khz) which, in my opinion, possess substantial advantages over supersonic observations, since they permit detailed study of velocity parameters of the cross-section in cased wells.

Influence of the surface and the upper portion of the cross-section on the seismogram

As our knowledge of the mechanism of the formation of the wavefield increases, the influence of the surface and the upper portion of the cross-section on the character and structure of the seismogram appears to become more important. In particular, as the penetration increases, the relative intensity of useful waves decreases because horizons become less sharp while an increase of charge size leads to a disproportionate increase in background noise. It is essential to learn to bring-out waves associated with deep boundaries and to suppress the wavefield that corresponds to the upper portion of the cross-section.

VSP experience demonstrates that the upper portion of the cross-section and the surface may, in many cases, exert a decisive influence on the character of seismograms. Primarily, this is expressed in the change of form of each individual wave as it propagates through the upper portion of the cross-section or only through the ZLV. This influence, however, refers only to the high-frequency components. But for waves connected with deep boundaries or propagating from remote shotpoints, the influence is of no substantial practical value. Waves formed and propagated within the upper portion of the cross-section exert a considerably higher influence on the structure of the entire seismogram.

In the study of the influence of the upper portion of the cross-section at large distances (CMRRW, DSS), VSP observations at great depths near the source and the region of reception permit the separate study of reflected-refracted and refracted-reflected waves and evaluation of their total influence.

Modeling of seismic waves in actual media

The study of the process of propagation of seismic waves at interior points of the medium for the seismic exploration frequency range, is the basis for development of modeling of seismic waves in actual media in their natural state. Such modeling is primarily of interest as it applies to problems requiring complex computations. To these we may allocate waveguides, shadow regions, transition zones, velocity jumps associated with a gradient in the underlying layer, etc.

Of great interest also is the modeling of surface waves. We may study the mechanism of formation and propagation of surface waves and the depth of penetration of the energy of surface waves as it depends on the wavelength. This aspect is essential to the investigation of long-period surface waves and appraisal of detailing capabilities of procedures based on their utilization.

VSP permits the detailed study of the structure of the medium and the construction of the dynamic model. This makes it possible to obtain a concept of the parameters of the model sufficiently complete to study in detail the process of propagation of waves, and to determine the significance of waves of various types in the overall wavefield. Probably, modeling of actual media in situ will permit more reliable transfer of the results of modeling into realistic situations, i.e., of longer waves and greater depths, than is presently possible for modeling by supersonic waves on samples under laboratory conditions. The great variety of seismogeological conditions in the upper portion of the cross-section facilitates the selection of the model. In particular, a

good model of a waveguide is provided in the layer underlying permafrost.

FUTURE DEVELOPMENT OF THE METHOD

To realize the potential of observations at interior points of the medium, it is necessary to develop the method further as follows:

1. Perfect the instrumentation and observation techniques. It is essential for borehole instrumentation to guarantee multichannel recording of the full vector of motion in space, with independent surface-controlled clamping of each probe to the wall of the hole with controlled spatial orientation of the cluster. Surface instrumentation should provide for digital registration that would guarantee an undistorted record of recorded waves within a broad range of amplitudes and frequencies. Production of instrumentation and equipment should be accelerated.

2. Development of the most rational systems of observation at interior points of the medium (one-dimensional, two-dimensional, and spatial), combinations of observations along vertical and horizontal profiles, and spatial systems of observation. It seems expedient to convert completely from seismic well shooting to VSP. It is necessary to develop the complex of VSP work within the frame of conventional geophysical and acoustic observations.

3. Development of rigorous quantitative dynamic interpretation procedures using digital recording and computers. At present some programs are already written for improvement of correlation in VSP and programs are available for CDR-I and CDR-II. Special attention should be devoted to improvement of conditions of enhancement and tracking of waves along the vertical profile, and improved accuracy of stratigraphic correlation of waves.

4. VSP work should be included with the standard suite of geophysical research dealing with parametric, prospecting and reconnaissance boreholes, and to anticipate them in projects of drilling of such wells. For each area, no less than two or three boreholes should be used for VSP.

The capabilities of VSP, based on the process of propagation of seismic waves in actual media, appear fundamental to a substantial improvement of reliability and authenticity of geologic interpretation of seismic data and to effective seismic investigations.

Much VSP potential has not been realized. As instrumentation, observational procedures, and the method itself are further developed, still more possibilities will emerge.

CONCLUSION

1. Transition from studies of the already formed wave pattern at the surface to an understanding of the process of formation itself led to development of the method of vertical seismic profiling based on observations at interior points of the medium. This is founded on correlative tracking and study, along the vertical profile, not only of first waves but also the entire subsequent portion of the seismogram. VSP at present is the most effective method for the study of seismic waves in actual media.

2. Utilization of both the first arrivals and the entire later portion of the record revealed by the vertical profile sharply increased the capabilities of seismic investigations. The same situation existed in surface investigations as well. Simultaneously with the study of the propagation of waves in actual media, VSP in particular permits objective study of (a) conditions of excitation, (b) determination of the nature of observed waves, (c) improvement of accuracy of stratigraphic correlation, (d) appraisal of possibilities of seismic exploration under concrete seismogeological conditions, and (e) selection of the optimal procedure of observation. All these aspects determine the effectiveness of seismic investigations and particularly the authenticity of results of geological interpretation of seismic data.

In addition, VSP permits the most general approach to the study of the actual medium as a conductor of seismic energy and to the acquisition of data necessary for the construction of simplified (effective) models of actual media corresponding to basic laws governing the observed wavefields.

3. In contrast to surface observations, the directions of particle motion for VSP basically correspond to directions of approach of waves which may be utilized in quantitative processing of data. Experimental study of trajectories of particle motion demonstrates that they provide the key to the wave pattern and acquisition of supplementary data on the structure of the medium. The study of wave polarization in space could be especially significant.

4. VSP confirmed the correctness of basic concepts of dynamic theory of propagation of seismic waves in reference to various wave types in actual media, and permitted evaluation of the capabilities of major methods of seismic exploration. In actual media, the basic mechanisms of energy return to the surface involve reflection and refraction.

Reflected waves appear to be the basic wave type appearing on the later portion of the seismogram. Actual media are thin layered and even a homogeneous medium determined from well shooting data contains numerous reflecting horizons. However, dominant waves are coordinated to definite elements of the cross-section (most frequently to discrete thin layers or packets of layers). Against their background, total waves possess a considerably smaller amplitude and are basically observed in layers involving weak velocity differentiation.

Thin high-velocity layers may exert a considerable influence on the wavefield. This is expressed in the formation of intense reflected and multiple waves.

VSP observations reveal that reflecting horizons involving reflected waves do exist at great depths. This is the premise on which the increase of penetration of seismic investigations rests. It is the depth of penetration that at present is basically restricted by multiples and by the influence of the upper portion of the cross-section. Best exploratory capabilities involve MRLW.

Head waves in all cases are weaker

than transcritically reflected waves and are not significant in formation of the wavefield. In the case of thin high-velocity layers, transcritically reflected waves may be more intense than head waves (by two or more orders of magnitude), so that the latter are not brought out in practice. This includes both subsequent and first arrivals. The visible first arrivals on seismograms, in these cases, may be due to transcritically reflected waves, rather than head waves.

For thick layers in actual media, velocity increases with depth; and for large distances, the first waves are refracted waves whose intensity strongly depends on the coefficient of velocity increase. On the later portion of the record, transcritically reflected waves are important.

In a thin-layered medium, there is usually a plurality of reflecting horizons, only a few of which are associated with head waves. The nature of waves observed at large distances are not clearly understood. Further research is necessary to develop physical fundamentals and exploratory capabilities of the method of refracted waves.

Converted waves are abundant in actual media. Reflected converted waves, in spite of the inadequacy of observational procedures, were brought out at all available depths and off almost all boundaries involving longitudinal waves, including the top of the crystalline basement. This permits an increase of penetration by means of the method of converted reflected waves. Converted reflected waves connected with thin layers may be distinguished by their high intensity. The low-frequency content of the waves is formed in the process of wave conversion.

Transmitted converted waves increase the effectiveness of regional investigations for the study of the top of the crystalline basement under conditions of weak velocity differentiation in the sedimentary bed. In media with sharp velocity contrasts, there are no physically substantiated criteria for identification of surface seismograms of longitudinal and converted waves associated with a single boundary. It is essential to step up experiments in physical fundamentals and appraisal of exploratory capabilities of the method of converted transmitted waves.

5. The ZLV and the upper portion of the cross-section exert a decisive influence on the wave pattern. This can be observed at all distances from the source on the surface as well as at interior points of the medium. In many cases, they seem to limit the exploratory capabilities of all seismic observations. This influence is observed primarily near the source where heterogeneities of the upper portion of the cross-section lead to the transformation of the comparatively simple impulse generated in the source into a complex train of incident waves. The explosion and the heterogeneities of the medium in its vicinity should be jointly considered as a complex focus. This influence is manifested further in the noise wavefield connected with the upper portion of the cross-section. For small distances from the shotpoint, the basic classes of unwanted waves are reflected waves, refracted waves, and their multiple waves; for large separations (CMRRW) they include total reflected-refracted and refracted-reflected waves on the initial portion of the record, as well as low-velocity interferential waves on the later portion of the record. Records obtained on the surface and at interior points of the medium indicate that the overwhelming number of waves are connected with the upper portion of the cross-section.

6. The most accurate results may be obtained by utilization of waves propagating in directions that are nearly vertical. In this regard, reflected waves for small separations from the shotpoint are

of special interest; for observations at large separations, converted transmitted waves are important.

7. The basic body of observations was accomplished for a frequency range similar to that used in conventional seismic exploration. However, available results may help us understand the wave pattern observed in other procedures of seismic investigation, i.e., for DSS and seismology. VSP may serve as the basis for development of modeling of seismic waves in actual media in their natural state.

8. The method of vertical profiling is being actively incorporated into the practice of commercial prospecting. It is expedient to replace conventional well shooting entirely by vertical profiling. VSP, incorporating all aspects of seismic investigations (well logging using P- and S-waves, seismic well shooting, etc.) should, within the immediate future become the basic method for observations in wells at seismic frequencies and should be included in the complex of required geophysical investigations of parametric, prospecting, and exploratory boreholes.

VSP capabilities may prove to be so essential that in most cases it might be expedient and economically advantageous to anticipate special drilling of wells for vertical profiling. This would apply particularly to areas where a large amount of seismic research is planned.

9. The results to date justify continuation of investigations for further development of the method. The basic directives in this respect are the perfection of investigational procedures, change to digital recording, and computer processing of data in order to acquire more complete quantitative results. The development of a rational combination of borehole (VSP, SWL, and commercial geophysical) and surface observations is essential. For the study of seismic waves in actual media, it is expedient to increase investigations of the upper portion of the cross-section to determine its influence on the seismic effect of the explosion, the structure of the seismogram, and the effectiveness of seismic investigations.

REFERENCES

Aki, H., 1960, Seismic waves in the region near explosive origin: J. Sci. Nagoya Univ., v. 8, no. 2.

Alekseyev, A.S., 1960, Seminar data on the dynamics of seismic waves: Moscow, VNIIGeofiz.

_____ 1962, On kinematic and dynamic properties of basic depth waves for the case of some theoretical models of the earth's crust: Glubinn. Seyzm. Zondir. Semn. Kory. V. SSSR, Moscow, Gostoptekhizdat.

Andreyev, S. S., 1967, Study of depth structure of the earth's crust by means of converted PS waves registered for earthquakes: Izv. Akad. Nauk SSSR, Geophys. Ser. no. 1.

Anonymous, 1962, Experimental investigations of transverse and converted waves: SO, Akad. Nauk, SSSR.

Anstey, N. A., 1958, A note on the seismic pulse recorded from a mine explosion: Geophys. Prosp., v. 6, no. 4, p. 433-437.

Artamanova, V. D., and Glan, Ym. R., 1969, Instrumentation and procedure for VSP and utilization of its results for the interpretation of MRLW data: Novyye tekhn. i metod. razrab. V seyzm. Moscow ONTI VIEMS.

Averbukh, A. G., 1961, On the identification of refracted waves for DSS in the northwestern portion of the Sea of Okhot: Glubinn. Seyzm. Zondir. Zemn. Kory. V. SSSR., Leningrad, Gostoptekhizdat.

Averbukh, A. G., Gorbach, L. M., and Sumerina, E. P., 1963, On the physical nature of waves registering as first arrivals for CMRRW observations: Priklad, Geofiz., no. 36.

Beranek, B., and Zounkova, M. A., 1964, A method of borehole refraction: Geophysics,

Berdennikova, N. I., 1959, On some manifestations of anisotropy in a layered medium for work with transverse waves: Vop. Din. Teor. Raspr. Seizm. Voln, v. 2.

Berdennikova, N. I., Zhadin, V. V., and Rudakov, A. G., 1959, On the question of procedure of seismic well-logging observations: Vop. Din. Teor. Raspr. Seizm. Voln, v. 2.

Berdennikova, N. I., and Limbakh, Yu. I., 1966, On spectral particulars of seismic impulses registered in boreholes: Vop. Din. Teor. Raspr. Seizm. Voln, v. 8.

Bereza, G. V., 1954, Means of registration of seismic oscillations in seismic exploration: Avt. svid. no. 98804, ki. 42, ot. May 22, 1953; Bull. Izobret. no. 8.

Berlage, H. P., 1924, Recherches sur le debut d'une phase Ir: Publ. du Bur. Cent. Seism. Int., Ser. AL.

Berzon, I. S., 1964, Some results of study of seismic waves for velocity well shooting: Izv. Akad. Nauk SSSR, Geophys. Ser., no. 9.

_____ editor, 1967, Models of actual media and seismic wave fields: Moscow, Nauka.

Berzon, I. S., et al, 1962, Dynamic characteristics of seismic waves: Moscow, Akad. Nauk SSSR.

Berzon, I. S., Ratnikova, L. I., and Ratz-Khizgiya, M. I., 1966, Seismic converted reflected waves: Moscow, Nauka.

Berzon, I. S., Mitronova, V. A., and Ratnikova, L. I., 1969, Comparison of calculated and experimental seismic wave fields corresponding to a thin layer with increased velocity: Geofiz. Sbornik AN. UkrSSR, no. 30.

Bogdanov, A. I., 1960, Theory of seismic TTC's: Moscow, Gostoptekhizdat.

Bokanenko, L. I., 1967, Dispersion and absorption of transverse waves in vinyl and Plexiglas slabs: Izv. Akad. Nauk SSSR, Phys. Earth Ser., no. 8.

Bol'shikh, S. F., Gorbatova, V. P., and

Davydova, L. N., 1961, Study of kinematic and dynamic characteristics of reflected and head waves on models of a layered medium: Priklad, Geofiz., no. 30.

Bondarev, V. I., 1965, Six-component borehole azimuthal seismic installation: Geofiz. Appar., no 26.

Bondarev, V. I., and Sivkov, N. F., 1963, Procedures for determination of azimuth and angle of emersion of the displacement vector according to results of azimuthal observations: Tr. Sverdle. Gorn. Inst., no. 44, Vop. Razved. Geofiz., Moscow, Gostoptekhizdat.

Brodov, L. Yu., 1967, Some questions of excitation of transverse waves: Poper. I Obmen. Volny V Seyzm., Moscow, Nedra.

Bulin, N. K., 1960, Determination of depth of folded basement by means of converted transmitted waves of PS type, registered in earthquakes: Izv. Akad. Nauk SSSR, Geophys. Ser., no. 6.

Calitzin, B. B., 1909, Zur Lage der Bestimmung des Asimuts des Epizentrum eines Bebens: Bull. Imperial Acad. of Sci., ser. 6.

Chekin, B. S., 1965, On the influence of a weak heterogeneity of the refracting medium on head waves: Isv. Akad. Nauk SSSR, Phys. Earth Ser., no. 3.

Clifford, E. L., et al, 1958, Method of surveying a borehole: U.S. Patent no. 2,842,220, 8.07.

Collins, F., and Lee, C. C., 1956, Seismic wave attenuation characteristics from pulse experiments: Geophysics, v. 21, no. 1. p. 16-40.

Davydova, N. I., 1962, Model study of the dependence of dynamic characteristics of longitudinal head waves on the thickness of the refracting layer: Izv. Akad. Nauk SSSR, Geophys. Ser., no. 1.

Demidenko, Yu. B., 1964, Vertical seismic profiling: Geol. interpr. i metod. geofiz. issled., Tr. Inst. Geofiz., Akad. Nauk SSSR, no. 7.

_____ 1966, Straightening-out of line-ups and of TTCs of reflected and multiple waves for VSP: Razved. Geofiz., no. 12.

_____ 1967, Tracking and utilization of multiply reflected waves for VSP: Metod. seyzm. issled., Kiev, Tekhnika.

Deryagin, B. V., 1931, On decay and dispersion of seismic waves: Geofiz., nos. 1-2.

Dix, C. H., 1945, The interpretation of well-shot data: Geophysics: v. 10, no. 2, p. 160-170.

Epinat'yeva, A. M., 1960, Study of longitudinal seismic waves propagating in certain actual layered media: Tr. Inst. Fiz. Semli, Akad. Nauk SSSR, no. 14.

_____ 1964, Multiple ghost waves: Seyzm. monogr. otrazh. volny, Tr. Inst. Geofiz., Akad. Nauk SSSR, no. 34.

Epinat'yeva, A. M., et al, 1963, Certain experimental data on the form of impulses excited by explosions in boreholes: Izv. Akad. Nauk SSSR, Geophys. Ser., no. 6.

Epinat'yeva, A. M., and Karus, E. V., 1967, Head waves off thin layers (according to field investigations): Modeli real. sred i seyzm. volnov. polya, Moscow, Nauka.

Faizulin, I. S., and Epinat'yeva, A. M., 1967, Reflected and head waves off thin layers according to observations on hard three-dimensional models: Izv. Akad. Nauk SSSR, Phys. Earth Ser., no. 6.

Flinn, E. E., 1965, Analysis of signals by means of spatial filtering: Tr. IEEE, v. 5, no. 12.

Futterman, W. I., 1962, Dispersive body waves: Geophys. Res., v. 67, no. 13.

Gal'perin, E. I., 1955, Azimuthal method

of seismic observations: Moscow, Gostoptekhizdat.

——————— 1956a, Solution of direct spatial problems in geometric seismics for multi-layered media having arbitrary forms of boundaries of separation: Izv. Akad. Nauk SSSR, Geophys. Ser., no. 4.

——————— 1956b, On azimuthal deflections of seismic rays: Izv. Akad. Nauk SSSR, Geophys. Ser., No. 11.

——————— 1957, Grouping of first kind and procedure for obtaining multi-component azimuthal seismograms: Izv. Akad. Nauk SSSR, Geophys. Ser., no. 9.

——————— 1962, On change of directions of particle displacement for transition of seismic waves through a zone of low velocities: Izv. Akad. Nauk SSSR, Geophys. Ser. no. 5.

——————— 1963a, Study of direction of displacement vector in seismic waves for borehole observations: Izv. Akad. Nauk SSSR, Geophys. Ser., no. 2.

——————— 1963b, On determination of elements of embedding of the refracting boundary by means of direction of displacement of first waves observed in boreholes: Izv. Akad. Nauk SSSR, Geophys. Ser., no. 4.

——————— 1964a, Kinematic particulars of multiples associated with deep boundaries: Stroyen. zemv. kory v oblasti perekhoda ot Aziat. Kontin. k Tikhom. okeanu, Moscow, Nauka.

——————— 1964b, On the question of the influence of the surface and the UPC on the character and structure of seismograms: Vop. Din. Teor. Raspr. Seizm. Voln, v. 7.

——————— 1964c, Experience with detailed study of velocity model of the UPC under conditions of weak velocity differentiation: Izv. Akad. Nauk SSSR, Geophys. Ser., no. 4.

——————— 1965a, Study of multiply-reflected waves by means of VSP: Izv. Akad. Nauk SSSR, Phys. Earth Ser., no. 12.

——————— 1965b, On some wave types observable for explosions in boreholes: Razved. Geofiz., no. 6.

——————— 1966a, Study of process of propagation of seismic waves in actual media: Vestnik A., no. 1.

——————— 1966b, On intensity of head and transcritically reflected waves: Izv. Akad. Nauk SSSR, Geophys. Ser., no. 10.

——————— 1966c, On correlatability of waves for VSP: Razved. Geofiz., no. 17.

——————— 1967a, Seismic observations in boreholes and their exploratory capabilities: Metod. tekhn. i rezult. geofiz. razved., Moscow, Nedra.

——————— 1967b, On the significance of some wave types in the formation of the seismogram: Razved. Geofiz.

——————— 1969, Present status, experience of application and paths for further development of the VSP method: Novyye tekhn. i metod. razrab. v seyzm., Moscow, ONTI VIEMS.

Gal'perin, E. I., and Kosminskaya, I. P., 1958, Particulars of the DSS at sea: Izv. Akad. Nauk SSSR, Geophys. Ser., no. 7.

Gal'perin, E. I., Frolova, A. V., 1960, Azimuthal and phase correlation of elliptically polarized waves: Izv. Akad. Nauk SSSR, Geophys. Ser., no. 2.

——————— 1961a, Three-component seismic observations in boreholes: Izv. Akad. Nauk SSSR, Geophys. Ser., no. 6.

——————— 1961b, Vertical seismic profiling: Izv. Akad. Nauk SSSR, Geophys. Ser., no. 7.

——————— 1963, Study of seismic waves by combination horizontal and vertical profilings: Izv. Akad. Nauk SSSR, Geophys. Ser., no. 9.

————— 1966, Study of converted waves by the VSP method: Izv. Akad. Nauk SSSR, Phys. Earth Ser., no. 9.

Gal'perin, E. I., et al, 1969, On the nature of noise waves registering on wide territories of low foothills bordering the Fergan depression of Mid-Asia: Metod i result. kompleks. glubin. geofiz. issled, Leningrad, Nedra.

Gal'perina, R. M., 1968, On the question of physical fundamentals and exploratory capabilities of the method of converted waves according to data of VSP: Dokl. A., v. 182, no. 2.

Gamburtsev, A. G., and Koptev, V. I., 1967, On the possibility of complex study of the characteristic of the UPC: Modeli real. sred i seyzm. volnov. polya, Moscow, Nauka.

Gamburtsev, A. G., Kuznetsov, V. V., and Isayev, V. S., 1967, On the possibility of determining the filtering properties of the UPC: Modeli real. sred i seyzm. volnov. polya, Moscow, Nauka.

Gamburtsev, G. A., 1937 & 1938, Seismic methods of exploration, parts I and II: ONTI VIEMS.

————— 1939, On the possibility of bringing out transverse reflected waves for seismic exploration by means of reflections: Izv. Akad. Nauk SSSR, Geophys. Ser., no. 2.

————— 1952, On a novel aspect of phase correlation in seismic observations: Dokl. A., v. 87, no. 1.

————— 1969, Fundamentals of seismic exploration: Moscow Gostoptekhizdat.

Gamburtsev, G. A., and Deryagin, B. V., 1934, Seismometry: Priklad. Geofiz., no. 2.

Gamburtsev, G. A., et al, 1952, Correlational method of refracted waves: Moscow, Akad. Nauk SSSR.

Gamburtsev, G. A., and Gal'perin, E. I., 1954, Azimuthal seismic observations using inclined seismometers: Izv. Akad. Nauk SSSR, Geophys. Ser., no. 2.

Gardner, L., 1953, Seismic exploration of a salt dome by means of a borehole seismometer placed at the flank of the dome: Vop. seyzm. razved, Moscow, IL.

Gel'chinskyi, B. Ya., 1960, Seminar data on questions of dynamics of seismic waves: Moscow, VNIIGeofiz.

Gil'bershteyn, P. G., and Gurvich, I. I., 1963, Study of two-dimensional models of head waves off layers of differing thickness; Izv. Akad. Nauk SSSR, Geophys. Ser., no. 11.

Gogonenkov, G.N., 1967, Application of synthetic seismograms for the clarification of the analysis of multiply reflected waves: Izv. Akad. Nauk SSSR, Phys. Earth Ser., no. 10.

Gorbatova, V. P., 1958: On the intensity of refracted and reflected transmitted waves for subcritical angles of incidence: Priklad. Geofiz., no. 18.

Gurevich, G. I., 1955, On the question of physical fundamentals of the propagation theory of elastic waves: Tr. Inst. Geofiz., Akad. Nauk SSSR, no. 30.

Gurvich, I. I., 1952, On reflections off thin layers in seismic exploration: Priklad. Geofiz., no. 9.

————— 1960, Seismic exploration: Moscow, Gostoptekhizdat.

————— 1967, Dependence of spectra of seismic waves on weight of charge in an absorptive medium: Izv. Akad. Nauk SSSR, Phys. Earth Ser., no. 1.

Gurvich, I. I., and Gil'bershteyn, P. G., 1961, On the determination of constants of absorption of seismic waves: Razved. Geofiz., no. 4.

Gurvich, I. I., Levyant, V. B., and Molotova, L. V., 1966, Experimental amplitude characteristics of explosion: Izv. Akad. Nauk SSSR, Phys. Earth Ser., no. 3.

Gvozdev, A. A. and Kuznetsov, V. V., 1967, Splintering phenomena in soils observable in seismic exploration, Izv.

Akad. Nauk SSSR, Phys. Earth Ser., no. 5.

Hagedoorn, L. C., 1962, In pursuit of the errant seismic pulse: Geophys. Prosp., v. 10, no. 2, p. 148-165.

Holste, W., 1959, Problems and results with refractions seismics in boreholes (Determination of salt-flanks and other interfaces): Geophys. Prosp., v. 7, no. 2, p. 273.

Horton, C. W., 1943, Secondary arrivals in a well velocity survey: Geophysics, v. 8, no. 3, p. 290-296.

I, Fyn-De, 1962, On the appraisal of the influence of surface layers on the field of seismic waves: Vop. Din. Teor. Raspr. Seizm. Voln, v. 6.

Isymbal, T. M., Gel'chinskyi, B. Ya., and Rudakov, A. G., 1962, Basic properties of wave field encumbering the tracking of reflected waves in the Surkhan-Dar depression and problems of its study: Vop. Din. Teor. Raspr. Seizm. Voln, v. 4.

Isymbal, T. M., and Krauklis, L. A., 1966, Study of surface waves registered in seismic investigations of the Surkhan-Dar depression: Vop Din. Teor. Raspr. Seizm. Voln, v. 8.

Ivakin, V. N., 1956, Head transmitted and other waves for the case of a thin hard layer within a liquid: Seyzm. razved., Tr. Inst. Geofiz., Akad. Nauk SSSR, no. 35.

Ivanov, L. I., 1957, Seismic well logging by means of refracted waves: Priklad. Geofiz., no. 17.

Ivanov, S. I., 1953, Seismic method in the study of lateral partitions of salt domes: Tr. NIIGA, v. 39.

Ivanova, T. G., 1960, On the utilization of frequency seismic sounding for the study of the UPC: Izv. Akad. Nauk SSSR, Geophys. Ser., no. 2.

Jolly, R. N., 1953, Deep-hole geophone study Gravin County, Oklahoma: Geophysics, v. 18, no. 3, p. 662-670.

_____ 1956, Investigation of shear waves: Geophysics, v. 21, no. 4, p. 905-938.

Kaplan, S. A., 1962, On selection of optimal conditions of excitation of elastic vibrations: Geofiz. Razved., no. 9.

Karayev, N. A., and Lukashin, Yu. P., 1964, Study of noise waves for MRLW work in central Kazakhstan: Vop. Razved. Geofiz., no. 4, Nedra.

Karus, E. V., 1958, Absorption of elastic vibrations in rocky formations for steady-state excitation: Izv. Akad. Nauk SSSR, Phys. Earth Ser., no. 4.

Karus, E. V., and Pasechnik, E. V., 1954, Procedure for study of elastic and absorptive properties of rocky formations in their natural embedding by means of seismo-acoustic methods: Izv. Akad. Nauk SSSR, Geophys. Ser., no. 6.

Karus, E. V., and Saks, M. V., 1961, Impulse supersonic well logging: Vestnik A, no. 5.

Kefeli, A. S., 1965, Determination of parameters of uninterrupted media from data of borehole observation: Geolog. i Geofiz., no. 4.

Khaikin, E. M., 1966, Appraisal of effectiveness of various procedures of utilization of sources of low interaction in seismic exploration: Tr. Kuibyshev, NII Neftyan. Promyl., no. 36.

Khalyevich, N. I., 1955, Supporting devices for geophones in seismic well logging: Razved. i Promysl. Geofiz., no. 14.

Khothe, G. H., 1961, Homogene Dreikomponentenanordnungen fur tiefenseismische Untersuchungen: Z. Geophys., v. 27, no. 2.

Kirnos, D. P., et al, 1934, Contributions of the seismo-geological institute of the Academy of Sciences of the USSR with reference to seismic exploration: Tr. Seism. Inst. A, no. 47.

Kogan, S. Ya., 1961a, On the influence of absorption on the form of the seismic impulse: Izv. Akad. Nauk SSSR, Geophys. Ser., no. 9.

———————— 1961b, On determination of the absorption coefficient of seismic waves: Izv. Akad. Nauk SSSR, Geophys. Ser., no. 12.

Kolsky, H., 1956, The propagation of stress pulses in viscoelastic solids: Phil. Mag., ser. 8, v. 1, no. 8.

Kondrat'yev, O. K., and Gamburtsev, A. G., 1963, Seismic investigations on the coastal portion of Antarctica: Moscow, Akad, Nauk SSSR.

Konovalov, M. M., 1961, Borehole seismic exploration: Razved. i Okhrana nedr., no. 8.

Koryagin, V. V., 1966, Results of experimental study of the form of seismic impulses in the Kuibyshev district: Razved. Geofiz., no. 10.

Kosminskaya, I. P., 1956, Analysis of interferential zones of seismic waves: Seyzm. razved., Tr. Inst. Geofiz., Akad. Nauk SSSR, no. 35.

Kosminskaya, I. P., and Krakshina, R. M., 1961, On transcritical reflections off the Mohorovčić boundary: Izv. Akad. Nauk SSSR, Geophys. Ser., no. 6.

Kozlov, E. A., 1961, On one aspect of noise in seismic exploration by means of MRLW in Kuban: Razved. i Promysl. Geofiz., no. 41.

Krauklis, L. A., Moiseyeva, L. A., and Gel'chinskyi, B. Ya., 1966, Program for computed correlation of seismic waves and experience with its utilization: Vop. Din. Teor. Raspr. Seizm. Voln, v. 8.

Krauklis, P. V., and Molotkov, L. A., 1968, On the theory of seismic well logging in cased boreholes: Izv. Akad. Nauk SSSR, Phys. Earth Ser., no. 9.

Kulichikhina, T. N., Yudina, R. I., and Karzheva, L. V., 1964, Distribution of velocities of P and S waves in the UPC: Razved, i Promysl. Geofiz., no. 51.

Kuz'mina, N. V., 1959, On utilization of converted waves in the study of the structure of the earth's crust in the southeastern part of the Kaukasus ridge: Izv. Akad. Nauk SSSR, Geophys. Ser., no. 7.

Kuznetsov, V. V., and Gamburtsev, A. G., 1967, Procedures for registration of direct longitudinal waves at the surface and at interior points of the medium: Modeli real. sred i seyzm. volnov. polya, Moscow, Nauka.

Lamb, H., 1898, On the velocity of sound in a tube as affected by the elasticity of the walls: Manchester Mem., v. 17, no. 9.

Lamb, G. N., 1962, The attentuation of waves in dispersive medium: Geophys. Res., v. 67, no. 13.

Lavergne, M., 1961, Etude sur modele ultrasonique du probleme des couches mines in seismique refraction: Geophys. Prosp. v. 9, no. 1, p. 60-73.

Levin, F. K., and Lynn, R. D., 1958, Deep-hole geophone studies: Geophysics, v. 23, no. 4, p. 639-664.

Levin, F. K., and Ingram, J. D., 1962, Head waves from a bed of finite thickness: Geophysics, v. 27, no. 6, p. 753-765.

Lynn, R. D., 1963: A low-frequency geophone for borehole use: Geophysics: v. 28, no. 1, p. 14-19.

Malinovskaya, L. N., 1959, On the problem on calculation of theoretical seismograms of interferential oscillation, Vop. Din. Teor. Raspr. Seizm. Voln, v. 3.

Malushin, I. I., 1967, On the excitation of transverse waves by explosions in the region of Ustyurt: Poper. i obmen. volny v seyzm., Moscow, Nedra.

McDonal, F. J., et al, 1958, Attenuation of shear and compressional waves in Pierre shale: Geophysics, v. 23, no. 3, p. 421-439.

Meissner, R. 1965, Multiple events in

refraction shooting: Geophys. Prosp., v. 13, no. 4, p. 617-658.

Meshbey, V. I., 1962, On the question of multiple reflections on the platform portion of the northwestern approaches of the Caucasus: Razved. i Promysl. Geofiz., no. 43.

Mirchink, M. F., et al, 1961, Appraisal of possibility of application of seismic exploration to the direct search of petroliferous deposits: IG and RGI, Akad. Nauk SSSR.

Mitrofanov, V. N., and Vavilova, T. L., 1961, On the nature of reflection in the Maicop clay formation of the northern approaches of the Caucasus: Vop. Rudnoy Geofiz., no. 3.

Molotkov, L. A., and Krauklis, P. V., 1963, On the formation of a low-frequency head wave in thin layers: Izv. Akad. Nauk SSSR, Geophys. Ser., no. 6.

Molotova, L. V., 1963, On the value of the ratio of P and S waves in terrigenous formations: Izv. Akad. Nauk SSSR, Geophys. Ser., no. 12.

Muzyka, I. M., 1969, Study of multiply reflected waves by VSP and experience in the selection of interferential systems based on acquired data: Novyye tekhn. i metod. razrab. v seyzm., Moscow, ONTI VIEMS.

Naidis, L. M., 1967, Experience in ultilization of converted waves in seismic work according to CMRRW in the Volgograd Volga region: Razved. Geofiz., no. 21.

Nekrasov, I. L., editor, 1962, Physics of earthquakes and seismics of explosions: Akad. Nauk SSSR.

Nersesov, I. L., 1960, Methods for detailed study of seismicity: Tr. Inst. Fiz. Zemli, Akad. Nauk SSSR, no. 9.

Nikolayev, A. V., 1965, Seismic properties of soils: Moscow, Nauka.

Ogurtsov, K. I., and Ozerov, D. K., 1959, On theoretical experimental work for 1952-1953: Vop. Din. Teor. Raspr. Seizm. Voln, v. 2.

Olhovich, V. A., 1964, The causes of noise in seismic reflection and refraction work: Geophysics, v. 29, no. 6, p. 1015-1030.

Ostrovskyi, A. E., 1944, On seismic well logging: Dokl. A, v. 45, no. 5.

Ozerov, D. K., Yermilova, N. I., and Litvinenko, I. V., 1962, Application of dynamic theory to the interpretation of seismic data in northern Karelia: Vop. Din. Teor. Raspr. Seizm. Voln: v. 4.

Pasechnik, I. P., 1952a, Results of experimental study of resonance phenomena for the oscillatory system soil geophone: Izv. Akad. Nauk SSSR, Phys. Earth Ser.

_____ 1952b, Comparison of results of theoretical and experimental investigations of resonance phenomena in the system soil geophone: Izv. Akad. Nauk SSSR, Phys. Earth Ser., no. 5.

Petkevich, G. I., 1957, On the vertical TTC of the reflected wave: Razved. i Promysl. Geofiz., no. 19.

_____ 1958, On the problem of revealing seismic boundaries in seismic well-logging investigations: Dop. AN URSR, no. 10.

Petrashen', G. I., 1957, General quantitative theory of reflected and head waves excited in layered media having flat parallel boundaries: Vop. Din. Teor. Raspr. Seizm. Voln, v. 1.

_____ editor, 1957, Data on quantitative study of dynamics of seismic waves, Vols. I and II: Leningrad Mining University.

Petrashen', G. I., Alekseyev, A. S., and Gel'chinskyi, B. Ya., 1959, Elementary theory of propagation of seismic waves, Vol., III: Leningrad, Leningrad Mining University.

Podyapolsyi, G. S., 1959, Approximate expression for displacement in the neighborhood of the basic wave front in the case of a small angle between the ray and the boundary of separation: Izv. Akad. Nauk SSSR, Geophys. Ser., no. 12.

Pogonyailo, G. G., 1966, On the determination of the reflection coefficient from data of seismic well logging: Vop. Din. Teor. Raspr. Seizm. Voln, v. 8.

―――――― 1968, Study of wave field in a borehole for remote SP's: Vop. Din. Teor. Raspr. Seizm. Voln, v. 9.

―――――― 1970, Theoretical-experimental investigations of the wave field observed in the vertical plane on one of the platforms of the lower Volga region: Vop. Din. Teor. Raspr. Seizm. Voln, v. 10.

Pomerantseva, I. V., 1962, Nature of waves associated with the surface of the crystalline basement: Priklad. Geofiz., no. 34.

Pomerantseva, I. V., and Margot'yeva, M. V., 1959, On the nature of waves registering for DSS: VNIIGeofiz.

Press, F., and Dobrin, M. B., 1956, Seismic waves over a high-speed surface layer: Geophysics, v. 21, no. 2, p. 285-298.

Problems of seismic exploration, 1962: Collection of papers, Moscow, Gostoptekhizdat.

Puzyrev, N. N., 1957, Variation of seismic velocities in boreholes: Tr. VNII-Geofiz., no. 3.

―――――― 1959, Interpretation of data of seismic exploration by means of MRLW: Moscow, Gostoptekhizdat.

―――――― editor, 1967, Transverse and converted waves in seismic exploration: Moscow, Nedra.

Puzyrev, N. N. and Khudobina, L. N., 1962, Review of experimental investigations and some theoretical concepts in the study of transverse and converted waves: Tr. Inst. Geol. i Geofiz., no. 16.

Puzyrev, N. N., Lebedev, K. A., and Lebedeva, G. N., 1967, Excitation of transverse seismic waves by explosions in cavities: Poper. i obmen. volny v seyzm., Moscow, Nedra.

Raikher, L. D., 1958, Seismic well logging with utilization of remote SP's: Tr. Geol. Inst. A, Geofiz. Ser., no. 2.

Razumovskiy, N. K., 1932, Stereographic projections, 2nd edition: Leningrad, Gorny. Inst. Im. Soyuza Gornorab. SSSR.

Ricker, N., 1940, The form and nature of seismic waves and the structure of seismograms: Geophysics, v. 5, no. 4, p. 348-366.

―――――― 1953, The form and laws of propagation of seismic wavelets: Geophysics, v. 18, no. 1, p. 10-40.

Ricker, N., and Sorge, W. A., 1954, The primary seismic disturbance in shale: Bull. Seism. Soc. Amer., v. 41, no. 3.

Riggs, E. D., 1955, Seismic wave types in a borehole: Geophysics, v. 20, no. 1, p. 53-67.

Riznichenko, Yu. V., 1946, Geometric seismics of layered media: Tr. Inst. Teor. Geofiz., v. 2.

―――――― 1956, On impulse-type supersonic seismic well logging: Izv. Akad. Nauk SSSR, Geophys. Ser., no. 11.

Rosenbaum, J. J., 1965, Refraction arrivals through thin high-velocity layers: Geophysics, v. 30, no. 2, p. 204-212.

Rudakov, A. G., 1962, Some problems in the study of noise waves and the recognition of reflected waves on their background. Study of wave field (according to results of experimental procedures in the Surkhan-Dar Depression): Vop. Din. Teor. Raspr. Seizm. Voln, v. 6.

Rudnitskiy, V. P., 1968, Seismic investigations in boreholes: Kiev, Naukova Dumka.

Ryabinkin, L. A., 1957, Controllable directional reception of seismic waves and fundamentals of its resolving power: Vop. regul. napravl. priyema seyzm. voln, Tr. Moscow Sci. Inst., no. 18.

―――――― editor, 1960, Application

of controllable directional reception of seismic waves: Moscow, Gostoptekhizdat.

Savarenskiy, E. F., and Kirnos, D. P., 1955, Elements of seismology and seismometry: Moscow, Gostekhizdat.

Seismic exploration, 1966, Vol IV of reference books on geophysics: Moscow, Nedra.

Seismic multiply reflected waves: Tr. Inst. Geofiz., Akad. Nauk SSSR, no. 34.

Sergeyev, L. A., et al, 1963, Impulse sonic well logging in cased boreholes: Geol. Nefti i Gaza, no. 1.

Shalimov, B. N., 1965, On selection of optimal conditions of excitation of elastic vibrations: Tr. Nizhne-Volzhsk. Inst. Geol. i Geofiz., no. 3.

Shamina, O. G., and Gurvich, I. I., 1960, Study of dynamic characteristics of longitudinal waves in layers of differing thickness: Izv. Akad. Nauk SSSR, Geophys. Ser., no. 8.

Shan'gin, N. V., 1958, Experience in utilization of decay phenomena of seismic waves: Uch Zapiski Leningrad Mining University, Ser. Fiz. i Geol. Nauk, no. 10.

Sharpe, J. A., 1942a, The production of elastic waves by explosion pressures, I. Theory and empirical field observations: Geophysics, v. 7, no. 2, p. 144-154.

_____ 1942b, The production of elastic waves by explosion pressures, II. Results of observations near an exploding charge: Geophysics, v. 7, no. 3, p. 311.

Shchepin, V. D., and Ruchiy, G. S., 1963, Arrangement for directional reception of elastic vibrations: Avt. svid. no. 157516, Bull. Izobret., no. 18.

Shcherbakova, B. E., 1966, Regional seismic investigations of surface of basement by means of converted refracted waves in the territory of the Russian platform: Priklad. Geofiz., no. 48.

Shmakov, V. N., 1962, Borehole seismic observations: Izv. Buzov. Gorny Zh., no. 4.

Shneyerson, M. V., 1959, Seismic well logging by means of refracted waves: Razved., i Promysl. Geofiz., no. 26.

Slutskovskiy, A. I., 1958, On the dynamic range of oscillations registered in seismic exploration by MRLW: Razved. i Promysl. Geofiz., no. 22.

Smirnova, N. S., and Yermilova, N. I., 1959, On the construction of theoretical seismograms in the neighborhood of starting points: Vop. Din. Teor. Raspr. Seizm. Voln, vol. 3.

Sollogub, V. B., and Raikher, L. D., 1955, Some recommendations for the conduct of seismic observations in boreholes: Razved. i Okhrana Nedr, no. 6.

Tatel, H. E., 1954, Note on the nature of a seismogram: Geophys. Res., v. 59, no. 2.

Tatel, H. E., and Tuve, M. A., 1954, Note on the nature of a seismogram: Geophys. Res., v. 59, no. 2.

_____ 1958, Seismic observations at one kilometer depth, in Contributions in geophysics: London, Pergamon Press.

Teplitskiy, V. A., 1969, Method of converted TTC's of reflected waves: Novyye tekhn. i metod. razrab. v seyzm., Moscow, ONTI VIEMS.

Tumilovich, N. I., 1962, Interpretation of borehole seismic exploration data for domes of southern Emba: Priklad. Geofiz., no. 34.

Urupov, A. K., 1966, Velocity study in seismic exploration: Moscow, Nedra.

Van Sandt, D. R., and Levin, F. K., 1963, A study of cased and open holes for deep-hole seismic detection: Geophysics, v. 28, no. 1, p. 8-13.

Vasil'ev, Yu. I., 1959, Some consequences resulting from the analysis of coefficients of reflection and refraction for elastic waves: Tr. Inst. Fiz. Zemli, Akad, Nauk SSSR, no. 6.

——————— 1961, Converted refracted waves in seismic exploration, *in* State-of-the-art and speculation on the development of geophysical methods for the search and exploration of useful mineral resources: Mater. Nauch. Tekhn. Geofiz. Konfer., Moscow, Gostoptekhizdat.

——————— 1962, Two resumes on absorption constants for elastic vibrations in rocky formations: Izv. Akad. Nauk SSSR, Geophys. Ser., no. 5.

Vinnik, L. P., 1968, Structure of microseism and certain questions on procedures of grouping in seismology: Moscow, Nauka.

Vinogradov, F. V., 1967, Some results of testing borehole three-component seismic receivers with automatic orientation: Poper. i Obmenn. Volny v seyzm. Moscow, Nedra.

Vinogradov, F. V., Golosov, V. P., and Yudina, R. P., 1967, On directivity of the source for an explosion of a small charge in a borehole: Poper. i Obmenn. volny v. seyzm., Moscow, Nedra.

Volin, A. P., and Rudakov, A. G., 1956, On seismic exploration by transverse waves: Priklad, Geofiz., no. 15.

Vol'vovskyi, B. S., Vol'vovskyi, I. S., and Tal'virskyi, B. B., 1960, Conditions of conducting seismic exploration in the Fergan valley: Razved. i promysl. geofiz., no. 35.

Voronin, Yu. A., and Zhadin, V. V., 1964, On frequency distortions of the seismic signal for registration by means of three-component borehole seismometers: Geolog. i Geofiz., no. 3.

Voyutskiy, V. S., 1937: On the problem of seismic well logging: Bull. Neft. Geofiz., no. 4.

White, J. E., 1965, Seismic waves. Radiation, transmission and attenuation: New York, McGraw-Hill Book, Co., Inc.

White, J. E., and Sengbush, R. L., 1963, Shear waves from explosive surfaces: Geophysics, v. 28, no. 6, p. 1001-1019.

Wuenschel, P. C., 1965, Dispersive body waves. An experimental study: Geophysics, v. 30, no. 4, p. 539-551.

Yakobson, A. N., 1956, Subsequent waves in seismic well logging: Razved. i Promysl. Geofiz., no. 15.

Yakovenko, Yu. N., 1966, Borehole clamping arrangement: Avt. svid. no. 185793 ot Nov. 23, 1965, Izobret. Promysl. Obrazov. Tovarn. Znaki, no. 18.

Zapol'skiy, K. K., 1955, On dynamic TTCs of seismic waves: Izv. Akad. Nauk SSSR, Geophys. Ser., no. 3.

Zhadin, B. V., 1960, Three-component measurements of amplitudes and velocities of propagation of longitudinal and transverse waves in a deep borehole: Geolog. i Geofiz., no. 10.

Zyuzin, P. I., 1954, Vertical TTC for a two-layered medium: Vop. razved. i dobychi nefti i gaza, Tr. Akad. Neft. Prom, no. 1.